FUNDAMENTALS
OF
DIGITAL ELECTRONICS

FUNDAMENTALS

OF

DIGITAL ELECTRONICS

A Laboratory Text

GEORGE B. RUTKOWSKI, P. E.

Head, Electronics Department
Electronics Technology Institute
Cleveland, Ohio
Consultant, Aptek, Inc.

JEROME E. OLEKSY, P. E.

Head, Physics Department
Electronics Technology Institute
Cleveland, Ohio
Consultant, Aptek, Inc.

PRENTICE-HALL, INC., *Englewood Cliffs, New Jersey* *07632*

Library of Congress Cataloging in Publication Data

RUTKOWSKI, GEORGE B
    Fundamentals of digital electronics.

    Includes index.
    1. Digital electronics.   I. Oleksy, Jerome E.,
joint author.   II. Title.
TK7868.D5R87   621.3815   77-794
ISBN   0-13-336115-2

Printed in the United States of America

10   9   8   7

PRENTICE-HALL INTERNATIONAL, INC., *London*
PRENTICE-HALL OF AUSTRALIA PTY. LIMITED, *Sydney*
PRENTICE-HALL OF CANADA, LTD., *Toronto*
PRENTICE-HALL OF INDIA PRIVATE LIMITED, *New Delhi*
PRENTICE-HALL OF JAPAN, INC., *Tokyo*
PRENTICE-HALL OF SOUTHEAST ASIA PTE. LTD., *Singapore*
WHITEHALL BOOKS LIMITED, *Wellington, New Zealand*

Contents

3 **Field Effect Transistors
for Logic Circuits**   **52**

4 NAND **Gates and**
NOR **Gates**   **68**

5 **Logic Gate Symbols
and Tables**   **78**

6 **TTL and** CMOS
Integrated Circuit Devices   **84**

7

Equivalent Gate Symbols and Signal Names   110

8

Combinations of Gates for Logic Functions   121

9

Binary Numbers and Their Applications   148

15   Shift Registers, Latches, and Up/Down Counters   276

16   Arithmetic Circuits   297

Preface

Digital electronics is among the most rapidly growing technologies. Virtually every industrial and commercial activity has been heavily penetrated with digital equipment. Electronic calculators, computers, and cash registers, to name just a few, can be seen almost everywhere. No other occupation offers the varied, interesting, challenging, and rewarding opportunities that the digital electronics industry does.

In the plant, digital electronics technicians work in research and development, engineering, quality control, production testing, troubleshooting, etc. This list could be endless. Outside the plant and on the road they serve in sales, field servicing and testing, and liaison between plant and customers. This list, too, goes on and on. For every personality type, there is a niche for the hardworking person with a digital background.

This laboratory text was developed during many years of experience in training technicians for industry. We have tuned in on the needs of a broad cross section of industries and therefore shall emphasize material that most digital electronics employers consider important. We have included fundamentals that make technicians adaptable to the immediate and long-term needs of their companies. Also, we have learned that when an employer asks for an experienced technician, he is often after someone who is *not* simply a textbook "expert." Hands-on experience with digital ICs, such as provided in the laboratory experiments here, is most welcome and usually more than satisfactory on the entry level. The laboratory experiments also serve to minimize abstractions. The concepts discussed in the text are immediately followed by exposure to the hardware that does the job. Even the few mathematical principles involved, although simple, are not introduced until their applications can be demonstrated with hardware.

In summary, our goals have been to

1. Provide laboratory experiments immediately after the related text to maximize students' interest and comprehension.

2. Teach digital electronics in an interesting and dynamic way by including easy to visualize problems and many blinking lights in the laboratory experiments.

3. Familiarize the students with computer industry language and jargon to make them better able to communicate with those already working in the digital industry.

4. Present the material in a progressive order so that useful knowledge and understanding are established with each chapter so that even students who do not complete this entire text will gain a foothold needed to step into the computer industry.

5. Encourage teamwork in more complicated laboratory experiments, which prepares students for typical work environments.

6. Emphasize applications and the practical uses of digital electronics.

7. Expose the students to a broad range of digital fundamentals and hardware, which prepares them to easily adapt to more extensive systems.

8. Introduce each mathematical concept at a time that its relevance can be demonstrated.

9. Allow a student to start this text after he or she has established an understanding of *basic* electrical principles.

G. Rutkowski

J. Oleksy

FUNDAMENTALS
OF
DIGITAL ELECTRONICS

Introduction

In each of the laboratory experiments presented, the list of EQUIPMENT always speci-
fies a *digital breadboard kit*. This kit enables us to quickly and accurately build the
experimental circuits discussed. There is a variety of breadboards commercially
available on which the circuits can be wired; for example, see Fig. I-1. Any
equivalent is suitable provided the digital breadboard kit, as a whole, includes

1. A terminal strip or sockets for plugging in integrated circuits (ICs) (the breadboard).

2. A +5-V dc regulated power supply that is capable of delivering up to about
   500 mA (see Fig. I-2).

3. Four indicator lamps and drivers (see Fig. I-3).

4. Four logic simulator toggle switches (see Fig. I-4).

5. One or two bounceless switches (see Fig. I-5).

6. A 1-Hz square-wave generator (see Fig. I-6).

7. Assorted lengths of #22 solid hookup wire.

Needless to say, without these circuits and components, the experiments will not
work properly.

Fig. I-1. Courtesy of Aptek, Inc.

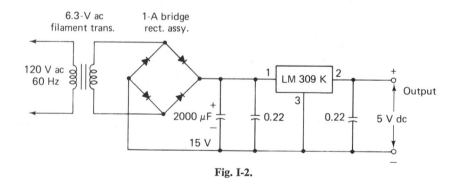

Fig. I-2.

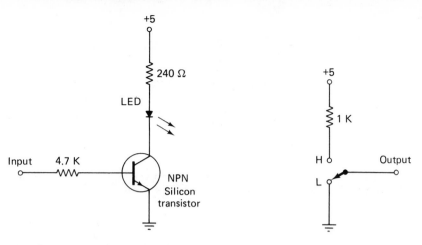

Fig. I-3. Lamp driver (discussed in Chap. 2).

Fig. I-4. Logic simulator toggle switch.

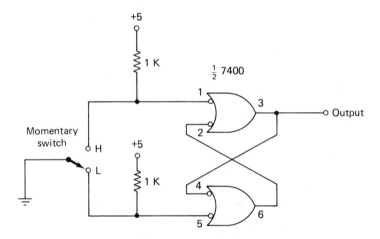

Fig. I-5. Bounceless switch (discussed in Chap. 12).

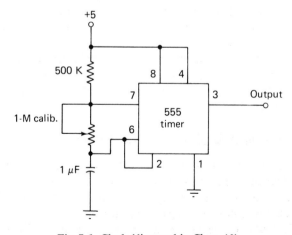

Fig. I-6. Clock (discussed in Chap. 10).

3

1

Diodes and Their Applications

Introduction

Diodes are the simplest of solid-state components. A diode has only two leads, an *anode* and a *cathode*. The symbol for a diode and a variety of packages used to contain diodes are shown in Fig. 1-1. The size of the package is a good indication of what current the diode is able to conduct safely. Larger packages usually mean larger current ratings. The manufacturers of diodes indicate the current ratings of their products in specification (spec) sheets.

Small diodes are used in great numbers in various types of electronic equipment. In amplifiers and communications equipment, such as found in home radio and TV receivers, diodes serve as temperature stabilizers, signal detectors, and regulators, to name just a few. Small diodes are also used in decision-making logic circuits within computers and automated industrial equipment.

Larger diodes are used in electrical power supplies. These power supplies typically convert ac voltages to dc. Most electronic equipment requires dc voltage as a source of power.

1-1 The Diode as a Unilateral Conductor

The diode is a *unilateral* conductor, which means that it conducts current well in one direction and not well in the other direction. The arrow, on the symbol of a diode, points in the direction that conventional current flows well, which means that electrons flow well against the arrow.

The least confusing way to determine whether a diode will or will not conduct is to note the polarity of the voltage to be applied to it. The voltage applied to a diode,

4

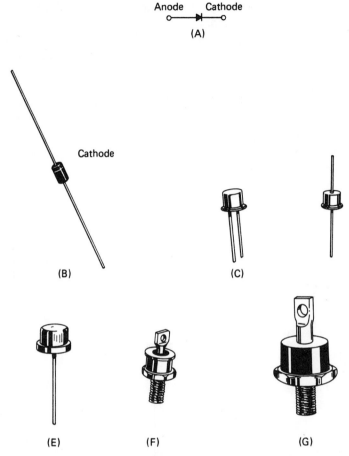

Fig. 1-1. (A) Schematic symbol for diode; (B) small signal diode; stripe indicates end to which the cathode is connected; (C) through (E) are moderate current diodes; (F) and (G) are high current diodes. The diodes (D) through (G) have one lead connected to the case, which can be either the cathode or anode as ordered by the circuit designer.

and to other solid-state components, is commonly called *bias.* When a diode's anode is more positive than its cathode, as shown in Fig. 1-2(A), the diode is said to be *forward biased* and able to conduct current well. If the applied voltage is such as to make the diode's anode more negative than its cathode, as shown in Fig. 1-2(B), it does not conduct current well and is said to be *reverse biased* or *back biased.*

A diode, therefore, can be shown to have low resistance when forward biased and high resistance when back biased. The ohmmeter in Fig. 1-3(A) will measure low resistance because its negative lead is applied to the cathode while its positive lead is applied to its anode; that is, the battery in the ohmmeter forward-biases the diode. On the other hand, if the leads are reversed, as shown in Fig. 1-3(B), the measured resistance is high because the diode is back biased.

For most practical purposes, a forward-biased diode can be considered equivalent to a short circuit having negligible resistance and voltage drop. Therefore, in the circuit of Fig. 1-2(A) nearly all of the supply voltage E is across the resistor R. If the values of the supply voltage E and the resistance R are known, we can estimate the current in R, which is the circuit current and the current in the diode, with Ohm's law:

$$I = \frac{E}{R}$$

A reverse-biased diode is very nearly equivalent to an open circuit. That is, in the circuit of Fig. 1-2(B) the diode behaves like an open switch, and nearly all of the supply voltage E appears across it.

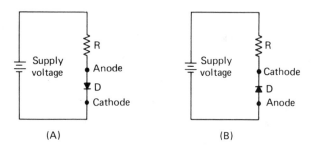

(A)   (B)

Fig. 1-2. (A) Forward-biased diode; (B) reverse-biased diode.

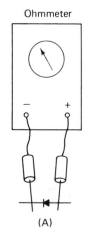

(A)

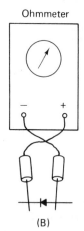

(B)

Fig. 1-3. (A) Ohmmeter measures low resistance; (B) ohmmeter measures high resistance.

Summary

1. Diodes are unilateral conductors.

2. A diode is forward biased when its anode is positive with respect to its cathode.

3. A diode is reverse biased when its anode is negative with respect to its cathode.

4. An ohmmeter will measure high resistance on a diode in one direction and low resistance in the other direction.

5. When forward biased, a diode behaves like a short circuit for most practical purposes.

6. When reverse biased, a diode behaves like an open circuit for most practical purposes.

7. The current in a series circuit with a supply voltage E, a resistance R, and a forward-biased diode D can be estimated by dividing the supply voltage E by the resistance R (Ohm's law).

Problems 1-1

1. The diode in the circuit of Fig. 1-4 is being measured with an ohmmeter. Should we expect to read a *high* or *low* resistance? Why?

    Ans. __High ResistANce   BecAuse it is Revere BIAsed__

2. If the ohmmeter leads in the circuit of Fig. 1-4 are reversed, what resistance should we read, *high* or *low*? Why?   *Ans.* __low   ForwARd BiAsed__

3. If the supply voltage $E = 20$ V and $R = 1$ kΩ in the circuit of Fig. 1-2(A), how much voltage can we expect to read across the resistor?

    Ans. ___ ~~2 milliamps~~   Almost   20V   __VoltAge ACRos3 Diode vary low__

4. With reference to Problem 3, how much current can we expect to flow in the circuit?   *Ans.* ___ 20   milliAmps___

5. With reference to Problem 3, how much voltage can we expect to measure across the diode D?   *Ans.* ___ Almost none___

$U = R i$

$$I = \frac{V}{R} = \frac{20v}{1000}$$

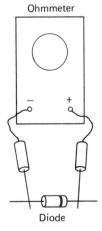

Ohmmeter

Fig. 1-4.   Diode

6. If the supply voltage $E = 20$ V and $R = 1$ kΩ in the circuit of Fig. 1-2(B), how much voltage can we expect to measure across the resistor?

   Ans.   Almost none

7. What is the current in the circuit described in Problem 6?

   Ans.   For all practical purposes (zero)

8. How much voltage can we expect to measure across the diode in the circuit described in Problem 6?   *Ans.*   20 v

ACT AS IF THE 9. If the diode in the circuit of Fig. 1-2 is defective (burned open), what voltage
DIODE WERE   drops would you expect to measure across the resistor R and across the diode
Rev-Biased D?   *Ans.*   Almost none across the resistor
                                      all across the open cht

1-2 Diodes as Rectifiers

An ac voltage is one whose amplitude and polarity vary as time passes. The continually changing polarity of ac voltage causes current to repetitively change direction. Since a diode conducts current in only one direction, a diode in an ac circuit will interfere with the usual two-directional current. When used in an ac circuit, the diode, or the circuit itself, is called a *rectifier*.

The simplest rectifier circuit is shown in Fig. 1-5. As the ac supply voltage repetitively changes polarity, the diode repetitively switches from being conductive (forward biased) to being nonconductive (reverse biased). That is, as shown in Fig. 1-5(B), each positive alternation of the supply voltage E puts a forward bias on the diode, causing it to act like a short for most practical purposes. All positive alternations of this supply, therefore, appear across the resistor R, and electrons flow in the direction indicated. On each negative alternation, the diode is reverse biased and behaves like an open, as shown in Fig. 1-5(C), and no current flows. Since the source voltage always appears across an open in a series circuit, all negative alternations appear across the diode D.

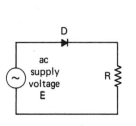

(A) Simple rectifier circuit

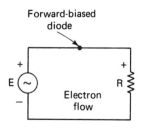

(B) Diode behaves as a short when forward biased by positive alternations of E

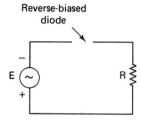

(C) Diode behaves as an open when reverse biased by negative alternations of E.

Fig. 1-5.

An electronic voltmeter (EVM), with its selector switch in the ac position, placed across the ac supply voltage *E*, will of course measure the value of this supply. If we change the selector switch to the +dc position, as shown in Fig. 1-6, the EVM will read zero. This is to be expected. There normally is no dc voltage available directly from an ac supply. Also shown, the scope in this case will display the entire waveform (both alternations) of the supply voltage.

If the scope and EVM are placed across the resistor instead, as shown in Fig. 1-7, only the positive alternations are displayed on the scope, and the EVM now reads a dc voltage. Thus the diode *D* in a series ac circuit enables us to convert ac voltages into dc. Some of the less expensive battery chargers use this simple circuit.

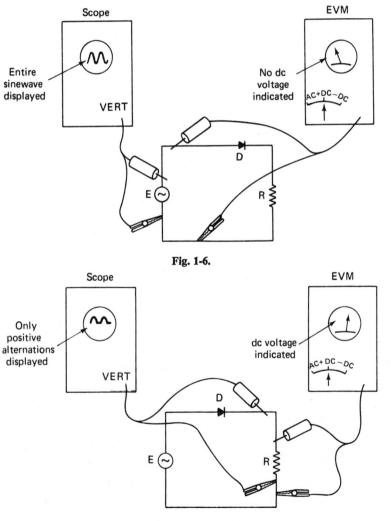

Fig. 1-6.

Fig. 1-7.

Since the diode *D* is like an open on the negative alternations, the negative alternations will appear across the diode. This fact can be observed with a scope, as shown in Fig. 1-8. Also shown, the EVM will now indicate a negative voltage. That is, the pointer reads up-scale when the selector switch is in the −dc position.

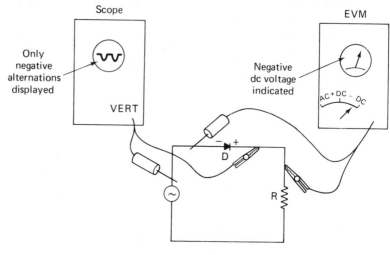

Fig. 1-8.

Summary

1. A diode in a series ac circuit will permit current flow on half the alternation only.

2. Diodes, therefore, are able to convert ac into dc voltage and are called rectifiers.

3. In a rectifier circuit, such as in Fig. 1-6, the alternations of the supply voltage that forward bias the diode *D* appear across the resistor *R* (load).

4. In a rectifier circuit, such as in Fig. 1-6, the alternations of the supply voltage that reverse bias the diode *D* appear across the diode.

5. If a rectifier circuit is working properly, dc voltages can be measured across the resistor *R* (load) and across the diode *D* (anode negative with respect to the cathode).

Problems 1-2

1. If in the circuit of Fig. 1-6, only the diode *D* is reversed so that the arrow points left instead of to the right, describe the waveform we should observe with the scope. *Ans.* _____SAME   FULL   SINE WAVE_____
How much voltage should we expect to measure with the EVM if the selector switch is in the dc position? *Ans.* _____no dc voltage_____

2. With reference to the circuit described in Problem 1, on what alternations, positive or negative, will current flow? *Ans.* _negative_

3. Still with reference to the circuit described in Problem 1, in which direction can electrons flow, clockwise or counterclockwise? *Ans.* _clockwise_

4. If we reverse the diode connection in Fig. 1-7 so that the arrow points to the left instead of to the right, what kind of waveform can we expect to see with the scope? Assume that the scope's and EVM's leads are across the resistor *R* as shown. Sketch your answer.

5. With reference to the circuit described in Problem 4, into what position must we place the EVM's selector switch to get an up-scale dc reading?

    Ans. _−dc_

6. If only the diode is reversed in the circuit of Fig. 1-8, sketch the waveform we should expect to see with the scope.

7. With reference to the circuit described in Problem 6, into what position must we place the EVM's selector switch to get an up-scaled dc reading?

    Ans. _+dc_

8. If the diode in the circuit of Fig. 1-8 burns open, what kind of waveform should we expect to see with the scope? Sketch your answer.

1-3   Diodes as Logic Circuit Components

In this age of computers and automation, logic circuits represent the largest and most rapidly growing segment of the electronics industry. Logic circuits are built with basic "building blocks" called gates. Among the most elementary gates are AND gates and OR gates, whose symbols are shown in Fig. 1-9. The gates themselves contain discrete components such as resistors, diodes, and transistors. As we shall see while progressing through this text, logic circuit gates are classified in logic families such as DTL (diode-transistor logic), RTL (resistor-transistor logic), ECL (emitter-coupled logic), and TTL or T²L (transistor-transistor logic). At this time we shall confine ourselves to gates made with diodes and resistors.

Generally, regardless of the logic family, logic circuits work with only two voltage levels at their inputs and outputs with respect to ground or common. These levels are typically 0 V and some positive voltage value. Frequent switching from one to the other occurs during normal circuit operation. Since these abruptly changing voltage levels are at inputs and outputs of logic circuit gates, they are called *logic signals*.

Commonly the term LOW or the letter L and sometimes the symbol 0 (zero) are used in reference to the 0-V logic level. On the other hand, the term HIGH or the letter H and sometimes the number 1 (one) are used in reference to the positive voltage level.

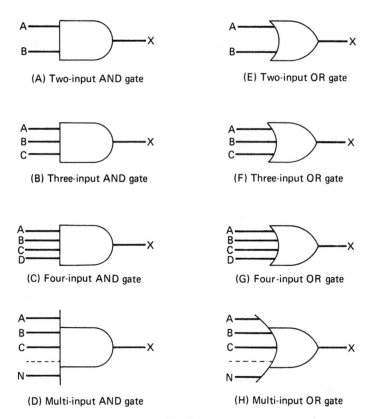

(A) Two-input AND gate

(E) Two-input OR gate

(B) Three-input AND gate

(F) Three-input OR gate

(C) Four-input AND gate

(G) Four-input OR gate

(D) Multi-input AND gate

(H) Multi-input OR gate

Fig. 1-9.

1-3.1 The AND Gate

Generally, the output signal of a logic circuit gate is HIGH or LOW depending on specific input requirements and the type of gate being used. The AND gate for example, has a LOW output if any one of its inputs is LOW. Only when all the inputs of an AND gate go HIGH will the output X go HIGH. Thus, referring to AND gate (A) of Fig. 1-9, the output X goes HIGH when both inputs go HIGH. Similarly, the output X of AND gate (B) goes HIGH only if all three of its inputs are pulled HIGH.

1-3.2 The OR Gate

Unlike the AND gate, the output of an OR gate remains LOW only if all its inputs are LOW. Thus, if any one of the inputs of an OR gate is made HIGH, its output becomes HIGH. For example, the output X of OR gate (G) in Fig. 1-9 is LOW only when all four of its inputs are LOW. If we drive any one or more of its inputs HIGH, the output X goes HIGH.

1-3.3 The Diode-Resistor AND Gate

Two-input diode-resistor AND gates are shown in Fig. 1-10. In part (A) of this figure, the input logic signals are applied to inputs *A* and *B* with the switches shown. In practice, input logic signals are not necessarily generated with mechanical switches. More likely, input signals are from the outputs of other logic circuits, as we shall see later. The two-input diode-resistor AND gate is more simply shown as in Fig. 1-10(B).

The way any logic circuit behaves can be itemized on a *truth table*. A truth table for a two-input AND gate is shown in Fig. 1-11. It itemizes all possible combinations of inputs *A* and *B* and the resulting output at *X* with each input combination. For example, in row 1, both inputs are L (LOW), representing 0 V, as is the case when both switches in the circuit of Fig. 1-10(A) are down in the L positions. As shown in the equivalent circuit in Fig. 1-12(A), both diodes are forward biased in this case, and behave as short circuits. The output voltage V_0 at *X* is 0 V or logic L because *X* is effectively grounded through these conducting diodes.

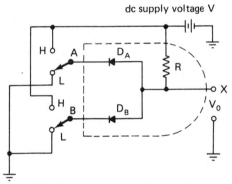

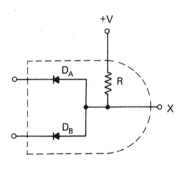

(A) Two-input diode-resistor AND gate
using switches to apply input
logic symbols

(B) Simple schematic diagram
of a two-input diode-resistor
AND gate

Fig. 1-10.

Truth Table

	Inputs		Output
	A	B	X
①	L	L	L
②	L	H	L
③	H	L	L
④	H	H	H

Fig. 1-11. Truth table for a two-input AND gate.

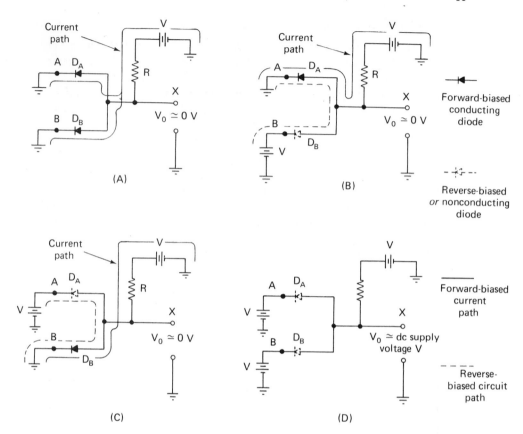

Fig. 1-12. Two-input diode-resistor AND gate with (A) both inputs L; (B) input A logic L and input B logic H; (C) input A logic H and input B logic L; (D) both inputs H.

If the switch at input B of the circuit in Fig. 1-10(A) is placed up in the H position while switch A remains in the L position, row 2 of the truth table indicates the input and resulting output signals. Diode D_A is forward biased and conducts current in the path shown in Fig. 1-12(B). In this case, however, diode D_B is reversed biased and nonconducting. That is, the HIGH logic signal at input B reverse-biases diode D_B through the diode D_A in the broken line circuit path shown. Conducting diode D_A, behaving like a short, holds the output X at ground potential, which is at logic level L.

When input A is HIGH and input B is LOW, the equivalent circuit can be shown as in Fig. 1-12(C). In this case diode D_B is forward biased and conducts current in the path indicated. Diode D_A is reverse biased by the HIGH logic level applied to input A through the conducting diode D_B as shown with the broken line circuit path. The output at X is still LOW because the conducting D_B holds this output at ground potential. Of course, row 3 of the truth table indicates the input and the resulting output conditions in this case.

Finally, when both switches are up in the H positions in the circuit of Fig. 1-10 its equivalent can be shown as the circuit of Fig. 1-12(D). Now the anode and cathode of each diode are at the same potential, assuming that each HIGH input voltage and the dc supply voltage are equal. With no potential difference across them, the diodes are nonconducting. With no current through either diode there can be no current in or voltage drop across resistor R, and the entire dc supply voltage appears at output X with respect to ground. That is, as shown in row 4 of the truth table, the output X is HIGH when both inputs are HIGH.

1-3.4 The Diode-Resistor OR Gate

Two-input diode resistor OR gates and their truth table are shown in Fig. 1-13. As with the AND gate, the inputs A and B of the OR gate can be mechanically switched HIGH or LOW, but more commonly the HIGH or LOW signals arrive from the outputs of other logic circuits.

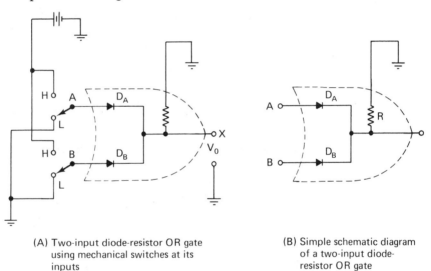

(A) Two-input diode-resistor OR gate using mechanical switches at its inputs

(B) Simple schematic diagram of a two-input diode-resistor OR gate

Truth Table

	Inputs		Output
	A	B	X
①	L	L	L
②	L	H	H
③	H	L	H
④	H	H	H

(C) Truth table for the two-input OR gate

Fig. 1-13.

As shown in the truth table of Fig. 1-13(C), the output voltage at *X* is LOW only when both inputs *A* and *B* are LOW. With both inputs LOW, there is no source of voltage, as shown in the equivalent circuit of Fig. 1-14(A), and the voltage at *X* to ground must be 0 V or logic LOW.

When input *A* is LOW but input *B* is HIGH, corresponding to row 2 of the truth table, the equivalent circuit in Fig. 1-14(B) applies. As shown, the voltage V_{in} (HIGH logic level) applied to input *B* forward-biases diode D_B, admitting current in the

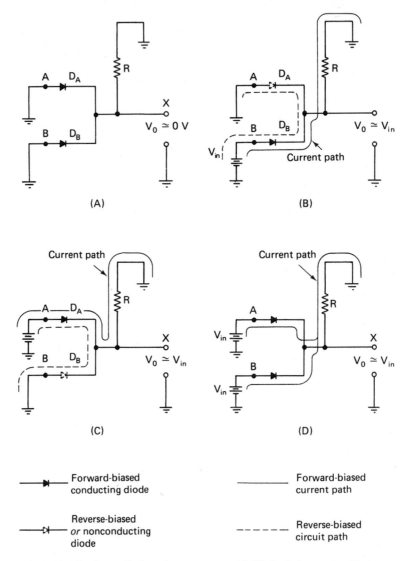

Fig. 1-14. Two-input diode-resistor OR gate with (A) both inputs L: (B) input *A* logic L and input *B* logic H: (C) input *A* logic H and input *B* logic L; (D) both inputs H.

path shown. Diode D_A, however, is reverse biased by V_{in} via the conducting diode D_B. Thus, the HIGH input voltage V_{in} is passed directly to output via the conducting diode D_B.

When input A is HIGH while input B is LOW, as shown in row 3 of the truth table, the circuit of Fig. 1-14(C) illustrates the situation. In this case diode D_A is forward biased and conducting, while diode D_B is reverse biased and nonconducting. That is, the HIGH input voltage V_{in} applies a reverse bias voltage across diode D_B through the conducting diode D_A. The output X is HIGH again because input A and output X are directly connected via the conducting diode D_A.

When both inputs are HIGH, as in row 4, both diodes conduct as shown in Fig. 1-14(D). As with input conductions of rows 2 and 3, the output X is HIGH. In this case, both of the HIGH inputs are directly connected to the output X via their respective diodes.

Summary

1. Logic circuits represent the largest and most rapidly growing segment in the electronics industry.

2. Logic circuits work with only two voltage levels at their inputs and outputs.

3. The two-level voltages at inputs and outputs of logic circuits are called logic signals, and they typically change from one level to the other quickly and frequently.

4. Commonly, the term LOW or the letter L is used to refer to the 0-V logic level, and the term HIGH or the letter H is used to refer to the positive voltage level of a logic signal.

5. An AND gate's output remains LOW if any one of its inputs is LOW. Only after all the inputs go HIGH can the AND gate's output go HIGH.

6. An OR gate's output is LOW only if all of its inputs are LOW. Its output goes HIGH if any one of its inputs goes HIGH.

7. Truth tables show how logic circuits behave by itemizing all possible input combinations and the resulting outputs.

8. AND gates can be made with diodes, resistors, and a dc supply voltage.

9. OR gates can be made with diodes and resistors.

10. The HIGH level output voltage of a diode-resistor logic gate is equal to the HIGH input voltage(s), assuming that the voltage drop across each conducting diode is negligible.

Problems 1-3

1. If we have a two-input AND gate with one of its inputs HIGH while the other is LOW, the output logic level will be _____*L*_____.

2. If both inputs of a two-input AND gate are LOW, the output will be __L__.

3. If both inputs of a two-input AND gate are HIGH, the output will be __H__.

4. If one input is LOW and the other HIGH on a two-input OR gate, the output logic level will be __H__.

5. If both inputs of a two-input OR gate are LOW, the output will be __L__.

6. If both inputs of a two-input OR gate are HIGH, the output will be __H__.

7. If a two-input AND gate's signal levels are 0 V and 5 V, show its truth table in Fig. 1-15(A). Use the voltage levels in place of the H and L letter symbols.

8. If a two-input OR gate's signal levels are 0 V and 12 V, show its truth table in Fig. 1-15(B). Use the voltage levels in place of the H and L letter symbols.

9. The circuit in Fig. 1-16(A) is a three-input __AND__ gate.

10. Referring to the circuit in Fig. 1-16(A) and its truth table [Fig. 1-16(B)], show its logic level outputs in column X for *each* combination of inputs A, B, and C shown.

11. The circuit in Fig. 1-17(A) is a three-input __OR__ gate.

12. Make the table in Fig. 1-17(B) the truth table for the circuit in Fig. 1-17(A). Show all possible combinations of inputs and the resulting outputs using the letter symbols H and L and the table in Fig. 1-16(B) as a guide.

For the following problems, assume that forward-biased diodes behave like shorts and that reverse-biased diodes behave as opens.

Fwd - short
Rev - open

13. With reference to the AND gate in Fig. 1-10(A), if the dc supply is 12 V and both switches are down in the L positions, what voltage values should we expect
    (a) At point X to ground?
    (b) Across resistor R?
    (c) Across diode D_A?
    (d) Across diode D_B?

    Ans. (a) __0 V__   (b) __12 V__   (c) __0 V__   (d) __0 V__

14. If the switch A is up in the H position and switch B is down in the L position in the circuit of Fig. 1-10(A), what are the answers to the questions listed in Problem 13?

    Ans. (a) __0 V__   (b) __12 V__   (c) __0 V__   (d) __0 V__

15. If both switches in the circuit of Fig. 1-10(A) are up in the H positions, what are the answers to the questions in Problem 13?

    Ans. (a) __12 V__   (b) __0__   (c) __0 V__   (d) __12 V__

Inputs		Outputs
A	B	X
(1) 0	0	0
(2) 0	5	0
(3) 5	0	0
(4) 5	5	5

(A)

Inputs		Outputs
A	B	X
(1) 0	6	0
(2) 0	12	12
(3) 12	0	12
(4) 12	12	12

(B)

Fig. 1-15. (A) Truth table for a two-input AND gate with 0 V and 5 V logic levels; (B) truth table for a two-input OR gate with 0 V and 12 V logic levels.

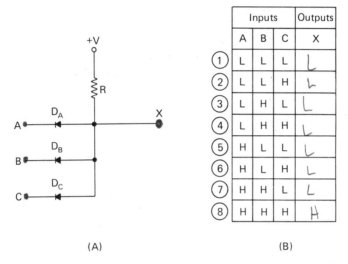

	Inputs			Outputs
	A	B	C	X
(1)	L	L	L	L
(2)	L	L	H	L
(3)	L	H	L	L
(4)	L	H	H	L
(5)	H	L	L	L
(6)	H	L	H	L
(7)	H	H	L	L
(8)	H	H	H	H

(A)   (B)

Fig. 1-16. (A) Three-input diode-resistor logic gate; (B) truth table for the three-input gate showing all possible combinations of inputs.

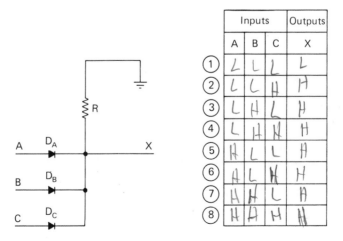

	Inputs			Outputs
	A	B	C	X
(1)	L	L	L	L
(2)	L	L	H	H
(3)	L	H	L	H
(4)	L	H	H	H
(5)	H	L	L	H
(6)	H	L	H	H
(7)	H	H	L	H
(8)	H	H	H	H

Fig. 1-17. (A) Three-input diode-resistor logic gate and its truth table (B).

16. With reference to the circuit of Fig. 1-13, if the dc supply voltage is 5 V and both switches are down in the L positions, what voltage values should we expect

    (a) At point X to ground?
    (b) Across resistor R?
    (c) Across diode D_A?
    (d) Across diode D_B?

Ans. (a) ___0___ (b) ___0 V___ (c) ___5 V___ (d) ___5 V___

17. If switch A is down in the L position and switch B is up in the H position in the circuit of Fig. 1-13(A), what are the answers to the questions listed in Problem 16?

Ans. (a) ___5 V___ (b) ___5 V___ (c) ___5 V___ (d) ___0___

18. If both switches in the circuit of Fig. 1-13(A) are up in the H positions, what are the answers to the questions in Problem 16?

Ans. (a) ___5 V___ (b) ___5 V___ (c) ___0 V___ (d) ___0 V___

Experiment 1-1   Forward-Biased and Reverse-Biased Diodes

Purpose

To become familiar with forward-biased and reverse-biased diodes.

Equipment

> Variable dc power supply voltage E
> Breadboard and appropriate interconnecting wires or clip leads
> 1-kΩ, $\frac{1}{4}$-W $\pm 5\%$ resistor
> 220-Ω $\frac{1}{4}$-W $\pm 5\%$ resistor
> Diode: 1N92 or equivalent

Procedure

1. Measure the diode's resistance with an ohmmeter as shown in Figs. 1-3(A) and (B). Measured forward bias resistance is _____. Measured reverse bias resistance is _____.

2. Breadboard the circuit of Fig. 1-2(A) and adjust the power supply voltage to 24 V. Use the 1-kΩ resistor and include a milliammeter if available. Measure the resistor's voltage drop V_R and the diode's voltage drop V_D. Measured $V_R =$ _____. Measured $V_D =$ _____.

3. What is the current I in this circuit? Calculated $I = E/R =$ _____. Measured with milliammeter, $I =$ _____ (optional).

4. Repeat steps 2 and 3 with circuit of Fig. 1-2(B). Measured $V_R =$ _____. Measured $V_D =$ _____. Calculated $I =$ _____. Measured $I =$ _____ (optional).

5. Breadboard the circuit of Fig. 1-2(A) using the 220 resistor and include a milliammeter if available. Adjust the power supply to 11 V. Measure the voltage drop of the resistor and diode, and determine the circuit current. Measured $V_R =$ _____. Measured $V_D =$ _____. Calculated I _____. Measured $I =$ _____ (optional).

6. Repeat step 5 but replace the diode with one that is known to be defective (open) or simply remove the diode, leaving an open in its place. Measured $V_R =$ _____. Measured $V_D =$ _____. Calculated $I =$ _____. Measured $I =$ _____ (optional).

Experiment 1-2   The Diode as a Rectifier

Purpose

To use a diode as a rectifier.

Equipment

Low-voltage 60-Hz ac supply: Isolated secondary or a 6.3-V or a
12.6-V rms filament transformer or an equivalent of either.
Electronic voltmeter (EVM)
Oscilloscope (scope)
Breadboard and appropriate interconnecting wires or clip leads
2.2-kΩ, $\frac{1}{4}$-W ±5% resistor
Diode: 1N92 or equivalent

Procedure

1. Construct the circuit of Fig. L 1-2(A), and place the scope and EVM to measure the voltage at point X to ground. Use Fig. L 1-2(B) to sketch the waveform
observed with the scope. Measure the ac and dc voltages of this supply with the

scope. Measured ac _____. Measured dc _____.

2. Next, place the scope and EVM across the resistor R and measure the voltage at point Y. Use Fig. L 1-2(C) to sketch the waveform observed and measure

the dc voltage. Measured dc _____.

3. Now place the scope and EVM across the diode D from point X to Y, with
the common at Y. Use part D to sketch the waveform observed and measure the

dc voltage. Measured dc _____.

4. Referring to the circuit described in step 3 above place a piece of wire (a
short) across the diode D and observe the effect this has on the resistor's voltage
waveform. Describe the change that occurs when the short is put in place.

_____

_____

5. Referring to the circuit described in step 3 above replace the diode D with one
that is known to be burned open or simply leave an open in its place. Observe the
effect that this has on the diode's voltage waveform. Describe the waveform
observed in this case comparatively with the waveform you have sketched in Fig.

L 1-2(D). _____

_____

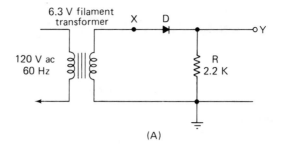

(A)

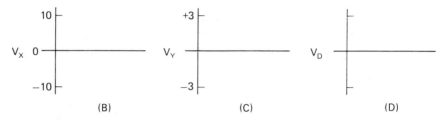

(B)   (C)   (D)

Fig. L 1-2.

Experiment 1-3 Diode Gates

Purpose

Familiarization with AND gate, OR gate, and truth tables.

Equipment

Low-voltage dc supply (1 to 15 V)
Electronic voltmeter (EVM)
4.7-kΩ, $\frac{1}{4}$-W $\pm 5\%$ resistor
Three diodes; any germanium type
Three switches; SPDT (single-pole, double-throw)
Breadboard and appropriate interconnecting wires or clip leads

Procedure

Construct the circuit of Fig. 1-10, and adjust the dc supply to 15 V. Measure the voltages V_0 at output X to ground, V_{D_A} across the diode D_A, V_{D_B} across the diode D_B, and V_R across the resistor R with each of the following four combinations of inputs:

1. Both switches are thrown into positions that ground (place 0 V to ground on) inputs A and B. Place measured voltage drops V_0, V_{D_A}, V_{D_B}, and V_R in the appropriate columns of row 1 of the table in Fig. L 1-3(A).

2. The switch at input A is not changed, causing 0 V to ground measured at A, but the switch at input B is thrown to place 15 V to ground at this input. Place the measured voltage drops in row 2 of the table in Fig. L 1-3(A).

3. Both switches are thrown, placing 15 V at input A and 0 V at input B. Place measured voltage drops in row 3 in Fig. L 1-3(A).

4. The switch at input B is thrown so that the voltage at input A remains at 15 V to ground and the voltage at input B rises to 15 V. Place the measured drops in row 4 in Fig. L 1-3(A).

Construct the circuit of Fig. 1-13, and adjust the dc supply to 15 V. Measure the voltages V_0 at output X to ground, V_{D_A} across the diode D_A, V_{D_B} across the diode D_B, and V_R across the resistor R with each of the following four combinations of inputs:

5. Both switches are thrown so that both inputs are 0 V to ground. Place the measured voltage drops in row 1 of the table in Fig. L 1-3(B).

6. The switch B is thrown so that the voltage at input A is 0 V to ground and input B is 15 V to ground. Place the measured drops in row 2 in Fig. L 1-3(B).

7. Both switches are thrown so that input A rises 15 V while input B drops to 0 V. Place the measured drops in row 3 in Fig. L 1-3(B).

8. The switch at input *B* is thrown so that input *A* remains at 15 V but input *B* rises to 15 V. Place the measured drops in row 4 in Fig. L 1-3(B).

9. Construct the circuit of Fig. 1-16(A) using switches at its inputs as a means of applying HIGH and LOW input logic levels. Adjust the dc supply to 8 V. Start by throwing the switches to get the input logic levels shown in row 1 of the table in Fig. L 1-3(C). Measure the resulting voltage drops, and record them in the appropriate blocks of this row. Then proceed to do the same with each of the remaining rows.

10. Construct the circuit of Fig. 1-17(A) using switches as its inputs as a means of applying HIGH and LOW input logic levels. Adjust the dc supply to 10 V. Start by throwing the switches so that the input levels match the inputs in row 1 of the table in Fig. L 1-3(D). Measure the resulting voltage drops, and record them in the appropriate blocks of this row. Repeat this procedure with each of the remaining rows.

	Input		X	V_{D_A}	V_{D_B}	V_R
	A	B				
1	L	L				
2	L	H				
3	H	L				
4	H	H				

(A)

	Input		X	V_{D_A}	V_{D_B}	V_R
	A	B				
1	L	L				
2	L	H				
3	H	L				
4	H	H				

(B)

	Input			X	V_{D_A}	V_{D_B}	V_{D_C}	V_R
	A	B	C					
1	0 V	0 V	0 V					
2	0	0	8					
3	0	8	0					
4	0	8	8					
5	8	0	0					
6	8	0	8					
7	8	8	0					
8	8	8	8					

(C)

	Input			X	V_{D_A}	V_{D_B}	V_{D_C}	V_R
	A	B	C					
1	0 V	0 V	0 V					
2	0	0	8					
3	0	8	0					
4	0	8	8					
5	8	0	0					
6	8	0	8					
7	8	8	0					
8	8	8	8					

(D)

Fig. L 1-3.

2

Transistors and Their Applications

Introduction

The invention of the transistor triggered the rapid growth of the electronics industry. Before transistors, electronic circuits were large, bulky, and unreliable. They consumed considerable power (energy) and therefore generated too much heat, which contributed to the deterioration of other circuit parts and materials, such as resistors, capacitors, and insulation. With transistors, circuits became much smaller, more efficient in the use of energy, and far more reliable. The higher reliability of transistor circuits compared to vacuum tube equivalents is an extremely important advantage. In a properly designed circuit, the transistor is much less likely to become defective than a tube. Since transistors work more efficiently (cooler), other circuit parts and materials are much less likely to fail due to excessive exposure to heat.

The techniques used to manufacture transistors led to developments that made it possible to mass-produce very small and highly reliable electronics circuits commonly known as *integrated circuits* (ICs). ICs have transistors, diodes, resistors, and all interconnecting leads formed on a single piece of semiconductor material. We need to become familiar with transistors and how they behave because

1. Large numbers of transistors are contained in ICs, which are discussed in later chapters, and

2. Transistors are so numerous in discrete parts circuits.

Discrete parts circuits are those made with individual components.

26

2-1 Transistor Packages

Individual (discrete part) transistors are available in a number of package types, as shown in Fig. 2-1. Generally, the larger packages contain transistors that are able to conduct larger currents. The packages in Fig. 2-1(A) are typical of transistors that are required to conduct small currents, up to about 200 mA. These small current transistors are frequently used in digital circuits and systems. The larger packages in Fig. 2-1(B) contain transistors capable of carrying up to a few amperes.

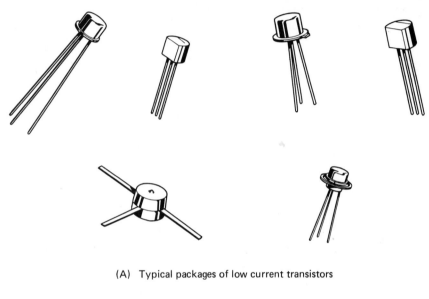

(A) Typical packages of low current transistors

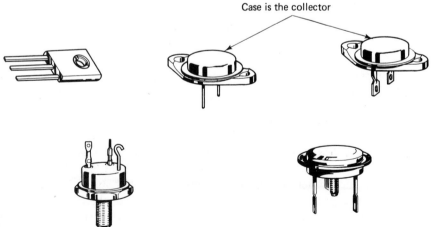

Case is the collector

(B) Packages for higher current transistors

Fig. 2-1.

Each of these larger packages is designed so that it can easily be mounted on a *heat sink*. A typical heat sink is a piece of metal with fins that efficiently draws heat away from the transistor package and transfers this heat to the surrounding air. Regardless of the package type, each transistor has three leads or terminals called its *base*, *collector*, and *emitter*, though with some larger current types the case serves as the collector terminal. Terminal identifications on common package types are shown in Fig. 2-2.

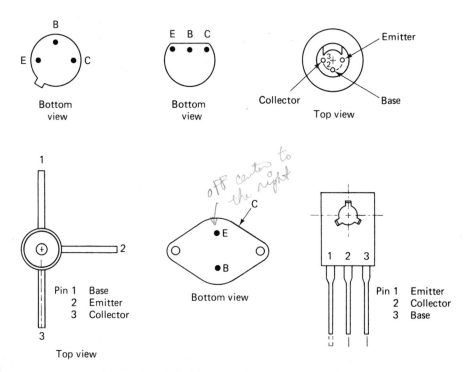

Fig. 2-2. Pin or terminal identifications of common transistor packages.

2-2 *NPN* and *PNP* Transistors

Regardless of their current ratings, transistors are available in two basic types. As shown in Figs. 2-3 and 2-4, these are *NPN* and *PNP* types. The arrow is always on the emitter *E* lead of the transistor symbol and points outward on the *NPN* transistor symbol and inward on the symbol for the *PNP* transistor. As shown in Fig. 2-3, the *NPN* transistor has its base *B* lead connected to a *P*-type semiconductor material which is formed between *N*-type materials of the collector *C* and emitter *E*. Of course, then, a *PNP*-type transistor consists of an *N*-type base *B* material between *P*-type collector *C* and emitter *E* materials.

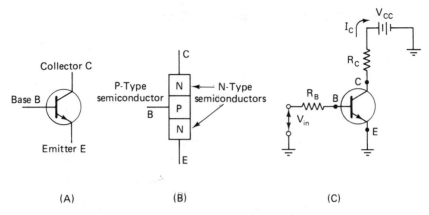

Fig. 2-3. (A) Symbol for the *NPN* transistor; (B) basic construction of the *NPN* transistor; (C) *NPN* transistor in a typical digital application.

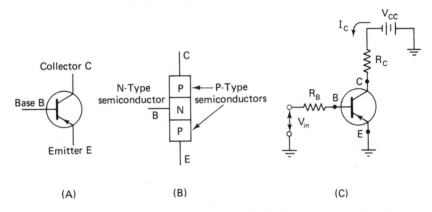

Fig. 2-4. (A) Symbol for the *PNP* transistor; (B) basic construction of the *PNP* transistor; (C) *PNP* transistor in a typical digital application.

We should note in Figs. 2-3(C) and 2-4(C) that either an *NPN*- or a *PNP*-type transistor is used depending on the polarity of the available dc source voltage V_{CC}. Application of a dc source voltage on a transistor is called *bias*. The *NPN* transistor is biased so that its collector C is positive with respect to its emitter E, whereas the *PNP* transistor is biased with its collector C negative with respect to its emitter E.

In typical digital applications, input signal voltages V_{in} are applied to the base B, through a resistor R_B, to control the current through the transistor. On the circuit of Fig. 2-3(C), if we increase V_{in} from zero to more *positive* values, the current through the transistor (between its collector C and emitter E) and through the resistor R_C increases. With the *PNP* transistor in Fig. 2-4(C), a larger *negative* input signal V_{in} causes a larger current through the transistor and resistor R_C. The current through the transistor and resistor R_C is called collector current I_C. In both circuits of Figs. 2-3(C) and 2-4(C), negligible collector current I_C flows when $V_{in} = 0$ V.

2-3   Testing Transistors with an Ohmmeter

A transistor should be checked before being used in a breadboard circuit. A quick method of testing an *NPN* transistor is shown in Fig. 2-5. First, as shown in Fig. 2-5(A), the *positive* lead of an ohmmeter is placed on the base *B*. The other *negative* lead is placed on the collector *C*, which should yield a low resistance reading with a normal transistor. That is, as the *equivalent of an NPN transistor* shows, this type of transistor consists of two diodes with their anodes connected (common) to the base *B*. The equivalent diode between the collector *C* and the base *B*, which is called the collector-to-base diode junction, is forward biased when the negative lead of the ohmmeter is applied to the collector *C* while the ohmmeter's positive lead is on the base *B*. Likewise we should have a low resistance reading when the negative lead of the ohmmeter is placed on the emitter *E*. In this case, the emitter-to-base diode junction is forward biased. Next, as shown in Fig. 2-5(B), higher resistance readings should result in these measurements when the *negative* lead of the ohmmeter is placed on the base *B* while the other (positive) lead is placed first on the collector *C* and then on the emitter *E*. In these measurements, both diode junctions are reverse biased. If the same resistance is measured across the collector-to-base junction or across the emitter-to-base junction, regardless of the polarity of the applied ohmmeter leads, the transistor is probably defective.

The *PNP* transistor can be checked with an ohmmeter much as is the *NPN* transistor. With the *PNP* transistor, however, we should observe low resistance measurements when the *negative* lead of the ohmmeter is on the base *B* while the *positive* lead is placed on either the collector *C* or the emitter *E*. In these measurements, the diode junctions within the transistor are forward biased. See Fig. 2-6. On the other hand, then, if we reverse the ohmmeter leads, as shown in Fig. 2-6(B), we should observe higher resistance measurements because the diode junctions are reverse biased. Of course, if little or no change in resistance measurements occur when the leads across the collector *C* and base *B* or across the emitter *E* and base *B* are reversed, the transistor is likely defective.

2-4   The Transistor as a Switch

Transistors work mainly as switches in digital electronic circuits. An input signal can make a transistor turn on and act like a short, while an absence of an input signal can make it turn off and act like an open. Figure 2-7(A) shows how an *NPN* transistor is frequently used as a switch. When a signal V_{in} of about $+5$ V with respect to ground is applied to the input *X* the transistor turns on; that is, it essentially acts like a short or closed switch and admits collector current I_C through the lamp, causing it to light. When the input signal $V_{in} = 0$ V (input *X* grounded) the transistor turns off and for practical purposes acts like an open, causing the lamp to go out. In this application the transistor, and the circuit as a whole, is called a

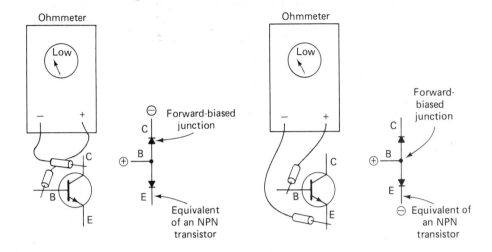

(A) Normally an *NPN* transistor has a low resistance reading when its base *B* is biased positively with respect to either its collector *C* or its emitter *E*.

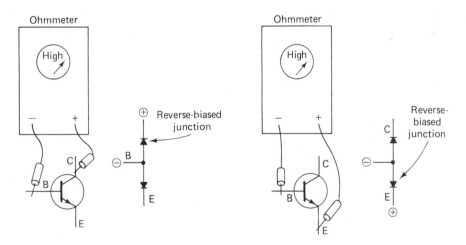

(B) Normally an *NPN* transistor has a high resistance reading when its base is biased negatively with respect to either its collector or its emitter.

Fig. 2-5. Checking *NPN* transistors with an ohmmeter.

lamp driver. In this circuit, the lamp will also go out when the input *X* is open. Normally, however, leads are never left hanging open in digital circuits; that is, a 0-V input signal is obtained by pulling the input lead down to ground potential (grounding it).

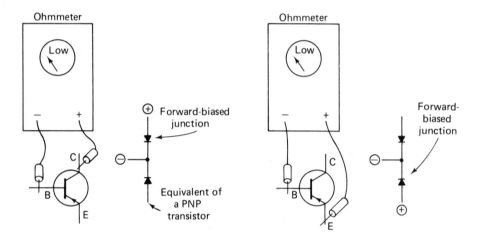

(A) Normally a *PNP* transistor has a low resistance reading when its base *B* is biased negatively with respect to either its collector *C* or emitter *E*.

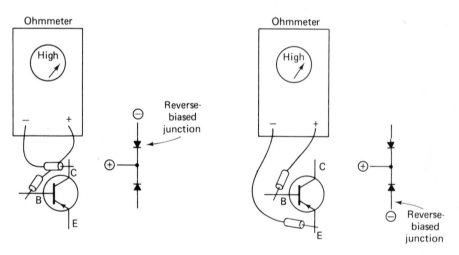

(B) Normally a *PNP* transistor has a high resistance reading when its base *B* is biased positively with respect to either its collector *C* or emitter *E*.

Fig. 2-6. Checking *PNP* transistors with an ohmmeter.

As shown in Fig. 2-7(B), if the input voltage V_{in} is positive enough, typically about 5 V to ground, it will forward-bias the emitter-to-base diode junction, causing base current I_B to flow. It is this base current I_B that actually turns on the transistor. That is, the transistor is a current-operated device. To turn one on we must apply an input voltage V_{in} in order to force enough base current I_B flow, which in turn admits flow of collector current I_C. The resistor R_B is necessary to limit the current I_B to safe and practical values. If R_B is too small, I_B might be large enough to destroy the transistor or it might *load down* the source of the input signal V_{in}. If R_B is too large, the current I_B might be too small to fully turn on the transistor. If the transistor does not turn on fully (hard), the lamp will not light to full brilliance. Usually, a transistor in a digital circuit is expected to turn on hard at certain times to act like a short or closed switch. At other times it is turned off to act like an open. When turned on hard a transistor is said to be *saturated,* and when turned off it is said to be *cut off.*

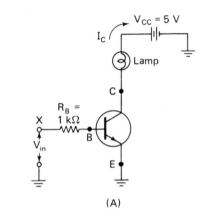

(A)

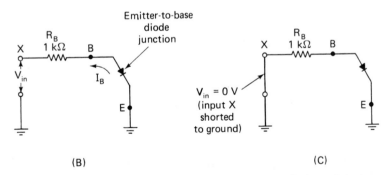

(B)   (C)

Fig. 2-7. (A) A transistor as a lamp driver; (B) input equivalent of the lamp driver circuit when V_{in} is positive enough to forward bias the emitter-to-base (EB) junction; (C) input equivalent of the lamp driver circuit when $V_{in} = 0$ V (input X is grounded).

Other circuits using *NPN* transistors as lamp or display drivers are shown in Fig. 2-8. The circuit in Fig. 2-8(A) is a more sophisticated lamp driver. Its advantages will become more apparent in a later chapter. For the present we should know that it offers less *loading* on the source of the input signal V_{in}. The circuit of Fig. 2-8(B) uses an LED as the light-emitting device. The resistor R_C is necessary to limit the current through the LED. If the resistance R_C is too small, the LED will illuminate brightly, become hot, and possibly be destroyed. If R_C is too large, the LED will light too dimly.

The display devices (lamps or LEDs) in the circuits of Figs. 2-7 and 2-8 light when the input $V_{in} \cong 5$ V and go out when $V_{in} \cong 0$ V. Therefore, they are called ACTIVE HIGH circuits. That is, a HIGH (about 5-V) input signal voltage causes each circuit to become ACTIVE (light a lamp or LED).

Another type of LED display circuit is shown in Fig. 2-9. In this case when we apply a $V_{in} \cong 5$ V the transistor turns on and effectively places a short across the LED. Thus while the transistor is on, practically all the current I_C flows through the transistor and the resistor R_C, resulting in little or no current for the LED, causing it to be unlighted. On the other hand, if we apply a $V_{in} \cong 0$ V (pull input X down to ground potential), the transistor turns off and acts like an open. Current will now flow through the LED, causing it to light. This display driver circuit is ACTIVE LOW. That is, this circuit is ACTIVE (lights the LED) when the input signal is LOW ($V_{in} \cong 0$ V).

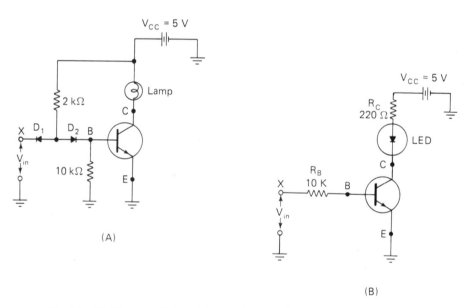

Fig. 2-8. (A) More sophisticated lamp driver circuit; (B) a transistor as an LED (light emitting diode) driver.

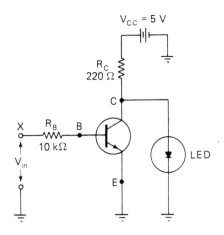

Fig. 2-9. LED driver circuit lights the LED when $V_{in} \cong 0$ V.

Summary

1. Transistors are more reliable and efficient than vacuum tubes.

2. Individual components such as transistors and resistors are called discrete parts.

3. Integrated circuits (ICs) contain transistors along with other components and interconnections all formed on a single piece of semiconductor.

4. Each transistor has three terminals (leads) called its collector, emitter, and base.

5. Transistors that are required to conduct larger currents are often mounted on heat sinks.

6. Transistors are available in two basic types: *NPN* and *PNP* types.

7. The dc voltage used across a transistor is called bias.

8. An *NPN* transistor is biased with its collector positive with respect to its emitter, whereas the collector is biased negatively with respect to the emitter on a *PNP* transistor.

9. The *NPN* transistor is equivalent to two diodes with their anodes connected (common) to the base while their separate cathodes are the collector and emitter.

10. The *PNP* transistor is equivalent to two diodes with their cathodes common to the base while their separate anodes are the collector and emitter.

11. Since transistors contain diode junctions, the resistances of these junctions can be checked with an ohmmeter to determine if they are OK.

12. In digital circuits, transistors are mainly used as switches that can be turned on (closed) or turned off (opened) by signal voltages.

13. Signal voltages can be used to turn lamps or LEDs on or off. In such applications, the transistors, or the circuits that contain them, are called lamp drivers, display drivers, or LED drivers.

Problems 2-1

Each pair of probes shown in Fig. 2-10 is from an ohmmeter. Indicate what we should read, *high* resistance or *low* resistance, if the transistor being tested is OK in each of the following 10 cases:

1. The transistor Q_1 is an *NPN* type, and probe *B* is positive with respect to probe *A. Ans.* ___High___

2. The transistor Q_2 is an *NPN* type, and probe *B* is positive with respect to probe *A. Ans.* ___High___

3. The transistor Q_1 is a *PNP* type, and probe *B* is positive with respect to probe *A. Ans.* ___~~High~~ LOW___

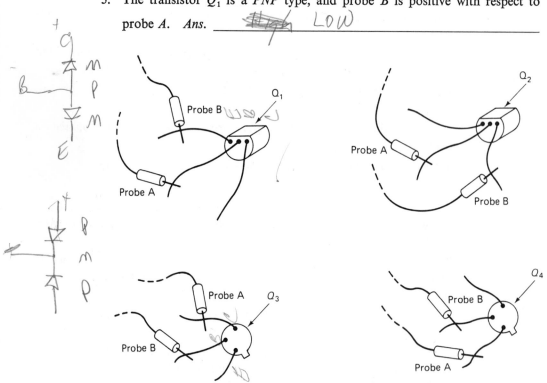

Fig. 2-10. Ohmmeter probes testing transistors.

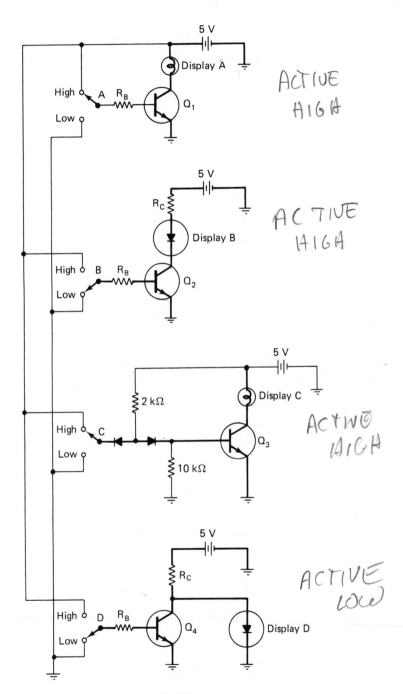

Fig. 2-11.

4. The transistor Q_2 is a *PNP* type, and probe B is positive with respect to probe A.   *Ans.* _____ LOW _____

5. The transistor Q_1 is an *NPN* type, and probe A is positive with respect to probe B.   *Ans.* _____ LOW _____

6. The transistor Q_2 is an *NPN* type, and probe A is positive with respect to probe B.   *Ans.* _____ LOW _____

7. The transistor Q_3 is an *NPN* type, and probe A is positive with respect to probe B.   *Ans.* _____ High _____

8. The transistor Q_4 is an *NPN* type, and probe A is positive with respect to probe B.   *Ans.* _____ High _____

9. The transistor Q_3 is a *PNP* type, and probe A is positive with respect to probe B.   *Ans.* _____ LOW _____

10. The transistor Q_4 is a *PNP* type, and probe A is positive with respect to probe B.   *Ans.* _____ LOW _____

   With reference to Fig. 2-11, each of the switches at inputs A, B, C, and D can be in either of two positions: the HIGH (H) position or the LOW (L) position. Table 2-1 has eight rows, each indicating a unique set of A through D input switch positions. As with the sample row, indicate the conditions that the transistors and displays are in with each row of conditions. Write ON if the transistor is acting like a short and OFF if it is acting like an open. Similarly, if a display is illuminated, indicate ON, and if it is not illuminated, write OFF.

2-5   The Transistor as a Logic Level Inverter

As mentioned in the previous section, a 5-V signal is called a HIGH signal, whereas a 0-V signal is called a LOW. The 5-V (HIGH) and 0-V (LOW) signals are commonly used in popular types of digital circuits and are called logic levels. Often, when a HIGH logic signal appears in one place in a digital system, a LOW logic level must simultaneously appear elsewhere in the system. In such cases, logic level inverters, simply called inverters, are used. A simple transistor inverter circuit is shown in Fig. 2-12. Input signals are applied to input A. The resulting output logic signals are then available at output X. A HIGH input signal causes a LOW output, whereas a LOW input causes a HIGH output. That is, when input A is HIGH, say at 5 V with respect to ground, base current I_B flows, causing the transistor to turn on and act like a short. A turned-on transistor *pulls* the output X to ground (0-V) potential.

On the other hand, if the input *A* is grounded (at 0 V), no base current flows, and the transistor turns off and acts like an open. In this case, little or no current I_C can flow, and therefore there is little or no voltage drop across the resistor R_C. This causes the entire V_{CC} supply voltage to appear across the transistor's collector *C* and emitter *E*, which means that it appears at output *X* to ground. The tables in Fig. 2-13 are called *functional tables* or *truth tables* and show how the inverter's output *X* responds to a given input *A*.

Table 2-1

	Inputs				Transistors				Displays			
	A	B	C	D	Q_1	Q_2	Q_3	Q_4	A	B	C	D
Sample	H	L	H	L	ON	OFF	ON	OFF	ON	OFF	ON	ON
11	H	H	H	H	ON	ON	ON	ON	ON	ON	ON	OFF
12	L	L	L	L	OFF	OFF	OFF	OFF	OFF	OFF	OFF	ON
13	H	L	L	L	ON	OFF	OFF	OFF	ON	OFF	OFF	ON
14	H	H	L	L	ON	ON	OFF	OFF	ON	ON	OFF	ON
15	H	H	H	L	ON	ON	ON	OFF	ON	ON	ON	ON
16	H	H	L	L	ON	ON	OFF	OFF	ON	ON	OFF	ON
17	L	L	H	H	OFF	OFF	ON	ON	OFF	OFF	ON	OFF

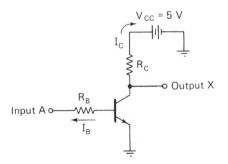

Fig. 2-12. Simple transistor inverter circuit.

The *square wave*, shown as signal *A* in Fig. 2-14, commonly appears in digital systems. If this square wave is applied to the input of an inverter, the output is also a square wave, but inverted, shown as waveform *X* in Fig. 2-14. These square waves can easily be viewed with an oscilloscope.

Symbols for logic circuit inverters are shown in Fig. 2-15. The circle on the symbol is shown on either the output or the input, *usually* depending on how the inverter is being used. If an inverter causes action in subsequent logic circuits when its output *X* goes LOW, its output *X* is said to be ACTIVE LOW. The symbol *A* in Fig. 2-15 is used to represent an inverter with an ACTIVE LOW output. On the other hand, when an inverter causes action in subsequent circuits when its output *X* goes HIGH,

Input	Output
A	X
LOW	HIGH
HIGH	LOW

Input	Output
A	X
0 V	5 V
5 V	0 V

Fig. 2-13. Functional tables, also called truth tables for the inverter.

Input A

5 V
0 V ──────────────────────────→ Time

Output X

5 V
0 V ──────────────────────────→ Time

Fig. 2-14. Typical input waveform *A* and resulting output waveform *X* of a logic inverter.

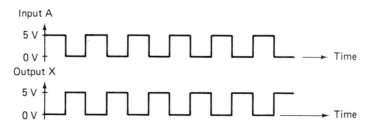

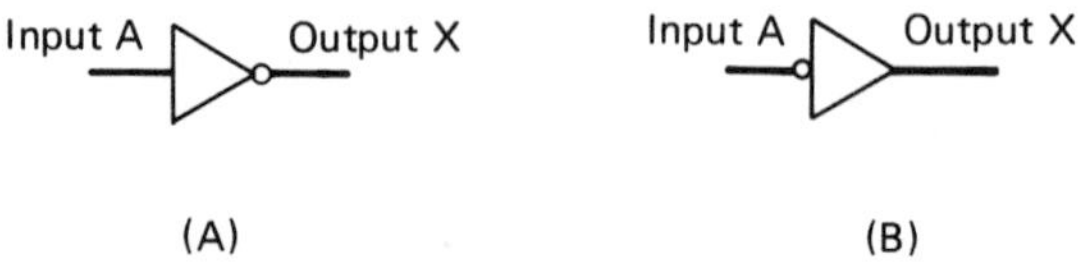

(A)   (B)

Fig. 2-15. Symbols for the logic inverter (A) ACTIVE LOW output; (B) ACTIVE HIGH output.

its output X is called ACTIVE HIGH, and the symbol B of Fig. 2-15 is used to represent this inverter. The term *action* can mean any number of things, as we shall see in later chapters. For the present, however, we can say that a lighted display means "action in subsequent circuits."

The circuit of Fig. 2-16(A) has an inverter with an ACTIVE LOW output. That is, when the signal at the inverter's output $\bar{X}$ goes LOW (becomes ACTIVE), the transistor Q_1 turns off, allowing the LED to light. On the other hand, the inverter in the circuit of Fig. 2-16(B) has an ACTIVE HIGH output. In this case, a HIGH signal at point X turns the transistor on, and this admits current through the LED, permitting it to light. Commonly, a line is drawn over the name or letter symbol of a signal that is ACTIVE LOW.

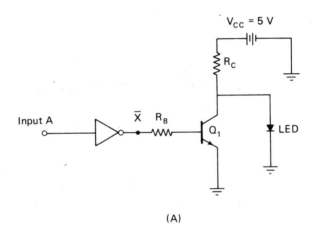

(A)

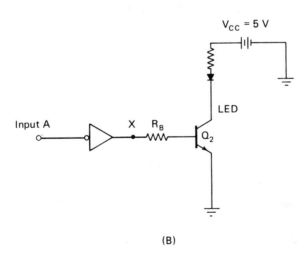

(B)

Fig. 2-16. (A) LED lights when the signal at $\bar{X}$ goes LOW (ACTIVE); (B) LED lights when the signal at X goes HIGH (ACTIVE).

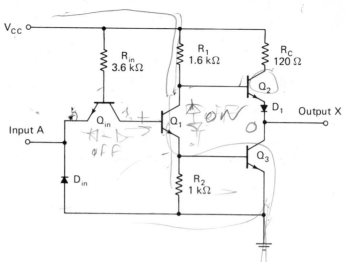

Fig. 2-17. Typical TTL (transistor-transistor logic) inverter circuit.

2-6 Transistors in Totem-Pole Connection

The circuit of Fig. 2-17 is a typical TTL inverter and has its output transistors Q_2 and Q_3 connected in a popular totem-pole arrangement. In logic circuit applications, one of these output transistors is turned on while the other is simultaneously turned off. The logic level of the input signal V_{in} determines which of the two is on or off. When a HIGH input signal V_{in} is applied, Q_2 turns off and Q_3 turns on which pulls the output X to ground (0-V) potential. Because of its job in this circuit, Q_3 is called a *pull-down* transistor. On the other hand, when the input V_{in} is LOW, Q_2 turns on while Q_3 turns off. The turned-on transistor Q_2 pulls the output X up to the V_{CC} voltage via resistor R_C. Q_2 is called a *pull-up* transistor because its job is to pull the output X up to a HIGH logic level. When Q_3 is on and conducting, it is said to be *sinking* current. When Q_2 is on and conducting, it is said to be *sourcing* current. The diode D_{in} in the inverter circuit of Fig. 2-17 is called a *clamping diode*. This diode prevents input signal oscillations, which can cause unreliable operation in digital circuits.

Summary

1. Transistors are used as logic level inverters.

2. An inverter's output logic level is opposite to its input logic level.

3. A square wave applied to the input of an inverter causes an inverted output square wave.

4. The inverter's logic symbol has a circle at *either* its input or output. Usually the circle is at the output when the inverter's output signal is ACTIVE LOW, whereas the circle is on the input of the symbol if the inverter's output signal is ACTIVE HIGH.

5.   If a LOW or LOW-going* logic signal causes action in circuitry that it is driving, it is called an ACTIVE LOW signal.

6.   If a HIGH or HIGH-going† signal causes action in circuitry that it is driving, it is called an ACTIVE HIGH signal.

7.   Transistors are also connected in a *totem-pole* arrangement in some types of inverter circuits.

8.   When two transistors are connected in a totem-pole arrangement, the one between the output X and the V_{CC} supply is called the *pull-up* transistor.

9.   The transistor between the output X and ground, in a totem-pole output arrangement, is called the *pull-down* transistor.

10.   In typical logic circuit applications, when the pull-up transistor is turned on (saturated), the pull-down transistor is turned off (cut off). On the other hand, when the pull-down transistor is on, the pull-up transistor is off.

11.   When a pull-up transistor is conducting, we can say that it is *sourcing current*.

12.   When a pull-down transistor is conducting, we can say that it is *sinking current*.

Problems 2-2

1.   A transistor that is turned on and acting like a short can be said to be
     <u>satu</u>   .

2.   A transistor that is turned off and acting like an open can be said to be
     <u>cutoff</u>   .

3.   If we make the transistor in the circuit of Fig. 2-18 turn on and act like a short, what are the voltages (a) at the output X with respect to ground, (b) across the transistor's collector C and emitter E, and (c) across the collector resistor R_C?

                                                        a) 0V
    b) 0V

4.   If in the circuit of Fig. 2-18 we make the transistor turn off and act like an open, what are the voltages (a) at the output X to ground, (b) across the transistor's collector C and emitter E, and (c) across the collector resistor R_C?

    c) 5V
    a) 5V
    b) 0V

5.   If the switch S in the circuit of Fig. 2-18 is in the 1 position as shown, the voltage at input A is   <u>5V</u>   V to ground, base current through R_B (does, does not) flow, and the voltage at output X is   <u>0</u>   V to ground.

    c) 0V

6.   With reference to the circuit and condition of the switch S described in Problem 5, the logic level at input A is   <u>H</u>   , while the logic level at output X is   <u>L</u>   .

---

*A LOW-going signal is one that is changing from a HIGH logic level to a LOW logic level.
†A HIGH-going signal is one that is changing from a LOW logic level to a HIGH logic level.

7. If we throw the switch in the circuit of Fig. 2-18 down in the 0 position, the voltage at input A becomes ____0____ V to ground, base current through R_B (does, does not) flow, and the voltage at output X becomes ____5____ V to ground.

8. With reference to the circuit and condition of the switch S described in Problem 7, the logic level at input A is ____L____, while the logic level at output X is ____H____.

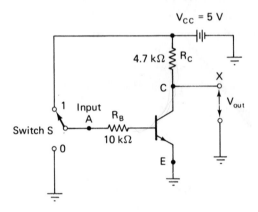

Fig. 2-18.

Experiment 2-1   Checking Transistors with an Ohmmeter

Purpose

You will now become familiar with the normal ohmmeter readings on transistors by identifying which transistors are *NPN* and which are *PNP*.

Materials

Ohmmeter
Six to eight transistors of different numbers, preferably three or four
NPN type and the remainder *PNP* type.

Procedure

Write down the transistor numbers in Table L 2-1 and make the measurements indicated. From your measurements, determine whether the transistor is *NPN* or *PNP*. Also tell whether it is defective or OK.

NOTE: Be sure you know the proper lead identification. Some types, particularly plastic-encased types, have different CBE locations from those shown in Fig. 2-2.

Table L 2-1

	Transistor number	Resistance with negative lead to base		Resistance with positive lead to base		Type NPN or PNP	Defective?
		B-E Ω	B-C Ω	B-E Ω	B-C Ω		
1	2N 3900	10Ω	10Ω	High	High	PNP	N
2	MPS 6521	∞	∞	10Ω	10Ω	NPN	N
3	MPS 6521	∞	∞	10Ω	10Ω	NPN	N
4	2N 3906	∞	∞	∞	∞	—	Y
5	MPS 6521	∞	∞	10Ω	10Ω	NPN	N
6	?T220	∞	∞	3.25Ω	2.8Ω	PNP	N
7	2N 6250	5.5Ω	∞	∞	∞	PNP?	Y
8	TIP 3055	6.5Ω	∞	∞	∞	PNP?	Y

Experiment 2-2   The Transistor as an LED Driver

Purpose

You will become familiar with using light emitting diodes as indicators. You will also use transistors as switching devices.

Materials

Digital breadboard kit
SPDT switch
(two) transistors—any silicon switching type
(two) LEDs
1-K pot
(two) 240-Ω, $\frac{1}{4}$-W $\pm 5\%$ resistors
(two) 4.7-K, $\frac{1}{4}$-W $\pm 5\%$ resistors

Procedure

1. Construct the circuit of Fig. L 2-2(A). With switch S_1 closed, vary the resistance of pot R_1, and notice the change in brightness of the LED. You can see that if the LED were to be used as an indicator in a darkened area, just a few mils of current would give sufficient brightness. But in a well-lit area, more current is needed.

The switch in the circuit represents a transistor being used either saturated or cut off. Flip the switch on and off a few times, and of course the LED will go on and off.

2. With the switch closed, measure the forward voltage drop, V_F, across the LED. $V_F =$ High ~ low *1.51—1.57* . How does this forward voltage compare to that of a *.7v* silicon diode? _TWICE AS HIGH_

3. Next, build the circuit of Fig. L 2-2(B). Notice that transistor Q_1 replaces the ON-OFF switch of the previous circuit. Place input switch S_1 in the L position. At this time the LED is (on, off) because the transistor is (on, off).

4. Then flip S_1 to the H position. Now the LED is (on, off) because the transistor is (on, off). Considering switch S_1 as the signal being monitored, the lamp driver is being used as an (ACTIVE HIGH, ACTIVE LOW) indicator.

5. With the LED on, measure the collector-to-emitter voltage, V_{CE}. $V_{CE} =$ _81.2 mV_ . The transistor is now in (cutoff, saturation). What voltage would you measure if the transistor were an ideal switch? _0v_

6. Connect a 1-Hz clock to the lamp driver as shown in Fig. L 2-2(C). Also connect an indicator lamp from your digital breadboard kit to the clock output as shown. Do the two lights blink on and off together or alternately?

 _together_

Do the lamps on your digital breadboard kit indicate ACTIVE HIGH or ACTIVE LOW signals? Leave this circuit wired for later use.

7. Next, build the circuit of Fig. L 2-2(D). Place input switch S_1 in the L position. At this time the LED is (on, off) because the transistor is (on, off).

8.   Then flip S_1 to the H position. Now the LED is (on, off) because the transistor is (on, off). Considering switch S_1 as the signals being monitored, the lamp driver is being used as an (ACTIVE HIGH, ACTIVE LOW) indicator.

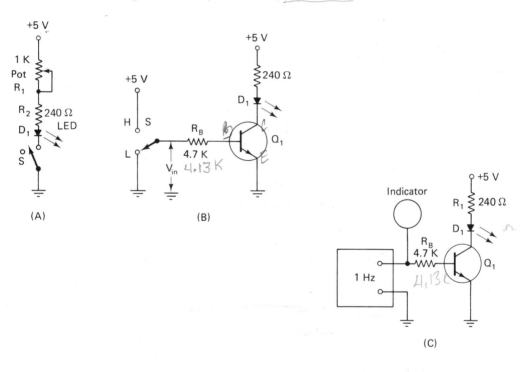

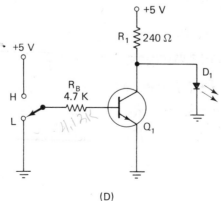

Fig. L 2-2.

9. Disconnect the left end of R_B from the switch in Fig. L 2-2(D). Then connect the resistor to the 1-Hz clock output of the circuit of Fig. L 2-2(C). That is, the clock should drive both the ACTIVE HIGH and ACTIVE LOW indicators. Apply power, and explain what you observe.   All LEDS ARE ON

C on when clock High
C off "   " low
D off "   " high
D on "   " low

Quiz for Experiment 2-2

1. In step 1, the lower the resistance in series with the LED, the (higher, lower) the current flow through it, and therefore the (higher, lower) the brightness.

2. In step 3, when switch S_1 was in the L position, base current (did, did not) flow into the transistor. Therefore, collector current (did, did not) flow.

3. In step 4, with the switch in the H position, base current (did, did not) flow into the transistor, turning it (ON, OFF).

4. The base current flowing into a transistor when it is ON is much (greater, less) than the collector current.

5. Since the LED of Fig. L 2-2(B) was (ON, OFF) when the input signal was HIGH, the LED is an ACTIVE (HIGH, LOW) indicator.

6. The following is a list of statements comparing the transistor switch to a mechanical toggle switch. Write A after each *advantage* of the transistor, and write D after each *disadvantage*.

   (a) Very fast ___Advantage___

   (b) Silent ___Advantage___

   (c) Consumes power _____

   (d) Long lasting ___Ad___

   (e) Has voltage drop when conducting ___dis___

   (f) Can be remotely controlled ___Ad___

   (g) Very small ___Ad.___

   (h) Must observe polarity ___disad___

Experiment 2-3 Totem-Pole Connection

Purpose

To become familiar with the totem-pole circuit, which is one of the most commonly used output circuits available in IC form. You will build the totem-pole circuit using discrete components in order to obtain a good understanding of how it works.

Materials

> Digital breadboard kit
> Voltmeter
> (Three) *NPN* transistors (any type)
> 4-K, $\frac{1}{4}$-W $\pm 10\%$ resistor
> 1.6-K, $\frac{1}{4}$-W $\pm 10\%$ resistor
> 1-K, $\frac{1}{4}$-W $\pm 10\%$ resistor
> (Two) 240-Ω, $\frac{1}{4}$-W $\pm 10\%$ resistors
> 120-Ω, $\frac{1}{4}$-W $\pm 10\%$ resistor
> Silicon diode
> (Two) LEDS
> SPDT switch

Procedure

1. Build the circuit of Fig. L 2-3. With the input switch in the L position, measure the collector-to-emitter voltage of Q_1. $V_{CE_1} =$ __4.16v__ . Is this as you would expect? Explain. _____

_____

_____

2. Measure the voltage at the emitter of Q_1 with respect to ground. (This is also the base-to-emitter voltage of Q_3.) $V_{E_1} =$ __0v__ .

3. Next, measure the output voltage V_0. (This is also the collector voltage of Q_3.) $V_0 =$ __3.48v__ .

4. Measure the collector voltage of Q_1 with respect to ground. $V_{C_1} =$ __4.16v__ .

5. Measure the collector-to-emitter voltage of Q_2. $V_{CE_2} =$ __21.9 mv__

6. Next, switch the input so that V_{in} is HIGH. Measure the collector-to-emitter voltage of Q_1. $V_{CE_1} =$ __23.3 mv__

7. Measure the voltage at the emitter of Q_1 to ground. $V_{E_1} = $ __.909 V__.

8. Measure the output voltage, V_0. $V_0 = $ __186 mV__.

9. Measure the collector-to-emitter voltage of Q_2. $V_{CE_2} = $ __184 mV__.

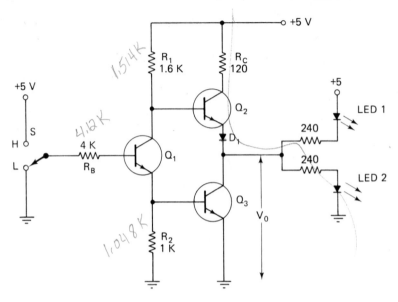

Fig. L 2-3.

Quiz for Experiment 2-3

All the following questions refer to the circuit of Fig. L 2-3. *open*

1 With $V_{in} = 0$, should Q_1 be ON or OFF? __OFF__

2. The voltage at the emitter of Q_1 when the switch was L caused Q_3 to be (ON, **OFF**).

3. The voltage at the collector of Q_1 when the switch was L caused Q_2 to be (**ON**, OFF).

4. In step 6, Q_1 was turned (ON, **OFF**).

5. The measurement of step 8 showed that Q_3 was turned (**ON**, OFF).

6. Step 9 showed that when Q_1 was (ON, **OFF**), Q_2 was turned (**ON**, OFF).

7. Summarizing the results of the experiment, when V_{in} is LOW, V_0 is (HIGH, LOW). Then when V_{in} is HIGH, V_0 is (HIGH, LOW).

8. LED 1 lit when the output was (HIGH, LOW). Current through the LED flowed from the power supply through the (current source Q_2, current sink Q_3).

9. LED 2 lit when the output was (HIGH, LOW). The current for LED 2 came from (current source Q_2, current sink Q_3).

10. With regard to Q_2 and Q_3 in the totem pole, Q_2 conducts only when the input is (HIGH, LOW). Q_3 conducts only when the input is (HIGH, LOW). The two transistors normally never conduct at the same time. Therefore, if the load is disconnected, the current through the totem pole will be (always HIGH, HIGH when the input is HIGH, HIGH when the input is LOW, always negligible).

3

Field Effect Transistors for Logic Circuits

Introduction

The field effect transistor (FET) is a voltage-operated device, which means that the current through it is controlled with an input signal voltage. An applied input voltage creates an electric *field* that penetrates the FET's semiconductor and thus controls its ability to conduct.

As are junction transistors, FETs in logic circuits are used as switches; that is, they serve as devices that can be abruptly turned on or off with electrical signals. Like the junction transistor, an FET has three terminals: a gate G, a drain D, and a source S. These are somewhat analogous to the base B, collector C, and emitter E, respectively, of the junction transistor. Generally, the resistance between the drain D and source S is controlled with a voltage applied to its gate G.

3-1 Construction and Behavior of the Field Effect Transistor

Parts (A) through (D) of Fig. 3-1 show basically how the FET is made. As shown in Fig. 3-1(A), the manufacturing process starts with a lightly doped semiconductor. A lightly doped semiconductor has few charge carriers, which makes it a poor conductor of current in the absence of external influences. As we shall see, a portion of this lightly doped material serves as the channel of the FET. The number of charge carriers in this channel and its ability to conduct current are increased when an electric field is applied.

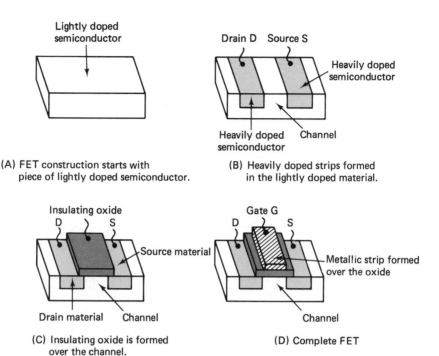

(A) FET construction starts with
piece of lightly doped semiconductor.

(B) Heavily doped strips formed
in the lightly doped material.

(C) Insulating oxide is formed
over the channel.

(D) Complete FET

Fig. 3-1.

As shown in Fig. 3-1(B), heavily doped semiconductor strips, which are good conductors, are formed in the channel material. Leads called the drain D and source S are then connected to these areas of heavily doped materials. The channel is between these drain and source materials.

Next, an insulating oxide is formed over the channel, as shown in Fig. 3-1(C).

Finally, a metal strip is formed over the oxide, and a gate G lead is connected to this metal; see Fig. 3-1(D). The gate G is thus insulated from the semiconductor materials. While currents cannot readily flow from the gate G to the channel, electric fields can easily penetrate the oxide and channel. Because of the insulating oxide, this device is called a metal oxide semiconductor field effect transistor (MOSFET) or an insulated gate field effect transistor (IGFET). Schematic symbols for the MOSFET, formed as in Fig. 3-1(D), are shown in Fig. 3-2.

When an appropriate polarity of voltage is applied across the gate and source of the MOSFET, an electric field penetrates into the channel and attracts (induces) charge carriers into it. The channel's conductivity is thus increased.

Negative charge carriers (electrons) are attracted into the channel of the N-channel MOSFET when its gate is made positive with respect to its source. Thus the N-channel MOSFET becomes more conductive when we apply a positive gate-to-source voltage. Positive charge carriers (holes) are attracted into the channel of the

(A) Schematic symbol for the
    N-channel metal oxide semiconductor
    field effect transistor (MOSFET)

(B) Schematic symbol for the
    P-channel metal oxide
    semiconductor field effect
    transistor (MOSFET)

Fig. 3-2.

P-channel MOSFET when its gate is made negative with respect to its source. The *P*-channel MOSFET therefore becomes more conductive when we apply a negative gate-to-source voltage. Both of these MOSFET types are called *induced channel* or *enhancement mode* MOSFETs because charge carriers must be attracted (induced) into their channels to improve (enhance) their conductivities. If we make the gate 0 V with respect to the source, with either the *N*-channel or the *P*-channel MOSFET, the channel is nonconductive and acts like an open switch for most practical purposes.

The circuit of Fig. 3-3 shows how an *N*-channel MOSFET can be used in a logic inverter circuit. When the switch Sw is down in the 0 position, the gate-to-source voltage is 0 V, and the MOSFET is nonconductive and acts like an open compared to the resistance of R_D. Therefore, practically all the V_{DD} supply voltage appears across the MOSFET and at the output X with respect to ground. Thus a LOW logic input (0 V) causes a HIGH logic (V_{DD} voltage) output. On the other hand, when the switch Sw is up in the 1 position, the gate-to-source voltage is positive. This turns the MOSFET on, causing it to act like a short compared to the R_D resistance. Thus the voltage across the MOSFET and the voltage at output X to ground drops to nearly 0 V. In this case a HIGH input (V_{DD} voltage) causes a LOW output (nearly 0 V).

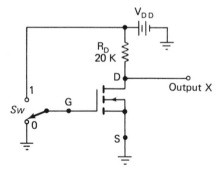

Fig. 3-3. Inverter circuit with a pull-up resistor R_D and *N*-channel MOSFET.

In much the same way, the *P*-channel MOSFET in Fig. 3-4 is used in an inverter circuit. Note that the drain is biased negatively with respect to the source in this case. Therefore, when the switch Sw is down in the 0 position, the gate is negative with respect to the source. For example, if we use a 10-V V_{DD} supply, the gate becomes -10 V with respect to the source when we place the switch in the 0 position. Such a negative gate-to-source voltage turns on the *P*-channel MOSFET, causing it to act like a short. This pulls the output X up to the V_{DD} voltage.

If the switch Sw is thrown up into the 1 position in the circuit of Fig. 3-4, the gate is raised to the source potential and the gate-to-source voltage becomes 0 V. This turns off the *P*-channel MOSFET, causing it to act like an open. Consequently, nearly the entire V_{DD} voltage appears across the drain and source, resulting in nearly 0 V across R_D and at the output X.

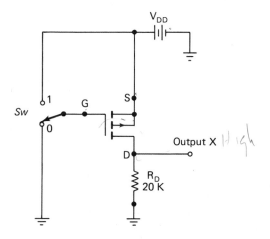

Fig. 3-4. Inverter circuit with a pull-down resistor R_D and a *P*-channel MOSFET.

3-2 A Practical CMOS Inverter

To reduce power consumption and increase switching speed, MOSFET inverters are commonly constructed without resistors, as shown in Fig. 3-5. Note that this inverter uses two MOSFETs: one *N*-channel and one *P*-channel. This arrangement of MOSFETs is called a *complementary pair*. Integrated circuits (ICs) using such pairs are called complementary metal oxide semiconductor (CMOS) ICs.

If we pull the input A on the circuit of Fig. 3-5 LOW, the MOSFET Q_1 turns on while Q_2 turns off, causing a HIGH at output X. That is, a grounded input A makes G_1 negative with respect to S_1, allowing Q_1 to become conductive. Simultaneously, G_2 and S_2 are at the same potential, keeping Q_2 nonconductive. The supply voltage V_{DD} thus appears across terminals D_2 and S_2 and at the output X.

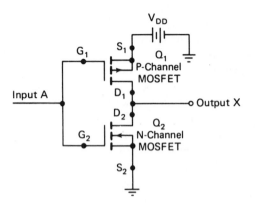

Fig. 3-5. Practical complementary-pair metal oxide semiconductor (CMOS) inverter.

By pulling the input A HIGH to the V_{DD} voltage, we cause Q_1 to turn off while Q_2 turns on, resulting in a LOW output X. That is, when input A is HIGH at the V_{DD} voltage, both G_1 and S_1 are at the same potential and Q_1 is nonconductive. Simultaneously, the HIGH input A makes G_2 positive with respect to S_2, causing Q_2 to become conductive, and about 0 V to ground at output X.

3-3   A Practical CMOS Integrated Circuit (IC)

Although we shall be studying and working extensively with CMOS and TTL ICs in later chapters, for the present we can become familiar with one simple and flexible CMOS IC. The 4007 in Fig. 3-6, for example, is such a CMOS IC. It is available in a number of package styles, though only the 14-pin DIP is shown. The numbered and circled terminals represent pins that are accessible outside of the package which can be used in a variety of connections.

The 4007 CMOS IC, as do most other CMOS devices, requires a dc supply voltage that is in the range from about 3 to 15 V. CMOS devices are particularly useful in applications where low power consumption is important. Battery-operated equipment, for example, works much longer between battery charges or replacements with a CMOS than with any other functionally equivalent logic circuits. This is partly true because of the full-on or full-off operation of each complementary output MOSFET. That is, as mentioned before, one of the complementary MOSFETs is on while the other is off. This keeps current drain from the V_{DD} supply down to insignificance. The extremely high input resistance of each CMOS device draws virtually no power which also contributes to its high efficiency.

Although efficient, the extremely high resistance of CMOS devices causes some problems. Static electrical charges cause few problems with low-resistance devices, but such charges can easily ruin a high-resistance CMOS IC. Because of this, CMOS manufacturers recommend the following precautions when using CMOS ICs:

1. The leads of CMOS devices should be in contact with conductive material, such as the conductive foam in which they are inserted during shipping, except when being used.

2. Metal parts, such as soldering iron tips and tools, should be grounded before being placed in contact with a CMOS pin. Grounding straps on the wrists of persons handling a CMOS is also recommended.

3. CMOS ICs should never be removed or inserted in a circuit while the power is on.

4. Input signals should never be applied while the supply power is off.

5. All unused inputs must be connected to either the V_{DD} supply or to ground.

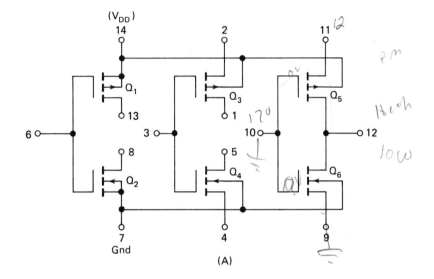

(A)

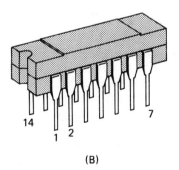

(B)

Fig. 3-6. (A) The contents of the 4007 CMOS IC; (B) a 14-pin dual in-line package (DIP) typically used to house a 4007.

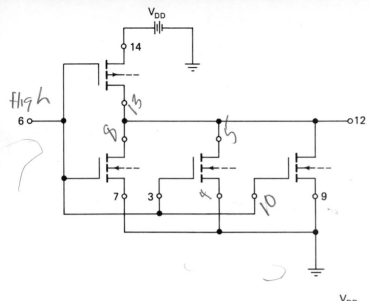

Fig. 3-7. Application of the 4007 CMOS IC; an inverter with improved current-sink capability.

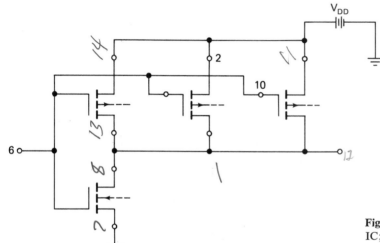

Fig. 3-8. Application of the 4007 CMOS IC; an inverter with improved current-source capability.

3-4 Applications of the 4007 CMOS IC

The circuit of Fig. 3-7 shows how a 4007 can be wired to work as an inverter with higher *current sink* capability. This means that if a HIGH signal is applied to the input (pin 6), the output (pin 12) is pulled LOW because the three lower MOSFETs are turned on. These three turned-on MOSFETs can conduct (sink) a larger current between the output (pin 12) and ground than can a single conducting MOSFET such as Q_2 in the simpler inverter of Fig. 3-5. Such a larger current sink capability might be required by some types of loads (other than CMOS inputs) connected to the right of pin 12.

The circuit of Fig. 3-8 shows how a 4007 can be wired to work as an inverter with a higher *current source* capability. This means that when a LOW input is applied to pin 6, the output at pin 12 is pulled HIGH by the upper three conducting MOSFETs.

These three turned-on MOSFETS can conduct (source) a larger current between the output (pin 12) and the V_{DD} supply than can a single conducting MOSFET, such as Q_1 in Fig. 3-5. Some logic circuit loads, other than CMOS, require such improved current source capability.

Summary

1. Field effect transistors (FETs) are voltage-operated devices, which means that the current through an FET is controlled with a voltage applied to its gate.

2. The FETs used in digital ICs have insulated gates, and therefore they are called insulated gate field effect transistors called (IGFETs). Since the insulating material is a nonconducting metal oxide, these FETs are also called metal oxide semiconductor field effect transistors (MOSFETs).

3. MOSFETs have three terminals: a gate G, a drain D, and a source S.

4. The resistance between the drain D and source S is controlled with a voltage applied to the gate with respect to the source S.

5. The gate G, drain D, and source S of a MOSFET are similar to the base B, collector C, and emitter E of the junction transistor.

6. *N*-Channel and *P*-channel types of MOSFETs are used in CMOS ICs.

7. The term CMOS means complementary metal oxide semiconductor.

8. An *N*-channel and a *P*-channel MOSFET connected as in Fig. 3-5 are called a complementary pair.

9. A positive gate-to-source voltage makes the *N*-channel MOSFET conductive.

10. The *N*-channel MOSFET is nonconductive when its gate-to-source voltage is 0 V.

11. A negative gate-to-source voltage makes the *P*-channel MOSFET conductive.

12. The *P*-channel MOSFET, like the *N*-channel type, is nonconductive when its gate-to-source voltage is 0 V.

13. The input resistances of MOSFETs are extremely high.

14. In typical logic applications of CMOS ICs, the resistances of the complementary output MOSFETs abruptly change in opposite directions; that is, when the *N*-channel MOSFET is conducting, the *P*-channel type is nonconducting and vice versa.

Problems 3-1

Circle the correct selections in Problems 1 through 6.

1. When the switch Sw in the circuit of Fig. 3-3 is down in the 0 position, the MOSFET is (ON, OFF) and the output X is (HIGH, LOW).

2. When the switch Sw in the circuit of Fig. 3-3 is up in the 1 position, the MOSFET is (ON, OFF) and the output X is (HIGH, LOW).

3. With reference to the circuit of Fig. 3-4, by placing Sw down in the 0 position we cause the MOSFET to turn (ON, OFF) and the output X to go (HIGH, LOW). But placing Sw up in the 1 position causes the MOSFET to turn (ON, OFF) and the output X to go (HIGH, LOW).

4. With reference to Fig. 3-6, MOSFETS Q_1, Q_3, and Q_5 are (N-channel, P-channel) types, while Q_2, Q_4, and Q_6 are (N-channel, P-channel) types.

5. If pin 11 in the circuit of Fig. 3-6 is connected to a +12-V dc supply and pin 9 is grounded, a +12-V signal applied to pin 10 will cause Q_5 to turn (ON, OFF) while simultaneously Q_6 turns (ON, OFF), causing the output at pin 12 to have about (+12 V, 0 V) to ground.

6. Still with reference to Fig. 3-6, if +12 V is at pin 11 while pins 9 and 10 are connected to ground, Q_5 turns (ON, OFF), Q_6 turns (ON, OFF), and pin 12 goes to about (+12 V, 0 V) with respect to ground.

7. On the circuits of Figs. 3-7 and 3-8, which are applications of the 4007 CMOS, show the missing pin numbers in the circles provided.

8. Using the Q numbers of the MOSFETS given in Fig. 3-6, which of the MOSFETS in the circuit of Fig. 3-7 are turned on and which are turned off when the input pin 6 is HIGH? _____ $Q_2 \, Q_4 \, Q_6 \quad ON$ _____

9. Which of the MOSFETS in the circuit of Fig. 3-7 are turned on and which are turned off when pin 6 is grounded? _____ $Q_1 \quad ON$ _____

10. By Q number, indicate which of the MOSFETS are missing (not used) in the circuit of Fig. 3-7. _____ $Q_3 \, Q_5$ _____

Experiment 3-1   MOSFETS

Purpose

To become familiar with the MOSFET as a switch.

Materials

> Digital breadboard kit
> Voltmeter
> 4007 IC
> 20-K, $\frac{1}{4}$-W $\pm 5\%$ resistor
> Clip leads

Procedure

1. Connect one *N*-channel MOSFET of the 4007 as shown in Fig. L 3-1(A). Be sure to wire the circuit *before* applying power. Connect pin 14 to $+5$ V dc and pin 7 to ground. (Pin 7 is often labeled V_{SS} in manufacturers' literature, but it will normally be tied to ground in these experiments.)

2. With switch *S* in the LOW position as shown, measure the output voltage V_0. $V_0 = $ _So 3 v_. What is the voltage V_R across the 20-K resistor? $V_R = $ ____0____. Current (is, is <u>not</u>) flowing through the MOSFET.

3. Flip the switch to the HIGH position, and again measure V_0. $V_0 = $ _ı o (3v)_. Now what is the voltage, V_R, across the 20-K resistor? $V_R = $ ____5.1____.The voltage across *R* shows that current (is, is not) flowing through the transistor. The output voltage is always the (same as, opposite of) the input voltage. Therefore the circuit is called a/an ___INVERTOR___

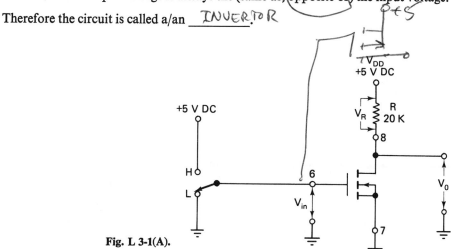

Fig. L 3-1(A).

(A)

4. Shut off the power and disconnect the switch from the gate of the MOSFET. Connect the voltmeter across pins 8 and 7 with the clip lead(s). Then apply power and touch a finger of one of your hands to power supply ground and a finger from the other hand to the gate, as shown in Fig. L 3-1(B). Observe and measure V_0.

$V_0 =$ ___5✓___ .

5. Next, keeping one finger on the gate lead, remove the other finger from ground and touch it to the +5-V supply. Measure V_0. $V_0 =$ ___0,3___ . Does the output change? ___Yes___ How? ___6ud → 6   0 in   Hi out___
___5-6   Hi in   low , w___

The input signal is being applied to the gate through your body resistance. Do you think there is much current flowing through your body? ___No___

What does this test tell you about the input resistance of the MOSFET? ___Very High___

6. Shut off the power and wire one of the *P*-channel MOSFETS as in Fig. 3-4. Draw your circuit in the space below and indicate the pin numbers you use. (Be sure to wire pin 14 to the +5-V V_{DD} supply and pin 7 to ground.)

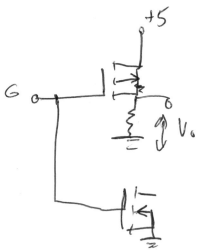

7. With switch S in position 0 (LOW), measure V_0. $V_0 =$ ___4.96___ .

8. Then switch the input to the 1 (HIGH) position, and measure V_0. $V_0 =$ ___0___ . What would you call this circuit? ___Inverter___ How does this circuit differ from the circuit using the *N*-channel MOSFET?

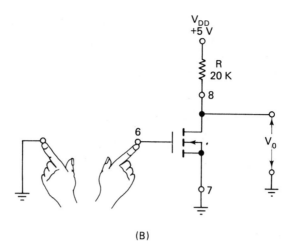

(B)

Fig. L 3-1. (*cont'd.*) (B).

see pg 67

Experiment 3-2 Complementary CMOS Inverter

Purpose

You studied the MOSFET inverter in the previous experiment. Recall that when the input voltage was HIGH, the output was LOW. And when the output was LOW, almost all the supply voltage was dropped across the 20-K load resistor. The current through the transistor at that time was about 5 V/20 K or $\frac{1}{4}$ mA. This might seem like quite a small current flow. But in even a small pocket calculator, there are as many as 40,000 or more transistors. Now if each of these transistors conducted only $\frac{1}{4}$ mA, the current drain from the power supply would be about 10 A. Think of the size of battery you would have to carry around to supply 10 A for any appreciable time.

Thus it is pretty obvious we need to build switching circuits that draw much less current. The complementary CMOS inverter is the answer. It draws almost no current in either output state. We shall see that in this experiment.

Materials

> Digital breadboard kit
> Voltmeter
> 4007 IC
> 20-K resistor
> 3.3-K resistor

Procedure

1. Connect the complementary inverter, as shown in Fig. L 3-2(A). With the input switch in the 0 (LOW) position, measure V_0. $V_0 =$ __5.03__.

2. Without changing the switch position, measure the voltage, V_R, across the 20-K resistor. $V_R =$ __6__. How much current is flowing through the resistor? $I =$ __·22 mA__.

3. Reconnect the voltmeter as in step 1. Flip the input switch to the 1 (HIGH) position. Measure V_0. $V_0 =$ __0__.

4. Again remove the voltmeter from the output, and connect it across the 20-K resistor, as in step 2. Measure V_R. $V_R =$ __0__. How much current flows through the resistor now? $I =$ __6__.

5. Connect a 3.3-K resistor from the +5-V power supply to the inverter output as shown in Fig. L 3-2(B). With the switch in the 0 position, measure V_0. $V_0 =$ __5.04__.

6. Next, flip the input switch to the 1 position and measure V_0. $V_0 =$

___+2V___. How does this differ from the unloaded measurement of step 3?

_____

_____

_____

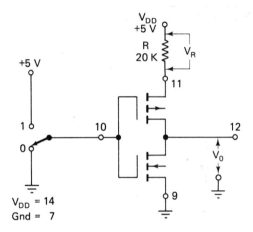

(A) Neither MOSFET is required to carry current while pin 12 is open

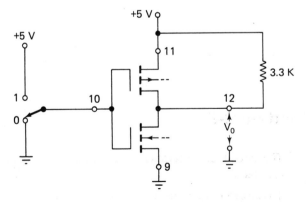

(B) *N*-Channel MOSFET required to sink current

Fig. L 3-2.

7. Now connect another *N*-channel transistor as shown in Fig. L 3-2(C). Repeat the measurements of steps 5 and 6. When $V_{in} = +0$ V, $V_0 = $ _5.04_ . When $V_{in} = +5$ V, $V_0 = $ _A 1_ . How do these measurements differ from those of step 6? _Y2_

___

Why? _____

___

Which circuit in Fig. L 3-2, (B) or (C), gives us a lower (better) LOW output?

___

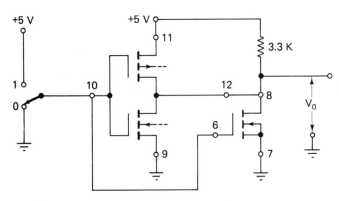

(C) Two *N*-channel MOSFET; sink current better

Fig. L 3-2. (*cont'd.*).

Quiz for Experiment 3-2

1. The circuit of Experiment 3-1 using the *N*-channel MOSFET (is, is not) an inverter.

2. The circuit of Experiment 3-2 (is, is not) an inverter.

3. The circuit of Experiment 3-1 (does, does not) draw current when its output is LOW.

4. The circuit (A) of Experiment 3-2 (does, ~~does not~~) draw current when its
    output is LOW.

5. Which circuit draws current when its output is HIGH (L 3-1, L 3-2(A), both,
    neither)?

6. The reason the complementary CMOS inverter is more efficient is that (neither
    the *N*-channel nor the *P*-channel MOSFET ever conducts, one or the other
    transistor is always off, both transistors have low resistance.)

7. If a load is connected from the output to V_{DD} of a complementary pair and
    if V_{in} is HIGH, current can flow through the (*N*-channel, *P*-channel) MOSFET.

8. If a load is connected from the output to ground of a complementary pair and
    if V_{in} is LOW, current can flow through the (*N*-channel, *P*-channel) MOSFET.

9. In step 5, current (did, did not) flow through the load resistor.

10. In step 6, V_0 is (higher than, ~~lower than, the same as~~) in the unloaded circuit
    of Fig. L 3-2(A) because (current flow through the *N*-channel MOSFET causes
    a drop across it, the resistor drags down the voltage).

11. When two *N*-channel MOSFETs are paralleled, as in step 7, the output voltage
    becomes (~~lower,~~ higher) than in step 6 because (the ON resistance of the two
    ~~transistors in parallel is~~ lower than that of the single transistor, both tran-
    sistor resistances add).

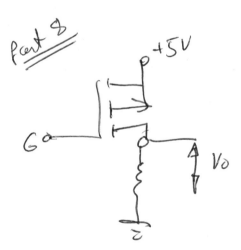

4

NAND Gates and NOR Gates

Introduction

The study of NAND gates and NOR gates is an important step in our becoming able to understand complicated digital electronic circuits. Although AND gates and OR gates have their uses, IC packages containing NANDs and NORs are far more commonly used. A digital circuit designer can achieve virtually any logic function he needs by using NAND gates only, or NOR gates only, or combinations of NANDs and NORs. A good understanding of how NAND gates and NOR gates work will enable us to understand how logic (electronic decision making) is performed in digital systems that are discussed in later chapters.

4-1 Basic NAND Gates

Logically, a NAND gate performs the same function as does an AND gate followed with an inverter. This combination and its equivalent, the NAND gate, are shown in Fig. 4-1. As indicated in Fig. 4-1(A), the output X of the AND gate is HIGH only when both inputs A and B are HIGH. Or, to put it in other words, the output X is LOW if either or both inputs are LOW. The inverter's output $\bar{X}$ (not X) is always an inversion of the AND gate's output X. This AND gate-inverter combination performs a NAND (not an AND) function. As shown in the $\bar{X}$ column of the tables, the NAND gate's output is LOW only when both inputs A and B are HIGH. Or, to put it another way, the NAND gate's output is HIGH if either or both of its inputs are LOW. The symbol in Fig. 4-1(B) is most often used to represent the NAND gate.

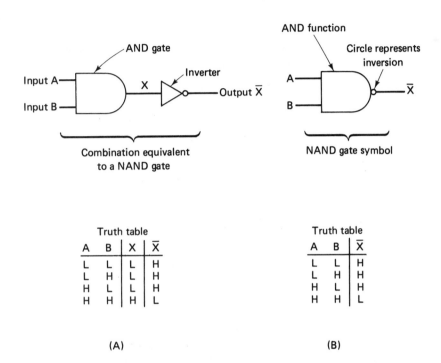

Truth table			
A	B	X	X̄
L	L	L	H
L	H	L	H
H	L	L	H
H	H	H	L

Truth table		
A	B	X̄
L	L	H
L	H	H
H	L	H
H	H	L

(A)   (B)

Fig. 4-1. (A) AND gate with inverter and their truth table; (B) the NAND gate and its truth table.

4-2   NAND **Gate Circuitry**

Figure 4-2 shows circuitry that a two-input NAND gate might contain. In Fig. 4-2(A), we have the simple diode AND gate previously discussed. In Fig. 4-2(B), we have a simple transistor inverter, also discussed previously. Because of the components it contains, this is called a resistor-transistor logic (RTL) inverter. A combination of the diode AND gate and RTL inverter is shown in Fig. 4-2(C) and, of course, it performs a NAND function.

The circuit of Fig. 4-3(A) is a basic TTL NAND gate. Its equivalent is shown in Fig. 4-3(B), which illustrates that the input transistor Q_1 of the TTL gate is equivalent to the input diodes used in the gates of Fig. 4-2.

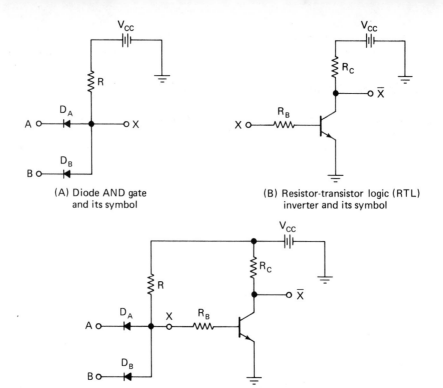

(A) Diode AND gate
and its symbol

(B) Resistor-transistor logic (RTL)
inverter and its symbol

(C) AND gate-inverter combination
forms a NAND gate

Fig. 4-2.

Fig. 4-3.

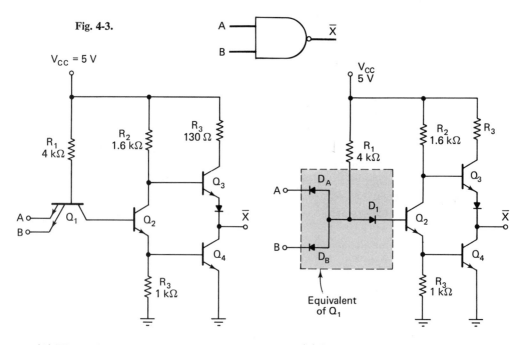

(A) TTL two-input NAND gate circuit

(B) Equivalent of the TTL two-input
NAND gate circuit

4-3 Basic NOR Gates and Their Circuitry

A NOR gate performs the same logic function as does an OR gate followed with an inverter. That is, as shown in both tables of Fig. 4-4, a two-input NOR gate's output $\bar{X}$ is HIGH only when both of its inputs are LOW. This means that its output $\bar{X}$ is LOW if either or both of its inputs are HIGH.

In the TTL family of ICs, the two-input NOR gate's circuitry is typically as shown in Fig. 4-4(C). With this circuit, if we pull both inputs LOW, the bases of transistors Q_2 and Q_3 are low and nonconducting. These transistors therefore turn

Fig. 4-4. (A) OR gate with inverter and their truth table; (B) the NOR gate and its truth table; (C) TTL two-input NOR gate circuitry.

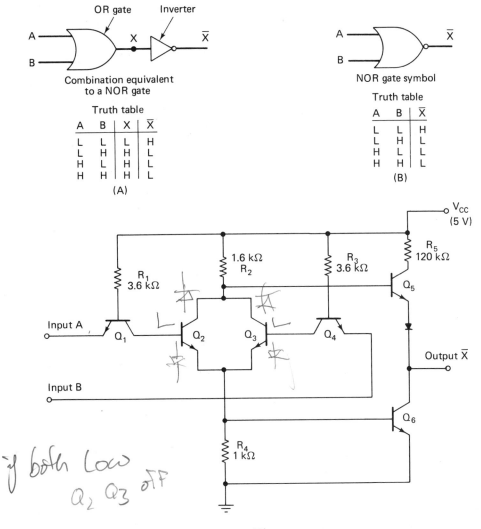

OR gate   Inverter

A
B   X $\bar{X}$

Combination equivalent
to a NOR gate

Truth table

A	B	X	$\bar{X}$
L	L	L	H
L	H	H	L
H	L	H	L
H	H	H	L

(A)

A
B $\bar{X}$

NOR gate symbol

Truth table

A	B	$\bar{X}$
L	L	H
L	H	L
H	L	L
H	H	L

(B)

(C)

off and raise the base voltage on Q_5 while reducing the base voltage on Q_6. This causes Q_5 to turn on and Q_6 to turn off, raising the output $\bar{X}$ to nearly the V_{CC} voltage via the conducting Q_5.

On the other hand, if input A is pulled HIGH, the voltage on the base of Q_2 increases, causing this transistor to turn on. While on, Q_2 raises the voltage at the base of Q_6 while simultaneously reducing the drive on the base of Q_5. Consequently, Q_5 turns off and Q_6 turns on, pulling the output $\bar{X}$ down to a LOW logic level. Similarly, if a HIGH is applied to input B, the transistor Q_3 turns on. This keeps Q_5 nonconducting and Q_6 conducting. Of course, then, output $\bar{X}$ remains LOW.

Needless to say, if both inputs A and B are HIGH, both Q_2 and Q_3 are conducting, which turns Q_6 on and pulls the output $\bar{X}$ LOW.

The circuit of Fig. 4-5 is a CMOS NOR gate. Its output $\bar{X}$ can go HIGH only if both MOSFETS Q_1 *and* Q_2 are on simultaneously. On the other hand, this output $\bar{X}$ is pulled LOW if either Q_3 *or* Q_4 turns on. Combinations of these MOSFETS turn on or off depending on the input signal conditions. For example, when both inputs are LOW, the MOSFETS Q_1 and Q_2 turn on while Q_3 and Q_4 turn off. Thus the output $\bar{X}$ is pulled up to the V_{DD} potential. However, if either or both of the inputs are HIGH, either or both MOSFETS Q_1 and Q_2 turn off, which prevents V_{DD} from appearing at the output $\bar{X}$. Simultaneously, either or both MOSFETS Q_3 and Q_4 turn on, which pulls the output $\bar{X}$ LOW to about ground potential.

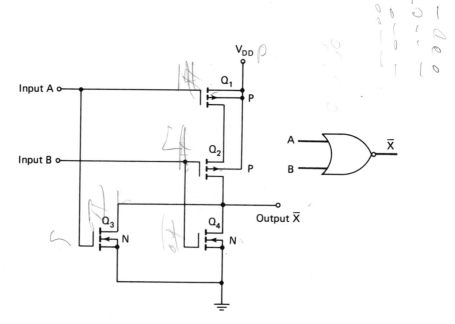

Fig. 4-5. CMOS IC NOR gate.

4-4   A Dynamic View of the NAND Gate/NOR Gate

In Fig. 4-6 we see how the NAND gate and the NOR gate respond to typical input signals. Note that the same input signals are applied to both gates and that the waveforms of these inputs are shown. The resulting output waveforms are also shown. In this case, we can see that the NAND gate's output $\bar{Y}$ remains HIGH as long as one or both inputs are LOW. That is, the output $\bar{Y}$ is LOW between 5 and 6 ms because both inputs are HIGH in this time segment. The NOR gate's output $\bar{Z}$, however, goes LOW whenever one or both of its inputs goes HIGH.

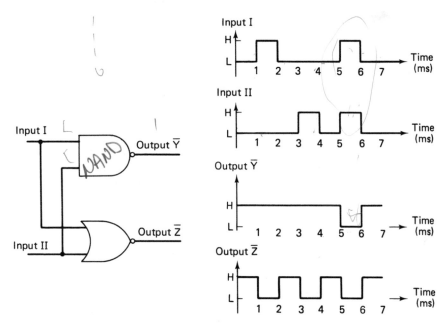

Fig. 4-6. Input waveforms applied to a NAND gate and a NOR gate with the resulting output waveforms at the gates' outputs.

4-5   Unused Inputs of NANDS and NORS

In the final wiring of logic circuit ICs, unused inputs are never left open. Open inputs can cause erratic and unreliable operation because they pick up noise by induction. Such noise might be interpreted, by the gate, as a logic input signal. In practice, therefore, unused inputs are connected to used inputs or to the dc supply voltage or to ground, whichever is appropriate. For example, Fig. 4-7 shows how two-input NANDS can be used as inverters. As shown in Fig. 4-7(A), both inputs can be tied together, therefore, with typical logic input signals; both inputs are either HIGH or LOW together. As row 1 of the NAND gate's truth table indicates, the NAND's output $\bar{X}$ is HIGH when *both* inputs are LOW. On the other hand, as shown in row 4, the NAND gate's output is LOW when *both* inputs are HIGH. Apparently, then, the gate connection in Fig. 4-7(A) works as an inverter.

When the NAND gate is wired as in Fig. 4-7(B), operation is in either row 3 or 4 and it likewise works as an inverter.

The NOR gate connections shown in Fig. 4-8 also work as inverters. When both inputs are tied together, as shown in Fig. 4-8(A), operation is in rows 1 and 4 of the NOR's truth table. In these rows we can see that if both inputs are LOW, the output $\bar{X}$ is HIGH, while, on the other hand, if both inputs are HIGH, the output $\bar{X}$ is LOW.

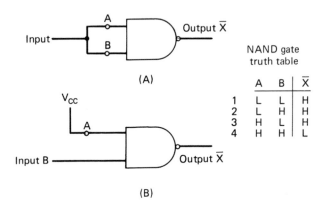

NAND gate
truth table

	A	B	$\bar{X}$
1	L	L	H
2	L	H	H
3	H	L	H
4	H	H	L

Fig. 4-7. NAND gates used as inverters.

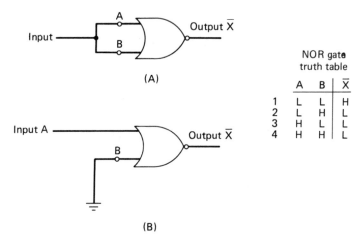

NOR gate
truth table

	A	B	$\bar{X}$
1	L	L	H
2	L	H	L
3	H	L	L
4	H	H	L

Fig. 4-8. NOR gates used as inverters.

If input *B* of the two-input NOR is permanently tied LOW, that is, grounded as shown in Fig. 4-8(B), operation is in rows 1 and 3 of the table. Thus when a LOW is applied to input *A*, the output $\bar{X}$ goes HIGH, whereas a HIGH on input *A* drives the output $\bar{X}$ LOW.

Other appropriate connections of NANDS and NORS are shown in Fig. 4-9. The four-input NAND gates in Fig. 4-9(A) are wired to work as two-input NANDS. The four-input NORS in Fig. 4-9(B) are wired to work as two-input NOR gates. Both four-input gates in Fig. 4-9(C) are wired to work as inverters.

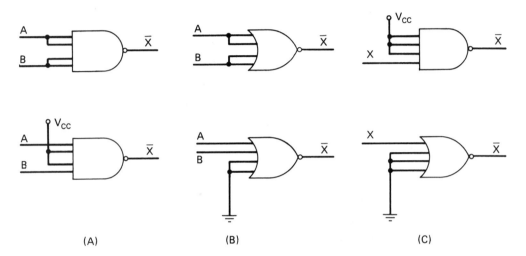

(A)   (B)   (C)

Fig. 4-9. (A) Four-input NAND gates used as two-input NANDS; (B) four-input NOR gates used as two-input NORS; (C) four-input gates used as inverters.

Summary

1. The term NAND gate can be interpreted to mean "not an AND gate" because the NAND's output is always opposite, logically, of an AND gate's output given the same set of inputs.

2. A NAND gate's output is LOW only if *all* its inputs are HIGH. This means that the NAND's output is HIGH if *any* one of its inputs is LOW.

3. The term NOR gate can be interpreted to mean "not an OR gate" because the NOR's output is always logically opposite of an OR gate's output with the same set of applied inputs.

4. A NOR gate's output is LOW if *any* one of its inputs is HIGH. This means that the NOR's output is HIGH only if *all* its inputs are LOW.

5. Either a NAND or a NOR gate can be used as a logic inverter by connecting all its inputs together or by connecting the unused inputs to an appropriate logic level permanently.

6. Unused inputs on a NAND gate can be connected permanently HIGH but never permanently LOW.

7. Unused inputs on a NOR gate can be permanently connected LOW but never HIGH.

8. Unused inputs on logic gates should never be left permanently open.

Problems 4-1

All the following problems refer to Fig. 4-10, in which the gate input waveforms are shown.

1. The output $\bar{S}$ is HIGH unless both inputs are ___High___ .

2. Sketch the waveform at output $\bar{S}$ directly on the scale provided.

3. The output $\bar{T}$ is LOW unless both inputs are ___Low___.

4. Sketch the waveform at output $\bar{T}$. Use the scale provided in Fig. 4-10.

5. The NAND gate III is wired to work as a logic ___INVERTER___.

6. Sketch the waveform at output $\bar{U}$. Use the scale provided.

7. The NOR gate IV is wired to work as a logic ___INVERTER___

8. Sketch the waveform at output $\bar{V}$.

9. Sketch the waveform at output $\bar{W}$.

10. Sketch the waveform at output $\bar{X}$.

11. Sketch the waveform at output $\bar{Y}$.

12. Sketch the waveform at output $\bar{Z}$.

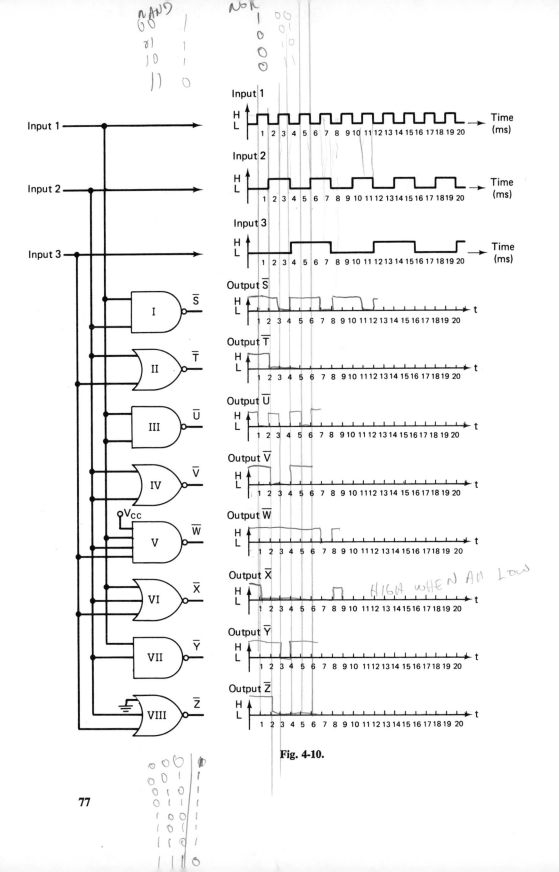

Fig. 4-10.

5

Logic Gate Symbols and Tables

Introduction

Like any specialized field, digital electronics has its own set of terms, expressions, and jargon. To the unfamiliar listener these have the sound of a foreign language. As we progress through this text and work its laboratory experiments, we not only obtain more understanding of the hardware but also we extend our vocabularies that help us to communicate in the "world of electronics." In these sections, we shall be introduced to techniques used when digital technicians and engineers communicate with each other about their work.

5-1 Boolean Expressions for Logic Functions

The way logic circuits and gates work can be expressed with a series of symbols called Boolean expressions or equations. Boolean equations are frequently used in logic diagrams, manufacturers' literature, reference books, and textbooks. They tell us what a given circuit or gate is doing in a simple and efficient way. For example, the output of the two-input AND gate shown in Fig. 5-1(A) is shown as $X = AB$. A multiplication sign, $\times$ or $\cdot$, is assumed to be between A and B if it is not shown. The multiplication sign means *and* in Boolean expressions. Thus $X = AB$ is pronounced "ex equals A and B." Similarly, the three-input AND's output, $X = ABC$, is pronounced "ex equals A and B and C." This simply means that the output X is HIGH only if input A *and* input B *and* input C are HIGH.

As shown in Figs. 5-1(C) and (D), the two- and three-input OR gates use plus (+) signs in their Boolean expressions. A plus sign means *or* when used in a Boolean equation. Therefore, $X = A + B + C$ is pronounced "ex equals *A or B or C*." This simply means that output X is HIGH if input *A or* input *B or* input *C* is HIGH.

Boolean expressions for NAND functions are shown at the outputs of the NAND gates in Figs. 5-1(E) and (F). The equations $\bar{X} = AB$ and $X = \overline{AB}$ are equivalent, as are $\bar{X} = ABC$ and $X = \overline{ABC}$. The equation $\bar{X} = ABC$ is pronounced "not ex (or bar ex) equals *A and B and C*," which means that the output $\bar{X}$ is LOW if all the inputs *A and B and C* are HIGH. The equivalent expression $X = \overline{ABC}$ can be pronounced "ex equals not the quantity *A and B and C*." The bars over the right-hand sides of $X = \overline{AB}$ and $X = \overline{ABC}$ simply mean that a NAND gate always has a logic level output that is opposite of an AND's output given the same set of inputs.

Equations for NOR functions are shown in Figs. 5-1(G) and (H). The equation $\bar{X} = A + B + C$, pronounced "not ex equals *A or B or C*," means that the output $\bar{X}$ is LOW if input *A or* input *B or* input *C* is HIGH. Its equivalent, $X = \overline{A + B + C}$, means that the NOR gate's output logic is always opposite of the OR gate's output if given the same set of inputs.

Fig. 5-1. Common logic gates and their Boolean expressions.

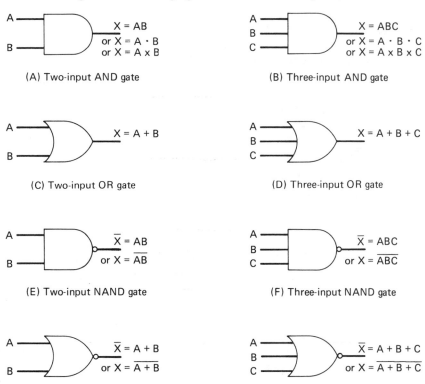

(A) Two-input AND gate   (B) Three-input AND gate

(C) Two-input OR gate   (D) Three-input OR gate

(E) Two-input NAND gate   (F) Three-input NAND gate

(G) Two-input NOR gate   (H) Three-input NOR gate

5-2 Constructing Truth Tables

When making a truth table, how do we know if we have shown every possible combination of input signals? To answer this we must first find the number of possible combinations, which is easy if we know the number of input signals. We can see in Fig. 5-2 that a truth table has more input combinations (rows) if the circuit for which it is written has more inputs. That is, as shown in Fig. 5-2(A), a two-input logic gate or circuit has 2^2 or 4 possible input combinations, which are shown in 4 rows of its truth table. Figure 5-2(B) shows that a three-input system has 2^3 or 8 possible input combinations (rows). A four-input gate has 2^4 or 16 input combinations, and its truth table requires 16 rows, as shown in Fig. 5-2(C). In the same way we could show that five-input systems have 2^5 or 32 combinations, six-input systems have 2^6 or 64 combinations, etc. Thus the number of inputs that a logic circuit has dictates the number of rows that we *must* provide when writing the circuit's truth table.

We should study Fig. 5-2 and note how the L's and H's (variables) are entered into each truth table. In each far-right input column, the entries are L, H, L, H, etc., from top to bottom. In the next input column to the left, the entries are in sets of twos; that is, they are L, L, H, H, etc., starting from the top downward. In the third from the far-right input column [see Fig. 5-2(C)] the entries are in sets of four starting with L's. Obviously, the number of L's and H's in each set simply doubles with each input column to the left. If we follow this format after establishing the proper number of rows, the truth table will have all possible input combinations.

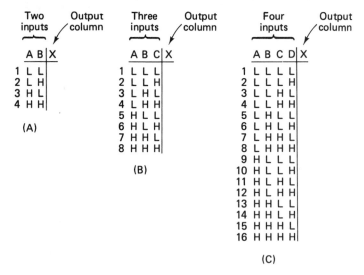

Fig. 5-2. Truth table input combinations for a (A) two-input (variable) logic system; (B) three-input system; (C) four-input system.

A number of four-input gates, their Boolean equations, and truth table are shown in Fig. 5-3. Note that the four inputs require 16 rows to cover all input combinations and that each input column to the left has twice as many L's and H's in each set as does the column to its immediate right.

The output column T in Fig. 5-3 represents the output of the four-input AND gate; that is, $T = ABCD$. We should note, in row 16, that output T is HIGH only when *all* inputs are HIGH.

Column U in Fig. 5-3 represents the output $U = \overline{ABCD}$ of the four-input NAND gate. In this case we can see that every entry in the U column is opposite of the T column's entry in the same row. Of course, then, the output U is LOW only when all inputs are HIGH.

Column V in Fig. 5-3 shows the output signals of the four-input OR gate. Obviously the OR's output $V = A + B + C + D$ is HIGH if any one of its inputs is HIGH. That is, V is LOW only when all inputs are LOW.

Finally, column W shows that the output $W = \overline{A + B + C + D}$ of the four-input NOR is LOW if any of its inputs is HIGH and that, generally, each entry in the W column is opposite logically to each adjacent entry in the V column.

Functional table

Inputs	Outputs
A B C D	T U V W
L L L L	L H L H
L L L H	L H H L
L L H L	L H H L
L L H H	L H H L
L H L L	L H H L
L H L H	L H H L
L H H L	L H H L
L H H H	L H H L
H L L L	L H H L
H L L H	L H H L
H L H L	L H H L
H L H H	L H H L
H H L L	L H H L
H H L H	L H H L
H H H L	L H H L
H H H H	H L H L

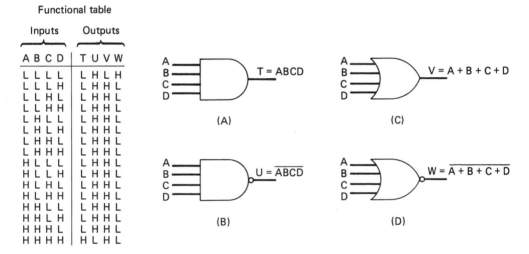

Fig. 5-3. Functional table for (A) four-input AND gate; (B) four-input OR gate; (C) four-input NAND gate; (D) four-input NOR gate.

5-3   Other Symbols for Logic Levels

Truth tables, which are also called functional tables, are commonly used in literature describing digital circuits. The logic signal levels in such tables are not always shown as L's and H's. Frequently, the numbers 0 and 1 are used to represent L and

H, respectively. Examples of this are shown in Fig. 5-4. With the use of 0's and and 1's in place of the L's and H's, the language decribing circuit action will be slightly different. For example, the AND gate is said to have a 1 output only if all its inputs are 1, which means that its output is 0 if any or both of its inputs are 0. Similarly, statements describing the action of the other gates can be made in terms of 1's and 0's instead of HIGHs and LOWs.

A	B	AB		A	B	A + B		A	B	$\overline{AB}$		A	B	$\overline{A + B}$
0	0	0		0	0	0		0	0	1		0	0	1
0	1	0		0	1	1		0	1	1		0	1	0
1	0	0		1	0	1		1	0	1		1	0	0
1	1	1		1	1	1		1	1	0		1	1	0

(A)   (B)   (C)   (D)

Fig. 5-4. Truth tables for (A) two-input AND gate; (B) two-input OR gate; (C) two-input NAND gate; (D) two-input NOR gate.

Summary

1. The Boolean expression $X = AB$ represents the function of a two-input AND gate.

2. The multiplication sign assumed to be between the A and B in the equation $X = AB$ means *and*.

3. The Boolean expression $X = A + B$ represents the function of a two-input OR gate. The plus sign between the A and B means *or*.

4. The expressions $\bar{X} = AB$ and $X = \overline{AB}$ represent the function of a two-input NAND gate.

5. The expressions $\bar{X} = A + B$ and $X = \overline{A + B}$ represent the function of a two-input NOR gate.

6. The number of possible input combinations on logic circuits or gates doubles with each additional input.

7. The logic level symbols L and H are frequently replaced with numbers 0 and 1, respectively.

Problem 5-1

1. In Fig. 5-5, show truth tables, using 0's and 1's instead of L's and H's, for the functions
    (a) $W = ABC$. (b) $X = \overline{ABC}$. (c) $Y = A + B + C$. (d) $Z = \overline{A + B + C}$.

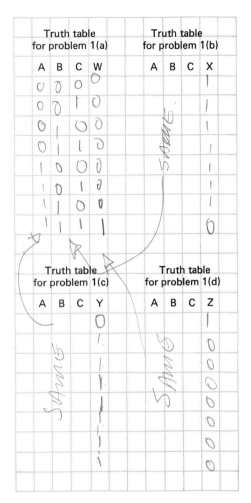

Truth table for problem 1(a)			
A	B	C	W
0	0	0	0
0	0	1	0
0	1	0	0
0	1	1	0
1	0	0	0
1	0	1	0
1	1	0	0
1	1	1	1

Truth table for problem 1(b)			
A	B	C	X
			1
			1
			1
			1
			1
			1
			1
			0

SAME

Truth table for problem 1(c)			
A	B	C	Y
			0
			1
			1
			1
			1
			1
			1
			1

SAME

Truth table for problem 1(d)			
A	B	C	Z
			1
			0
			0
			0
			0
			0
			0

SAME

Fig. 5-5.

6

TTL and CMOS Integrated Circuit Components

Introduction

In this chapter we shall become familiar with several integrated circuit (IC) devices that are in the popular TTL and CMOS families. The ICs discussed here are SSI (small-scale integration) types that contain logic gates. Because of ICs, electronic circuits became much smaller and less expensive. This expanded the possible uses of electronics in industry and in the home. Computers and hand calculators are just two of many we could mention. On the foundation laid here, we shall build an understanding of modern electronics, which is rapidly becoming the "brains" and "nerves" of our complicated society.

6-1   Transistor-Transistor Logic

Transistor-transistor logic (TTL), also called T^2L ("tee squared ell"), is one of the most popular of digital IC logic families. Therefore, most of the ICs that we shall discuss and work with are of the TTL type. TTL ICs are known for their high switching speeds and good *noise immunity*. For the present, we should know that good noise immunity means reliable operation of a digital system even though heavy electrical equipment (motors, high current relays, etc.) is nearby. The TTL family of ICs requires dc supply voltages in the range of 4.5 to 5.5 V. Typically 5-V well-regulated power supplies are used. TTL ICs will not work reliably with dc supply voltages outside of this recommended range and will likely be destroyed if the recommended maximum of 5.5 V is exceeded.

Most TTL ICs have totem-pole output transistors, as shown in Fig. 6-1(C), and we should become familiar with the output levels of such ICs. In a previous chapter it was implied that if the dc supply voltage V_{CC} is 5 V on a logic circuit, then its HIGH output signal is *about* 5 V and its LOW output is *about* 0 V. This, in fact, is true with many digital circuits. In the case of totem-pole output TTL devices, however, the HIGH output signal might be as low as 2.4 V even though $V_{CC} = 5$ V. On the other hand, its LOW output might be as high as 0.5 V. Although we should be aware of these HIGH and LOW output levels, they cause no difficulty in circuits built entirely with TTL devices. That is, though a HIGH output of a digital IC might be as low as 2.4 V, the next TTL device will definitely interpret it as a HIGH input. of course, then, any signal above 2.4 V, up to 5.5 V, will likewise be interpreted as a HIGH input. Similarly, a LOW output of 0.5 V or less will definitely be interpreted as a LOW input by the TTL device being driven by this output signal.

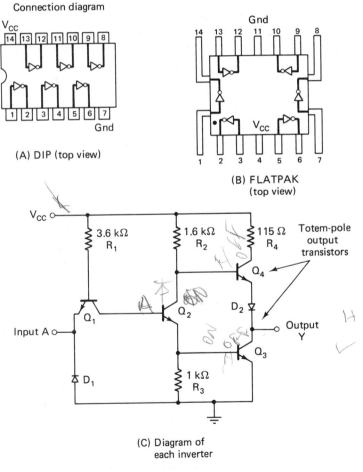

Connection diagram

(A) DIP (top view)

(B) FLATPAK
(top view)

(C) Diagram of
each inverter

Fig. 6-1. The 7404 hex inverter (totem-pole outputs).

Some TTL ICs have *open collector* outputs instead of totem-pole arrangements. For example, see Fig. 6-2(C). The open collector TTL devices require an externally wired pull-up resistor R_x, as shown in Fig. 6-3. When the transistor Q_3 is turned on, the output X is pulled down to ground potential. On the other hand, when Q_3 is turned off, the output X is pulled up, through R_x, to very nearly the entire V_{CC} voltage value. The open collector TTL devices are capable of HIGH output signals that are higher than HIGHs out of totem-pole arrangements. In fact, the top of the pull-up resistor R_x can be connected to a V_{CC} source that is significantly larger than the 4.5- to 5.5-V recommended supply for the TTL ICs. This feature makes the open collector TTL IC able to work into (be compatible with) other logic family ICs that work better with or require larger V_{CC} supply voltages and larger HIGH input signals. For example, if $V_{CC_2} = 12$ V in the circuit of Fig. 6-3, the output X goes HIGH to about 12 V when Q_3 is turned off. Note, however, that the V_{CC_1} supply on the TTL device is 5 V and therefore is in the recommended range. This 12-V HIGH output could be the input to a CMOS (complementary metal oxide semiconductor) or a DTL (diode-transistor logic) family IC. A 12-V logic level cannot be used as a HIGH into a TTL device whose maximum HIGH must be limited to 5.5 V.

Fig. 6-2. The 7405 hex inverter (open collector outputs).

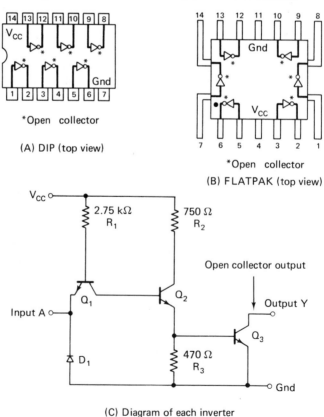

*Open collector

(A) DIP (top view)

*Open collector

(B) FLATPAK (top view)

(C) Diagram of each inverter

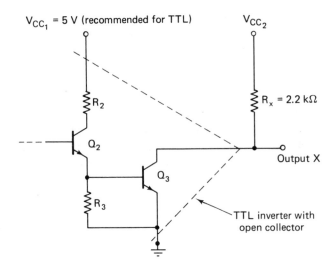

Fig. 6-3. ICs with open cell collector outputs require pull-up resistors R_x connected externally.

6-2 Numerical Identifications of TTL ICs

A large variety of TTL logic ICs is available. The various types, which perform various logic functions, have numerical identifications that are somewhat standard in the electronics industry. For example, in this chapter we shall discuss the hex inverter with totem-pole outputs whose number is 7404, the hex inverter with open collector outputs whose number is 7405, and the quad two-input AND whose number is 7408, to name just a few.

6-3 Output and Input Unit Loading of TTL ICs

Typically the output of one logic circuit drives one or more inputs of other logic circuits. We can determine the output drive capability of a logic circuit or IC from its fan-out or output unit load (U.L.) specification which is provided by the manufacturer. For example, the 7404 Hex Inverter TTL IC is specified as having a fan-out of 10. This means that each Inverter is able to drive up to 10 standard TTL inputs.

6-4 TTL Hex Inverters

The 7404 TTL hex inverter IC is shown in Fig. 6-1. Parts (A) and (B) of this figure show that either package type contains six complete inverters. As mentioned before, each 7404 inverter has a totem-pole output arrangement, shown in Fig. 6-1(C). As with inverters discussed in previous chapters, each inverter in the 7404

package can be used to invert the logic level of a digital signal. That is, a HIGH on
its input causes a LOW on its output or vice versa. Each hex inverter package has
one dc supply pin and one ground pin that provide power to all six inverters.

Although the inverter symbols shown in each package type in Fig. 6-1 have
the circles at the outputs, they can also be drawn with the circles at the inputs.
That is, on an engineering drawing, the six inverters might be drawn as shown in
Fig. 6-4(A) if their outputs are ACTIVE LOW. On the other hand, they might be
shown as in Fig. 6-4(B) if their outputs are ACTIVE HIGH. The pin numbers for the
DIP (dual in-line package) are shown at the inputs and outputs in this figure.

The IC in Fig. 6-2 is a 7405 type. It features open collector outputs on each
inverter. This means that each inverter output must be externally connected to
a V_{CC} supply through a pull-up resistor. In practice, then, each of these inverters

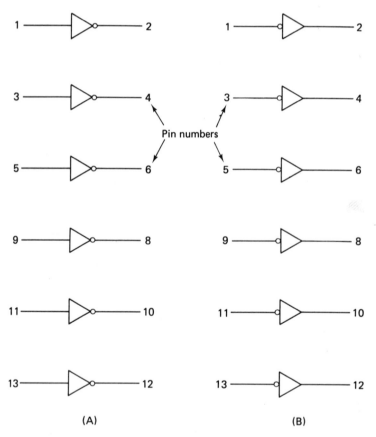

(A)   (B)

Fig. 6-4. Hex inverters of the 7404 DIP package as they might appear on
an engineering logic diagram; (A) with ACTIVE LOW outputs, and (B) with
ACTIVE HIGH outputs.

would be used as shown in Fig. 6-5. Sometimes, for simplicity on engineering diagrams, the 7405 inverters are shown without the pull-up resistors, that is, as in
Fig. 6-4. In the actual circuit, however, the pull-up resistors must be used with this
IC. As with the inverters with totem-pole outputs, the symbols for open collector
inverters can be drawn with the circles at the outputs or the inputs depending on
whether they are used with ACTIVE LOW or ACTIVE HIGH outputs, respectively.
With either hex inverter, the 7404 or the 7405 type, an *open* (unconnected) input
is interpreted as a HIGH input and causes a LOW output. Normally, however, TTL
inputs are not left open.

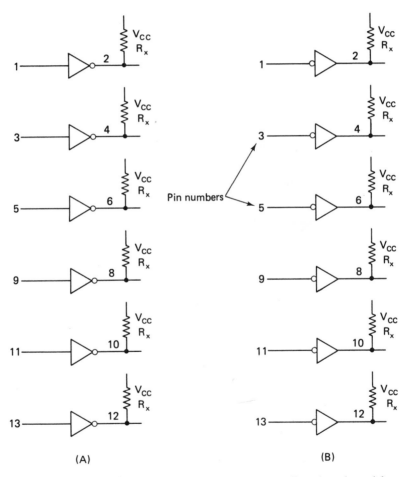

(A)   (B)

Fig. 6-5. Hex inverters of the 7405 DIP package (open collector) as they might
appear on an engineering logic diagram (A) with ACTIVE LOW outputs, and (B)
with ACTIVE HIGH outputs.

Summary

1. The TTL family is among the most popular of digital ICs.

2. TTL ICs are known for their high switching speeds and good noise immunity.

3. The TTL family requires a dc supply in the range of 4.5 to 5.5 V; typically a regulated 5-V dc supply is used.

4. Most TTL logic devices have totem-pole outputs that can simply be connected to inputs of other TTL devices.

5. The output HIGHs of totem-pole TTL devices are usually considerably less than the 5-V dc supply voltage. This is no problem provided that such signals drive other TTL inputs.

6. TTL ICs are available with open collector outputs, which require externally connected pull-up resistors.

7. When the output transistor of an open collector TTL device is turned off, the output is pulled HIGH to nearly the entire dc supply voltage through the pull-up resistor.

8. Open collector outputs are capable of higher HIGH outputs than are totem-pole output TTL ICs.

9. Open collector outputs can be used to *interface* TTL circuits with other logic families, such as the CMOS and DTL.

10. Each TTL IC device has a specified *fan-out* that tells us its output drive capability.

Problems 6-1

1. With reference to Fig. 6-6, what are the logic levels at (a) pin 2, (b) pin 4, and (c) pin 6?   *Ans.* (a) __LOW__   (b) __LOW__   (c) __HIGH__

2. With reference to Fig. 6-6, if the switch Sw is alternately thrown to the H and L positions so as to cause waveform *A* in Fig. 6-7 on pin 13, what do the resulting waveforms at pins 12, 10, and 8 look like? Sketch your answers on the appropriate scales in Fig. 6-7.

3. If two inverters are in cascade (the output of the first is driving the input of the second), how do the logic levels at the input of the first inverter and the output of the second compare?   __SAME__

4. If a totem-pole output TTL device has a 2.5-V output signal while being powered by a 5-V dc supply, what logic level is this signal?   __High__

5. What type of TTL ICs require externally connected pull-up resistors?   __open collector__

6. What maximum dc supply voltage can we use with TTL devices?   __5.5V__

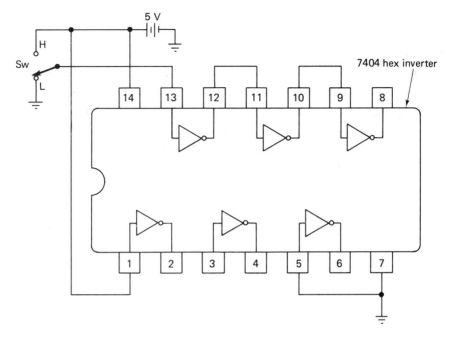

Fig. 6-6.

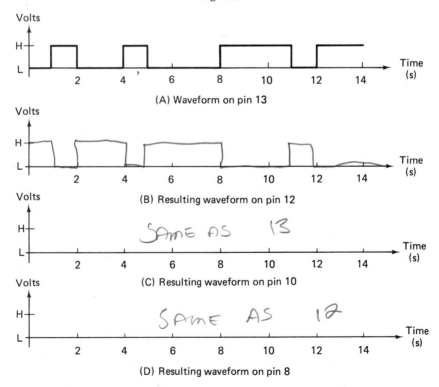

(A) Waveform on pin 13

(B) Resulting waveform on pin 12

SAME AS 13

(C) Resulting waveform on pin 10

SAME AS 12

(D) Resulting waveform on pin 8

Fig. 6-7. Waveforms associated with the circuit of Fig. 6-6.

6-5 Quad AND Gates

As are inverters, various logic gates are available in IC packages. The 7408 TTL IC, shown in Fig. 6-8, is a quad two-input AND gate. Functionally, each individual AND gate works like the two-input AND gate described in a previous chapter. Since each gate in the 7408 has a totem-pole output, a HIGH output signal might be as low as 2.4 V. A LOW logic output signal can be as high as 0.5 V. Input signals from about 2 to 5.5 V, applied to the 7408 gates, are interpreted as HIGH logic inputs. Signals of about 0.8 V or less are interpreted as LOW logic inputs.

The 7409 quad two-input AND is shown in Fig. 6-9. Since each of its gates has an open collector output, a pull-up resistor R_x must be used with it. As is the case with the open collector inverter, the open collector AND gate is capable of a higher voltage HIGH logic output signal. Also, the outputs of several open collector AND gates can be directly wired together, which is sometimes useful, as we shall see in a later chapter.

Fig. 6-8. The 7408 quad two-input AND gate (totem-pole outputs).

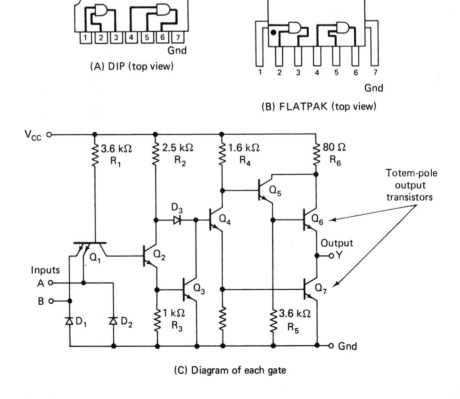

(A) DIP (top view)

(B) FLATPAK (top view)

(C) Diagram of each gate

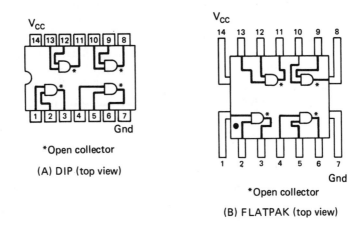

*Open collector

(A) DIP (top view)

*Open collector

(B) FLATPAK (top view)

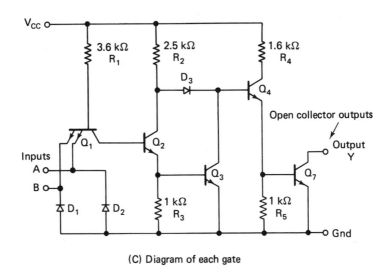

(C) Diagram of each gate

Fig. 6-9. The 7409 quad two-input AND gate (open collector outputs).

6-6 Quad NAND Gates

NAND gates are available in TTL ICs such as the 7400 quad two-input NAND shown in Fig. 6-10. Each individual NAND gate in the 7400 package functionally works like the two-input NAND gate discussed previously*. That is, the two-input NAND gate's output goes LOW only if both its inputs are HIGH. Or, to put it another way,

*See the truth table for the two-input NAND gate in Fig. 4-1(B), Chapter 4.

we can say that the NAND gate's output goes HIGH if either or both of its inputs are pulled LOW.

The 7401 TTL IC, shown in Fig. 6-11, is a quad two-input NAND with open collector outputs. Each gate in this package must be used with an externally connected pull-up resistor. These open collector NANDs are capable of higher HIGH outputs than are the totem-pole outputs of the 7400 package. An open collector gate can be directly wired to other open collector outputs, as shown in Fig. 6-12. The usefulness of this is discussed later.

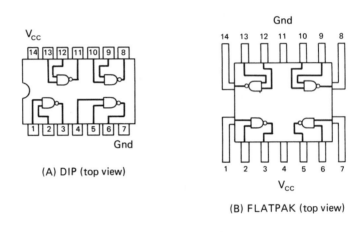

(A) DIP (top view)

(B) FLATPAK (top view)

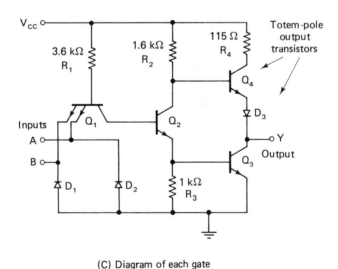

(C) Diagram of each gate

Fig. 6-10. The 7400 quad two-input NAND gate (totem-pole outputs).

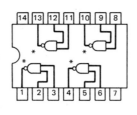

Fig. 6-11. The 7401 quad two-input NAND gate (open collector outputs).

*Open collector

(A) DIP (top view)

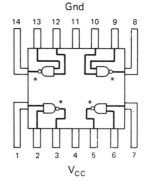

Gnd

Vcc

*Open collector

(B) FLATPAK (top view)

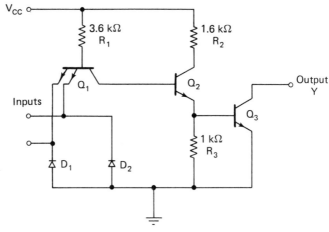

(C) Diagram of each gate

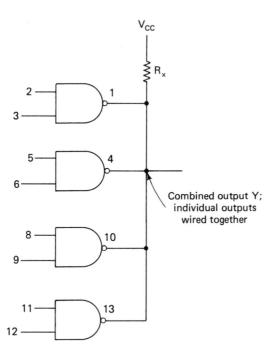

Combined output Y;
individual outputs
wired together

Fig. 6-12. Open collector NAND gates with outputs wired together and to a pull-up resistor.

6-7 Quad NOR Gates

The packages and circuit in Fig. 6-13 are those of the 7402 quad two-input NOR TTL IC. Functionally it works like the two-input NOR discussed in Chapter 4. That is, its output goes LOW if either or both of its inputs are pulled HIGH. Or in other words, the output of the two-input NOR goes HIGH only if both of its inputs are pulled LOW.

Fig. 6-13. The 7402 quad two-input NOR gate (totem-pole outputs).

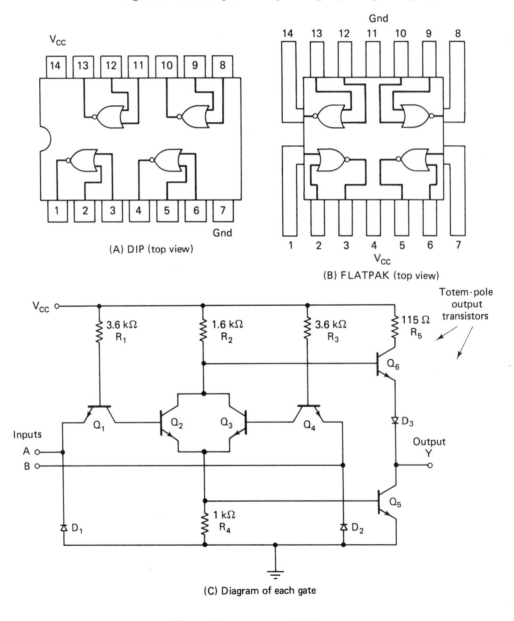

(A) DIP (top view)

(B) FLATPAK (top view)

(C) Diagram of each gate

CMOS 3-15V

Another type of quad two-input NOR is shown in Fig. 6-14. This package is a CD 4001A, which is a CMOS type. As mentioned before CMOS ICs work with dc supply voltages from about 3 to 15 V. Obviously, the power supply requirements for CMOS ICs are not so narrow as the 4.5- to 5.5-V range required with TTL ICs. Each gate in the CD 4001A works like any two-input NOR gate. Unlike the TTL gate, a CMOS gate interprets an input signal as HIGH or LOW depending not only on the input signal voltage value but also on the value of the dc supply voltage. Generally, a CMOS gate recognizes a signal that is about 0.9 of the dc supply voltage or larger as a HIGH input. Signals about 0.1 of the dc supply or less are recognized as LOW inputs by CMOS gates. Thus if the dc supply on a CMOS is 5 V, a HIGH input signal should be larger than 0.9×5 V, or 4.5 V approximately, whereas LOW input signals should be less than about 0.1×5 V, or 0.5 V.

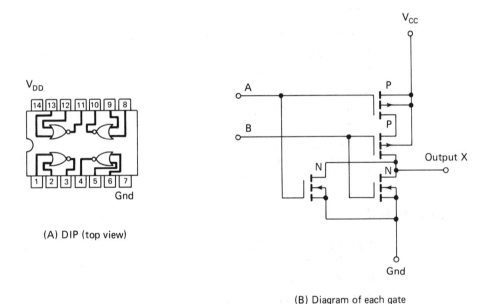

(A) DIP (top view)

(B) Diagram of each gate

Fig. 6-14. The CD 4001A quad two-input NOR CMOS IC.

Summary

1. Logic gates, such as ANDS, NANDS, and NORS, are available in IC packages.

2. The term *quad* means *four*, and therefore a quad NAND package contains four individual NAND gates.

3. Totem-pole output TTL gates are able to work directly into other TTL devices. Normally, no pull-up resistors are required.

4. A totem-pole output TTL gate can be used with a pull-up resistor R_x on its output to work into CMOS devices if the TTL and CMOS are on the same dc supply voltage.

5. Open collector output TTL gates, with pull-up resistors, are able to work into a CMOS system that is using larger than a 5-V supply.

6. Signals from about 2 to 5.5 V applied to TTL ICs are recognized as HIGH input signals.

7. Input signals from about 0.8 to 0 V are recognized by TTL as LOW inputs.

8. A CMOS recognizes an input signal as HIGH if its voltage is about 0.9 of the dc supply or larger.

9. A CMOS recognizes an input of about 0.1 of the dc supply or less as a LOW input signal.

10. CMOS systems will work with dc supply voltages from about 3 to 15 V.

11. A two-input AND gate's output goes HIGH if HIGHs are applied to both inputs. This gate's output goes LOW if either or both inputs are pulled LOW.

12. A two-input NAND gate's output goes LOW if HIGHs are applied to both of its inputs. In other words, this gate's output is HIGH if a LOW is on either or both of its inputs.

13. A two-input NOR gate's output goes LOW if a HIGH is applied to either or both of its inputs. In other words, we can say that the NOR gate's output goes HIGH if LOWs are applied to both inputs.

Problems 6-2

1. The circuit of Fig. 6-15 shows an application of the 7408 quad two-input AND. Indicate the missing pin numbers directly on this diagram. Note that this 7408 is in a DIP package.

    Problems 2 through 7 refer to the circuit of Fig. 6-15.

2. If both the DATA 1 and ENABLE signals are LOW, the logic level at pin 11 is ___Low___ .

3. If the DATA 1 signal is HIGH while the ENABLE signal is LOW, the logic at pin 11 is ___Low___ .

4. If the DATA 1 and ENABLE signals are both HIGH, the logic at pin 11 is ___High___ .

5. If the DATA 1 signal is LOW while the ENABLE signal is HIGH, the signal at pin 11 is ___Low___ .

6. If DATA 1 is HIGH, DATA 2 is LOW, DATA 3 is HIGH, DATA 4 is LOW, and the ENABLE signal is LOW, the logic level at pin 11 is ___L___, at pin 8 is ___L___, at pin 6 is ___L___, and at pin 3 is ___L___.

7. With the same DATA inputs, indicate the logic outputs when the ENABLE signal is HIGH. The logic level at pin 11 is ___H___, at pin 8 is ___L___, at pin 6 is ___H___, and at pin 3 is ___L___.

Problems 8 through 13 refer to the circuit of Fig. 6-16.

8. Indicate the missing pin numbers directly on the diagram. Place the even-numbered pins on the EXECUTE line. Note that this 7400 is in a FLATPAK.

9. If both the ADRS I and EXECUTE signals are LOW, the logic at pin 3 is ___H___.

10. If the ADRS I line is HIGH while the EXECUTE signal is LOW, the logic level at pin 3 is ___H___.

11. If both the ADRS I and EXECUTE signals are HIGH, the logic at pin 3 is ___L___.

12. If the ADRS I line is LOW while the EXECUTE input is HIGH, the signal at pin 3 is ___H___.

Fig. 6-15. Application of the 7408 quad two-input AND IC (DIP package).

Fig. 6-16. Typical application of the 7400 quad two-input NAND IC (FLATPAK).

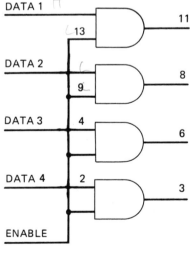

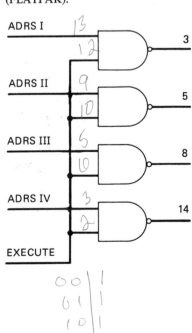

13. With the ADRS (address) and EXECUTE signals shown in Fig. 6-17 applied, sketch the output signals that we could expect to see at pins 3, 5, 8, and 14. Use the scales in Fig. 6-17.

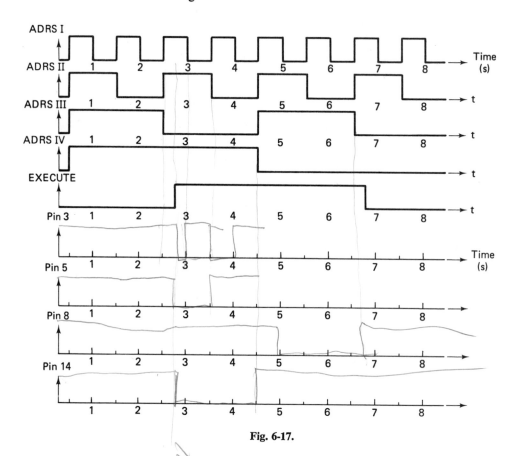

Fig. 6-17.

Experiment 6-1 Integrated Circuit Inverter

Purpose

You will become familiar with using the integrated circuit inverter, one of the simplest, yet most useful, logic circuits. You will work with the 7404 TTL inverter and thus get to know some of the characteristics of *all* TTL circuits.

Materials

> Digital breadboard kit
> 7404 hex inverter

Procedure

1. Wire the 7404 hex inverter into the socket strip as shown in Fig. L 6-1(A). Be sure to connect pin 7 to your power supply ground and pin 14 to V_{CC}. *Note: In this and all other experiments using TTL circuits, V_{CC} must be 5 V, regulated. A higher voltage can ruin the chips. You must connect every chip you use to V_{CC} and ground, even though these connections are often omitted on logic diagrams for simplicity.*

2. Flip the toggle switch up and down a few times. What do you notice about lamps *A* and *B* connected to the output and input? _____

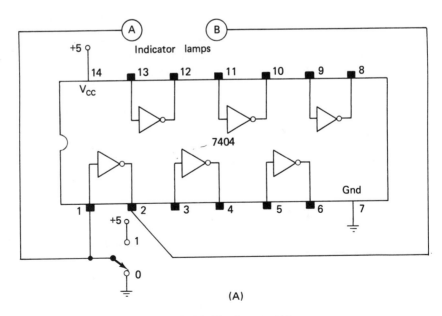

(A)

Fig. L 6-1. Hex inverter (A).

3. Connect a jumper from the output of the first inverter (pin 2) to the input of the second (pin 3), as shown in Fig. L 6-1(B). Flip the toggle switch up and down a few times. Are pins 1 and 4 always at the same logic level? _____ Should they be? _____ Explain. _____

_____

Since the 7404 is typical of the TTL logic family, we shall make some measurements at the inverter input and output to become familiar with the characteristics.

4. Connect a voltmeter from ground to pin 2. What is the LOW, or logic 0, voltage level? $V_L =$ _____ . What is the HIGH, or logic 1, voltage level? $V_H =$ _____ .

(Normally, you do not measure the outputs of logic circuits with a voltmeter but rather with a scope, so that you can see fast-changing signals, such as square waves.)

5. Suppose the square wave of Fig. L 6-1(C) is applied to pin 1 of the 7404. In Fig. L 6-1(D), draw accurately, and to scale, the waveform you would expect to see at pin 2. Label the HIGH and LOW voltage levels.

5a (optional). If you have access to a dual trace scope and a square-wave generator, drive pin 1 with a square wave and observe both input and output waveforms. Any frequency square wave will do, from about 100 Hz to a few kilohertz.* Be sure not to let the input amplitude get larger than 5 V p-p or you will ruin the chip.

Explain what you observe. _____

_____

6. To show that a single inverter can drive several other circuits, connect jumper wires from all other inverter inputs, pins 3, 5, 13, 11, and 9 to output pin 2. Leave the indicator lamps connected as in Fig. L 6-1(B). Then flip the toggle switch up and down a few times. Do the outputs still act as before? _____

Fig. L 6-1. (*cont'd.*) (B) and (C).

*See sine-to-square-wave converter circuits, Fig. L 10-5, and square-wave generators, Chapter 10.

One important point often overlooked by beginners is that unconnected inputs on logic circuits can be troublesome. You might think that leaving an input just "hanging open" will not affect the output of a circuit. But to get reliable operation of the circuit, the logic level must be either HIGH or LOW.

7. Disconnect all inputs from pin 1. That is, leave the pin hanging open. Is the output HIGH or LOW? _____ Does an unconnected input act like a 1 or a 0 input? _____

Quiz for Experiment 6-1

1. The normal LOW output level for an IC inverter is about _____ V.

2. The normal HIGH output level for a TTL circuit is at least _____ V.

3. A single IC inverter can drive up to _____ other similar loads.

4. The driving capability is called its _____.

5. If you needed a buffer amplifier to give you more driving capability with no polarity inversion, you could use (one, two, three) inverters in series.

Experiment 6-2 IC AND Gates

Purpose

To become acquainted with simple logic gates.

Materials

Digital breadboard kit
7408 quad two-input AND gate

Procedure

1. Wire the AND gate, whose input terminals are connected to pins 1 and 2, as shown in Fig. L 6-2(A).

2. Apply HIGH and LOW signals to the AND gate inputs by means of the toggle switches, and fill in Table L 6-2. Express in your own words what you find.

_____

_____

B	A	Output
L	L	
L	H	
H	L	
H	H	

Table L 6-2.

3. To demonstrate an important application of an AND gate, wire a 1-Hz clock and a bounceless switch to pins 12 and 13 as shown. (Since all four AND gates are indentical, it does not matter which one we use.) Experiment with the circuit by alternately depressing the bounceless switch for several seconds and then releasing it for several seconds. The bounceless switch in this application is called an

enabling input. Explain what you observe. _____

_____

_____

4. If you understand the idea brought out in step 3, you should be able to figure out what the AND gate will do for any square-wave inputs. Refer to Fig. L 6-2(B). Assume that two different high-frequency square waves are applied to pins 12 and 13 as shown. Sketch the output you would expect to see at pin 11 with a scope.

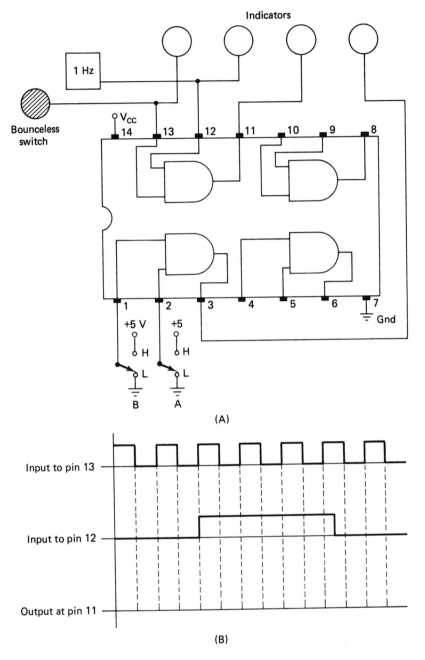

Fig. L 6-2. 7408 AND gates.

The circuit of step 3 can be used as a simple electronic stopwatch. For example, try measuring how long you can hold your breath by depressing the bounceless switch and counting the number of flashes you see at pin 11. Of course, if you wanted to measure a short interval event, you would use a higher-frequency clock and connect an automatic counter to the AND gate output.

5. Last, let's try a bit of troubleshooting. Occasionally connecting wires become broken, causing malfunctions. Disconnect the wire between the bounceless switch and pin 13. What do you notice at the AND gate output? _____

_____

Explain *why* the circuit acts as it does. Be specific—remember, there is nothing wrong with the gate itself. _____

_____

_____

_____

Quiz for Experiment 6-2

1. The AND gate output is HIGH only when both inputs are _____.

2. The AND gate output is LOW if (either, both, either or both) input(s) is/are LOW.

3. In Fig. L 6-2(B), the input to pin 12 enables the gate. When the enabling input is HIGH (the output is continually HIGH, the pulses applied to pin 13 appear at the output).

4. In Fig. L 6-2(B), if a pulse counter were connected to the output, how many counts would it register in the time the gate is enabled? _____

5. Step 5 demonstrated that an input left "hanging open" acts like a (HIGH, LOW).

Experiment 6-3   IC NAND Gates

Purpose

To become familiar with the 7400 quad two-input NAND gate, the basic building block of the TTL family.

Materials

Digital breadboard kit
15-mA LED (any color)
240-Ω, $\frac{1}{4}$-W $\pm 5\%$ resistor
7400 quad two-input NAND

Procedure

1. Wire the circuit of Fig. L 6-3(A). Apply power and observe the output at pin 3 with the toggle switches both at 0. Then switch the inputs as necessary and fill in Table L 6-3. How does this circuit compare with the AND gate of Experiment 6-2? _____

B	A	Output
L	L	
L	H	
H	L	
H	H	

Table L 6-3.

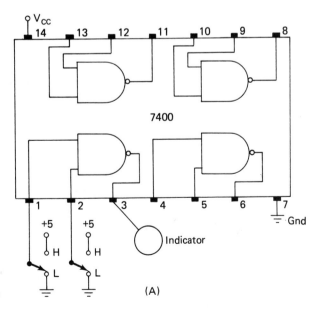

Fig. L 6-3. NAND gates.

(A)

107

2. Assume that waveforms *A* and *B* of Fig. L 6-3(B) are applied to pins 1 and 2. On the axis provided, sketch the output you would expect to see.

3. Next, wire the circuit shown in Fig. L 6-3(C). Again flip the toggle switches connected to pins 1 and 2 through all four possible combinations. What is the relationship between the output at pin 3 and the output at pin 6? _____ In this application, the NAND gate whose output is pin 6 is being used as a/an _____. If we want to consider the two gates in cascade acting as a single gate, what would you call it? (The inputs to the gate are pins 1 and 2, and the output is pin 6.)

The two-input NAND gate is one of the most useful logic circuits available, so it is worthwhile spending a little time thinking about how it works.

4. Hook up the circuit of Fig. L 6-3(D). Depress the bounceless switch a few times. The LED is lighted when the switch input is (HIGH, LOW). Why? _____

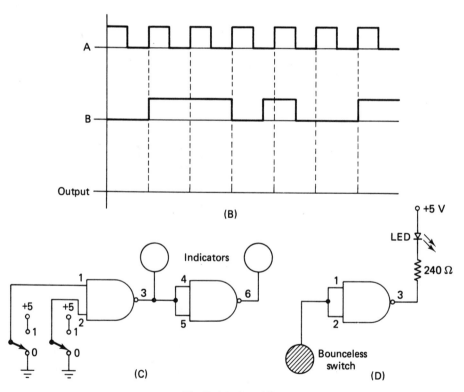

Fig. L 6-3. (*cont'd.*)

From what you learned in an earlier experiment, what is the normal forward voltage
drop across the LED? $V_F =$ _____.   So when the LED is on, how much current
flows through the gate output? Show your calculations.

5. The current* through the LED flows from the +5-V supply, through the LED
and resistor, and finally to ground through the lower transistor of the totem-pole
output of the gate. Manufacturers list the maximum "sink" capability of the lower
transistor as 16 mA. Has it been exceeded? _____

Quiz for Experiment 6-3

1. How many inverters could be made from one 7400 chip? _____

2. How many AND gates could be made with one 7400 chip? _____

3. In step 4 you should have found the current through the LED to be about 15 mA.
    Is it safe to sink this much current through the gate? _____

4. If a single 7400 has a fan-out of 10, what is the normal *input* current (unit load)
    for a TTL circuit? _____

5. Does the LED in Fig. L 6-3(D) indicate an ACTIVE HIGH or ACTIVE LOW signal
    from the switch? _____

*Conventional current flows as described here. Electron flow direction is opposite; *see* p. 4.

7

Equivalent Gate Symbols and Signal Names

Introduction

A very useful language is evolving in the use of gate symbols and signal names in logic circuit diagrams. After some experience, this language enables us, at a glance, to see what a given logic circuit is doing. Also, signal names are often shown at various points on a logic circuit diagram. The way that these signal names are expressed, with or without overbars, tells us which logic level of a given signal causes the circuit to perform the function for which it was designed. We shall find this language particularly useful when *trouble shooting* digital circuits.

7-1 ACTIVE HIGH/ACTIVE LOW Logic Signals

An understanding of the terms ACTIVE HIGH and ACTIVE LOW is very useful when we are required to determine how a given digital logic circuit works from its diagram. Logic circuit diagrams usually show names or symbols to identify logic signals. These signal names or symbols are printed with capital (uppercase) letters and are overbarred if they represent ACTIVE LOW signals. For example, a signal name such as $\overline{\text{LIGHT}}$ probably means that a lamp or indicator in the system will turn on when this signal is LOW. The absence of an overbar on a signal name or symbol means that it is ACTIVE HIGH. For example, a signal name such as DISPLAY probably means that a display in the system is activated when this signal is HIGH. Generally, then, a signal that causes action, in circuitry that it is driving, when it goes HIGH is called an ACTIVE HIGH signal. Therefore, a signal that causes action in subsequent circuitry when it goes LOW is called an ACTIVE LOW signal.

The circuit of Fig. 7-1(A) shows an example of an ACTIVE HIGH signal. The input signal ON is ACTIVE HIGH because the LED lights when this signal goes HIGH. That is, a HIGH ON signal saturates the transistor, forcing current through the LED, causing it to light. Of course, then, when the ON signal is LOW the transistor is cut off and the LED is not lit.

An example of an ACTIVE LOW signal is shown in Fig. 7-1(B). In this case, the input signal $\overline{\text{DISPLAY}}$ is overbarred, which means that it is ACTIVE LOW. That is, the LED lights when the $\overline{\text{DISPLAY}}$ input signal is LOW. A LOW input $\overline{\text{DISPLAY}}$ signal causes the transistor to cut off, which allows current to flow through the resistor R and the LED. On the other hand, a HIGH $\overline{\text{DISPLAY}}$ input signal saturates the transistor. A saturated transistor bypasses the LED.

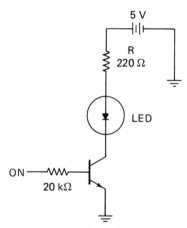

(A) The input signal ON is ACTIVE HIGH because the LED lights when ON is HIGH.

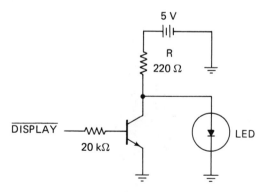

(B) The input signal $\overline{\text{DISPLAY}}$ is ACTIVE LOW because the LED lights when $\overline{\text{DISPLAY}}$ is LOW.

Fig. 7-1. The ON signal without an overbar indicates that it is an ACTIVE HIGH signal whereas the overbar on the $\overline{\text{DISPLAY}}$ input signal indicates that it is an ACTIVE LOW.

7-2 Logic Gate Symbols: AND-Form and OR-Form

Every type of logic gate can be represented by either of two symbols. A list of these symbols is shown in Fig. 7-2. The common symbols for the AND, OR, NAND, and NOR gates are shown in the left column of this figure. Alternative symbols for each of these gates are shown in the right column. Usually, depending on how a gate is used in a logic circuit, one or the other of its symbols is used.

Typically, the AND gate symbol of Fig. 7-2(A) is used when a HIGH logic signal output from the gate it represents causes action in subsequent gates or circuitry. That is, if an AND gate's output is ACTIVE HIGH, the symbol of Fig. 7-2(A) is used to represent this gate. An AND gate's output is ACTIVE HIGH when its ANDing function is being used or emphasized, which is the function shown in row 4 of the truth table in Fig. 7-2(A). An application of an AND gate with an ACTIVE HIGH output is shown in Fig. 7-3(A). In this case, both inputs A and B must be HIGH (ACTIVE) to

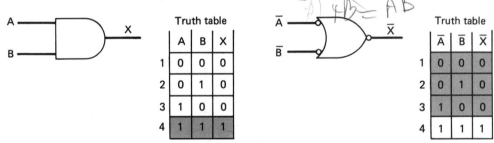

Truth table (A)

	A	B	X
1	0	0	0
2	0	1	0
3	1	0	0
4	1	1	1

Truth table (B)

	$\overline{A}$	$\overline{B}$	$\overline{X}$
1	0	0	0
2	0	1	0
3	1	0	0
4	1	1	1

(A) AND gate symbol used when the fact that two HIGH inputs cause a HIGH output (shaded area on truth table) is being used or emphasized.

(B) AND gate symbol used when the fact that either or both inputs being LOW cause a LOW output (shaded area on truth table) is being used or emphasized

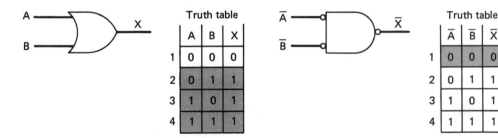

Truth table (C)

	A	B	X
1	0	0	0
2	0	1	1
3	1	0	1
4	1	1	1

Truth table (D)

	$\overline{A}$	$\overline{B}$	$\overline{X}$
1	0	0	0
2	0	1	1
3	1	0	1
4	1	1	1

(C) OR gate symbol used when the fact that either or both inputs being HIGH cause a HIGH output (shaded area on truth table) is being used or emphasized

(D) OR gate symbol used when the fact that both inputs have to be LOW to cause a LOW output (shaded area) is being used or emphasized

Fig. 7-2. Common logic gate symbols (left column) and their alternate symbols (right column).

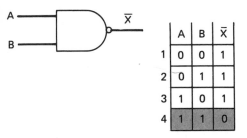

	A	B	X̄
1	0	0	1
2	0	1	1
3	1	0	1
4	1	1	0

(E) NAND gate symbol used when the fact
that two HIGH inputs cause a LOW
output (shaded area) is being used
or emphasized

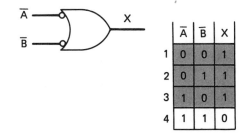

	Ā	B̄	X
1	0	0	1
2	0	1	1
3	1	0	1
4	1	1	0

(F) NAND gate symbol used when the fact
that either or both inputs being LOW
cause a HIGH output (shaded area)
is being used or emphasized

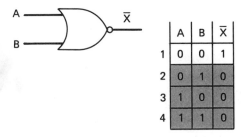

	A	B	X̄
1	0	0	1
2	0	1	0
3	1	0	0
4	1	1	0

(G) NOR gate symbol used when the fact
that a HIGH on either or both inputs
causes a LOW output (shaded area)
is being used or emphasized

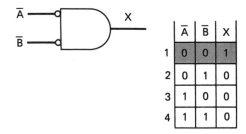

	Ā	B̄	X
1	0	0	1
2	0	1	0
3	1	0	0
4	1	1	0

(H) NOR gate symbol used when the fact
that both inputs have to be LOW to
cause a HIGH output (shaded area)
is being used or emphasized

Fig. 7-2. (Cont.)

cause a HIGH (ACTIVE) output X. These inputs and output are ACTIVE HIGH because
they all must be HIGH to light the LED. The AND gate, in this application, is obviously
used to perform an AND function, and therefore the common AND-form symbol of
this gate is used.

An ACTIVE LOW application of the AND gate is shown in Fig. 7-3(B). In this case,
an ACTIVE LOW signal on input $\bar{A}$ *or* input $\bar{B}$ or both pulls the output $\bar{X}$ LOW (ACTIVE)
and lights the LED. In this application, the AND gate is used to perform an OR function. That is, the AND gate is being used to OR LOW logic inputs, and therefore the
OR-form symbol for this gate is shown. As shown in rows 1, 2, and 3 the table of
Fig. 7-2(B), the AND gate can be viewed as an OR-performing gate if we are interested
in LOW logic signals in and out.

A similar point of view can be taken with other types of gates. The common
symbol for the OR gate shown in Fig. 7-2(C) is used when ACTIVE HIGH inputs and
outputs are being used or emphasized. In such cases, the OR gate's behavior indicated in rows 2, 3, and 4 of the table in this figure is of interest. An application of

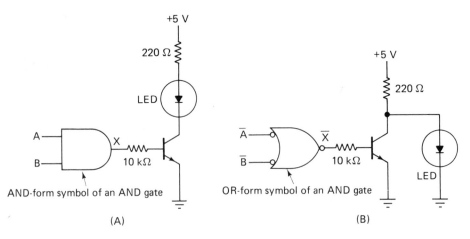

Fig. 7-3. (A) LED lights when input *A* **AND** input *B* go (ACTIVE) HIGH; (B) LED lights when input *Ā* **OR** input *B̄* goes (ACTIVE) LOW.

an OR gate with ACTIVE HIGH signals is shown in Fig. 7-4(A). In this circuit, a HIGH input *A or* a HIGH input *B* causes an ACTIVE HIGH output *X* which lights the LED. The OR-form symbol is shown because the OR gate is being used to OR input signals.

The OR gate can be used to perform an AND function with ACTIVE LOW inputs. That is, as shown in row 1 of the table in Fig. 7-2(D), the OR gate's output *X̄* is ACTIVE LOW only when its input *Ā and* input *B̄* are LOW (ACTIVE). An application of an OR gate with an ACTIVE LOW output is shown in Fig. 7-4(B). Since this circuit requires two LOW inputs to cause a LOW output *X̄* and a lighted LED, the AND-form symbol is shown to represent the OR gate.

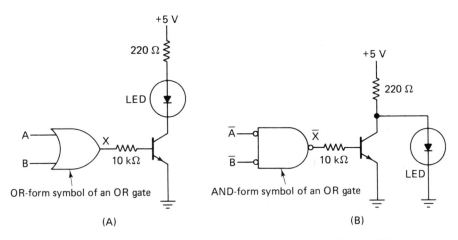

Fig. 7-4. (A) LED lights when input *A* **OR** input *B* goes (ACTIVE) HIGH; (B) LED lights when input *Ā* **AND** input *B̄* go (ACTIVE) LOW.

The NAND gate symbol of Fig. 7-2(E) is used when a LOW logic signal output from the gate it represents causes action in gates or circuitry that it is driving. That is, if a NAND gate's output is ACTIVE LOW, row 4 of the table in Fig. 7-2(E) is of interest to us. This row shows that both input *A and* input *B* have to be HIGH to cause an ACTIVE LOW output, and therefore the AND-form symbol for the NAND gate is appropriate. An application of a NAND gate with an ACTIVE LOW output is shown in Fig. 7-5(A). A HIGH on input *A and* on input *B* of this circuit pulls the gate's output $\bar{X}$ LOW, causing the LED to light.

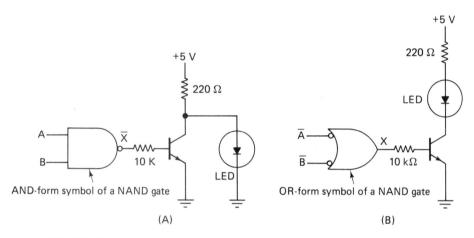

Fig. 7-5. (A) LED lights when inputs *A* **AND** *B* go (ACTIVE) HIGH; (B) LED lights when input $\bar{A}$ **OR** $\bar{B}$ goes (ACTIVE) LOW.

The NAND gate can also be used to OR ACTIVE LOW inputs for an ACTIVE HIGH output. In this case, the OR gate form of the NAND gate, shown in Fig. 7-2(F), is used, and this gate's behavior listed in rows 1, 2, and 3 of the table is of main interest to us. An application of a NAND gate having an ACTIVE HIGH output is shown in Fig. 7-5(B). A LOW logic signal applied to input $\bar{A}$ *or* to input $\bar{B}$ causes a HIGH (ACTIVE) output that saturates the transistor and lights the LED.

When the NOR gate is used to perform an OR function on ACTIVE HIGH inputs to obtain an ACTIVE LOW output, the common OR-form symbol, shown in Fig. 7-2(G), is used. In this case, the behavior of the NOR gate as indicated in rows 2, 3, and 4 of the table is being used and therefore is of interest. For example, the NOR gate used for its ORing capability is shown in Fig. 7-6(A). That is, input *A or* input *B* being HIGH causes a LOW output $\bar{X}$. A LOW output $\bar{X}$ is ACTIVE because it cuts off the transistor, causing the LED to light.

The NOR gate can also be used to perform an AND function on LOW input signals. In this case, the AND-form symbol for the NOR gate, shown in Fig. 7-2(H), is used, and the behavior indicated in row 1 is important. A NOR gate in this application is shown in Fig. 7-6(B). This circuit requires LOW logic on input $\bar{A}$ *and* on input $\bar{B}$ to drive the gate's output X HIGH (ACTIVE). The ACTIVE HIGH output X saturates the transistor and lights the LED.

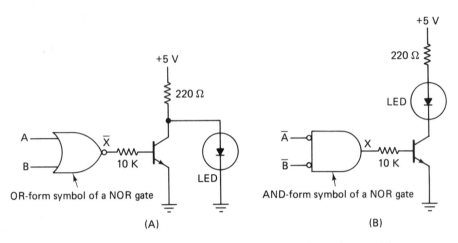

Fig. 7-6. (A) LED lights when input A **OR** input B goes (ACTIVE) HIGH; (B) LED lights when inputs $\bar{A}$ **AND** $\bar{B}$ go (ACTIVE) LOW.

7-3 Various AND-Form and OR-Form Symbols

If we compare an AND-form of any gate to its equivalent OR-form in Fig. 7-2, we can see a pattern in these equivalents. We should note that if an AND-form symbol of a gate has a circle on any input or output, the same input or output is shown without a circle in the OR-form of the same gate. Conversely, if no circle is on an input or output of an AND-form symbol of a gate, the OR-form of the same gate is drawn with a circle on the same input or output. More examples of this are shown in Figs. 7-7 and 7-8.

The gate in Fig. 7-7(A) has an inverter in series with one of its inputs, a common occurrence in practical logic circuits. This inverter can be replaced with a circle at the input of the gate as shown in Fig. 7-7(B). Both diagrams, Figs. 7-7(A) and (B), use AND-form symbols, and the circle at each of the outputs implies that each output is ACTIVE LOW. The overbarred signal names also imply ACTIVE LOW outputs. Row 3 of the truth table shows the input conditions that cause an ACTIVE LOW output. The OR-form shown in Fig. 7-7(C) can be used to represent this same logic function. In this case the output is ACTIVE HIGH, and rows 1, 2, and 4 indicate the input conditions that cause a HIGH output. By comparing the truth tables for the symbols (B) and (C) we can see that their entries, the L's and H's, are identical, indicating identical logic functions. The signal names, however, differ in the use of overbars. The presence or absence of overbars gives us a hint of how a logic gate or circuit is being used.

In Fig. 7-8, we can see how a three-input NOR gate with an inverter at one of its inputs, as shown in (A), can also be drawn as in (B) or as in (C). The symbol (B) or (C) is used depending on whether the gate's output is ACTIVE LOW or ACTIVE HIGH, respectively.

Fig. 7-7.

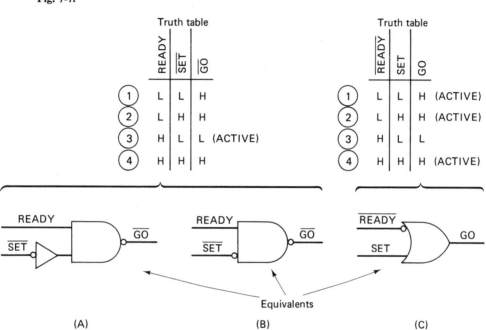

(A)   (B)   (C)

Fig. 7-8.

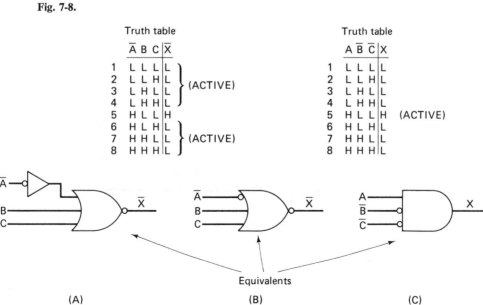

(A)   (B)   (C)

Summary

1. Logic signals can be classified into two categories called ACTIVE HIGH and ACTIVE LOW.

2. An ACTIVE HIGH signal causes action in the circuit when its logic level is HIGH or at the instant it goes HIGH.

3. An ACTIVE LOW signal causes action in the circuit when its logic level is LOW or at the instant it goes LOW.

4. Overbars are used on ACTIVE LOW signal names and symbols. Therefore, a signal name such as $\overline{\text{EXECUTE}}$ represents an ACTIVE LOW signal, whereas a signal name such as GO represents an ACTIVE HIGH signal.

5. The symbol for a logic gate can be drawn in either an AND-form or an OR-form, depending on how they are used.

6. Circles that are on inputs or the output of an AND-form of a gate are not shown on the same inputs and output of its OR-form equivalent. And where there are no circles on the inputs or the output of an AND-form of a gate, circles must be shown on the same inputs and output of its OR-form equivalent.

Problems 7-1

Referring to the gates shown in Fig. 7-9, match each gate in the left column with an equivalent in the right column.

1. Gate 1 and gate ____C____ are equivalent.

2. Gate 2 and gate ____B____ are equivalent.

3. Gate 3 and gate ____A____ are equivalent.

4. Gate 4 and gate ____F____ are equivalent.

5. Gate 5 and gate ____G____ are equivalent.

6. Gate 6 and gate ____D____ are equivalent.

7. Gate 7 and gate ____E____ are equivalent.

8. Gate 8 and gate ____H____ are equivalent.

9. Indicate by letters and numbers which of the gate symbols in Fig. 7-9 are shown in AND-form. ____1, 3, 5, 7, B, D, F H____

10. Indicate the letters and numbers of the gate symbols in Fig. 7-9 that are shown in OR-form. ____2, 4, 6, 8, A, C, E, G____

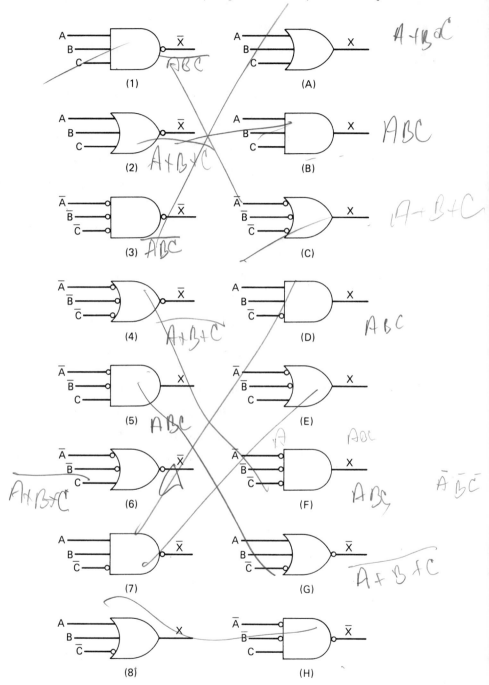

Fig. 7-9.

All of the following problems refer to Fig. 7-9.

11. Which symbol represents a gate whose output is LOW only if all its inputs are HIGH? I

12. Which symbol represents a gate whose output is LOW if any one of its inputs is HIGH? B

13. Which symbol represents a gate whose output is HIGH if any one of its inputs is LOW? C

14. Which symbol represents a gate whose output is HIGH only if all its inputs are HIGH? 4

15. Which gate symbol represents a gate whose output is LOW if any one of its inputs is LOW? 4

16. Which symbol represents a gate whose output is HIGH if any one of its inputs is HIGH? A

17. Which symbol represents a gate whose output is HIGH only if all its inputs are LOW? F

18. Which symbol represents a gate whose output is LOW only if two of its inputs are HIGH while one input is LOW? E

19. Which symbol represents a gate whose output is LOW only if two of its inputs are LOW while one input is HIGH? H

20. Which symbol represents a gate whose output is HIGH if its input $\bar{A}$ is LOW or its input $\bar{B}$ is LOW or if its input C is HIGH? H

8

Combinations of Gates for Logic Functions

Introduction

Within a typical digital system subassemblies exist, each of which performs its own function. This is similar to the human body in which there are many organs, which, like subassemblies, have specific functions. The combined efforts of these organs enable the body as a whole to work. The typical digital system similarly has many parts or subassemblies. Each part, when called on, must do its job if the system is to perform the task for which it was made. Decision-making circuits, called *combinational logic* circuits, are usually associated with each subassembly. These circuits are able to decide when and how their subassemblies do "their thing." For example, a combinational logic circuit can decide when a digital counter is to start and stop counting. Or a digital voltmeter (system) can automatically be placed in the appropriate voltage range by the decision-making circuit in its range selector (subassembly). By learning the principles of the few combinational logic circuits discussed in this chapter, we shall be able to see how gate combinations work with digital devices and subassemblies that are discussed in later chapters and are found in practical systems.

8-1 Combinations of AND Gates, OR Gates, and Inverters

Logic gates can be combined to perform any required logic function. A typical combination of AND gates, an OR gate, and inverters is shown in Fig. 8-1. This combination performs an exclusive OR function. The exclusive OR function differs from the simple two-input OR function in its behavior when both inputs are HIGH (last

121

row of their truth tables). Examine the output *Y* column (column 6) in Fig. 8-1 and compare it with the output *X* column in Fig. 1-13 of Chapter 1. We should note that the exclusive OR and the two-input OR gate work identically when both inputs are LOW or if one input is LOW while the other is HIGH. However, when both inputs are HIGH on the exclusive OR, its output *Y* is LOW, whereas the OR's output is HIGH.

In the Table of Fig. 8-1, all combinations of inputs *A* and *B* are shown in column 1. The signal outputs of inverter 1 are shown in column 2. Similarly, the outputs of inverter 2 are shown in column 3. Note that the entries in columns 2 and 3 are opposite of the entries in columns *A* and *B*, respectively. The outputs of AND gate 1 are shown in column 4. Each entry in this column is the result of ANDing the *A* and $\bar{B}$ inputs one row at a time. The outputs of AND gate 2 are shown in column 5. Each entry in this column is the result of ANDing the $\bar{A}$ and *B* inputs one row at a time. The resulting signals at output *Y* are shown in column 6. These final outputs are obtained by ORing the OR gate's inputs $A\bar{B}$ and $\bar{A}B$ (columns 4 and 5) one row at a time. Thus we can see that the exclusive OR's output can be expressed with the Boolean equation $Y = A\bar{B} + \bar{A}B$. ·

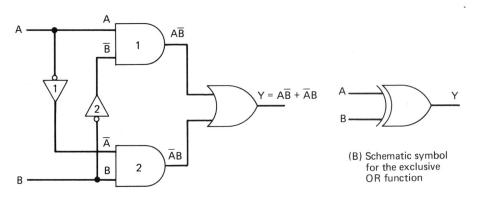

(A) Combination of AND gates, OR gate, and Inverters that performs an exclusive OR function

(B) Schematic symbol for the exclusive OR function

1		2	3	4	5	6
Inputs		Output of Inverter 1	Output of Inverter 2	Output of AND gate 1	Output of AND gate 2	Output of OR gate
A	B	$\bar{A}$	$\bar{B}$	$A\bar{B}$	$\bar{A}B$	Y
L	L	H	H	L	L	L
L	H	H	L	L	H	H
H	L	L	H	H	L	H
H	H	L	L	L	L	L

(C) Functional Table for the combination of gates shown above

Fig. 8-1.

A bit more involved, but commonly used, logic function is performed by the combination in Fig. 8-2. This logic circuit has three inputs and therefore eight possible input combinations. Inverted versions of input signals A, B, and C are at the outputs of inverters 1, 2, and 3, respectively; compare columns 1 through 4.

As shown in the circuit of Fig. 8-2, the inputs of AND gate 1 are A, $\bar{B}$, and $\bar{C}$. Therefore, its output has the Boolean expression $A\bar{B}\bar{C}$. The output signals of AND gate 1, for all combinations of inputs, are shown in column 5 of the table. Its entries are obtained by ANDing the A, $\bar{B}$, and $\bar{C}$ inputs (columns A, 3, and 4) one row at a time. Of course, then, the expressions at the outputs of the other AND gates, and

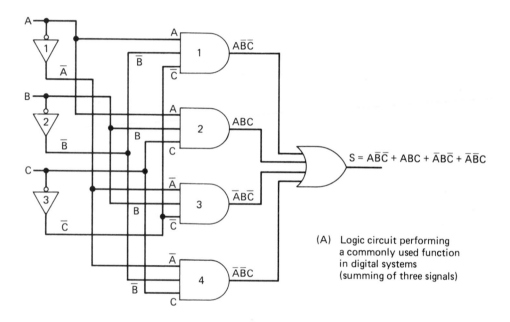

$$S = A\bar{B}\bar{C} + ABC + \bar{A}B\bar{C} + \bar{A}\bar{B}C$$

(A) Logic circuit performing
a commonly used function
in digital systems
(summing of three signals)

1	2	3	4	5	6	7	8	9
Inputs	Output of inverter 1	Output of inverter 2	Output of inverter 3	Output of AND gate 1	Output of AND gate 2	Output of AND gate 3	Output of AND gate 4	Output of OR gate
A B C	$\bar{A}$	$\bar{B}$	$\bar{C}$	$A\bar{B}\bar{C}$	ABC	$\bar{A}B\bar{C}$	$\bar{A}\bar{B}C$	S
L L L	H	H	H	L	L	L	L	L
L L H	H	H	L	L	L	L	H	H
L H L	H	L	H	L	L	H	L	H
L H H	H	L	L	L	L	L	L	L
H L L	L	H	H	H	L	L	L	H
H L H	L	H	L	L	L	L	L	L
H H L	L	L	H	L	L	L	L	L
H H H	L	L	L	L	H	L	L	H

(B) Functional table for the above logic circuit

Fig. 8-2.

their actual output signals, are similarly determined. Since the AND gates drive an OR gate, their outputs are ORed. That is, as shown, the OR gate's output $S = A\bar{B}\bar{C} + AB\bar{C} + \bar{A}B\bar{C} + \bar{A}BC$ and the entries in column 9 are obtained by ORing the entries in columns 5, 6, 7, and 8 one row at a time. By examining the inputs A, B, and C and the output S, we can see that this logic circuit's output is HIGH only when *one* or all *three* inputs are HIGH. As we shall learn later, this circuit is performing a commonly used *summing* function, which is addition of logic signals.

The summing function can be performed with several different combinations of gates, another of which is shown in Fig. 8-3. In this case, instead of AND gates working into an OR gate, we have OR gates working into an AND gate. As shown,

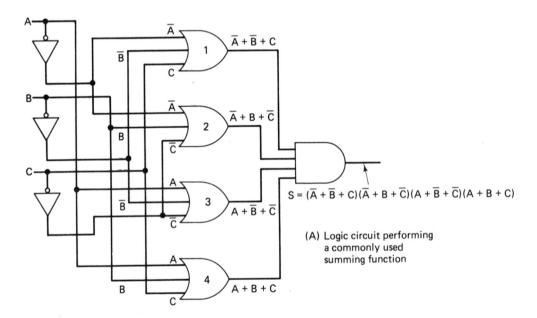

$$S = (\bar{A} + \bar{B} + C)(\bar{A} + B + \bar{C})(A + \bar{B} + \bar{C})(A + B + C)$$

(A) Logic circuit performing a commonly used summing function

1	2	3	4	5	6	7
Inputs	Outputs of inverters	Output of OR gate 1	Output of OR gate 2	Output of OR gate 3	Output of OR gate 4	Output of AND gate
A B C	$\bar{A}$ $\bar{B}$ $\bar{C}$	$\bar{A} + \bar{B} + C$	$\bar{A} + B + \bar{C}$	$A + \bar{B} + \bar{C}$	$A + B + C$	S
1 L L L	H H H	H	H	H	L	L
2 L L H	H H L	H	H	H	H	H
3 L H L	H L H	H	H	H	H	H
4 L H H	H L L	H	H	L	H	L
5 H L L	L H H	H	H	H	H	H
6 H L H	·L H L	H	L	H	H	L
7 H H L	L L H	L	H	H	H	L
8 H H H	L L L	H	H	H	H	H

(B) Functional table for the above logic circuit

Fig. 8-3.

OR gate 1 ORs its inputs $\bar{A}$, $\bar{B}$, and C, causing an output $\bar{A} + \bar{B} + C$. Each of the other OR gates similarly ORs its inputs. The outputs of these OR gates are then ANDed by the AND gate, whose resulting output is

$$S = (\bar{A} + \bar{B} + C)(\bar{A} + B + \bar{C})(A + \bar{B} + \bar{C})(A + B + C)$$

The table in Fig. 8-3 shows how the function of this circuit can be determined. By comparing the S columns of the tables in Figs. 8-2 and 8-3, we can see that they are identical, and therefore the circuits of these figures perform identical functions.

Summary

1. Any logic function can be performed with combinations of AND gates, OR gates, and inverters. Such combinations are called logic circuits.

2. We can sketch functional tables to determine what a given logic circuit is doing.

3. The columns in a functional table show all input signal combinations and the resulting outputs of the individual gates and inverters.

4. By writing Boolean expressions at the output of each gate or inverter, we can more easily select the correct entries for the table and thus accurately determine what the circuit as a whole does.

Problems 8-1

The input signals to the circuits of Fig. 8-4 are A, B, C, and D. When inverted, they can be shown as $\bar{A}$, $\bar{B}$, etc.

1. Write a Boolean expression representing the output of OR gate 1. $\overline{A + B}$

2. What is the Boolean expression for the output of OR gate 2? $A + B$

3. What is the Boolean expression for the output of AND gate 3? $L = \overline{(A + B)}(A + B)$

4. What are the Boolean expressions for the outputs of AND gates a and b and for OR gate c? For AND gate a, $A\bar{B}$; for AND gate b, $\bar{A}\bar{B}$; and for OR gate c, $M =$ $(A\bar{B}) + (\bar{A}\bar{B})$

5. Show the Boolean expressions representing the outputs of the following gates: AND gate i, $B\bar{C}\bar{D}$; AND gate ii, $BC\bar{D}$; AND gate iii, $\bar{B}CD$; OR gate iv, $N =$ $B\bar{C}D + BC\bar{D} + \bar{B}CD$

     Problems 6 through 8 refer to the circuits of Fig. 8-4 and the tables of Fig. 8-5.

6. Fill in table I for logic circuit I.

7. Fill in table II for logic circuit II. Use 0's and 1's instead of L's and H's.

8. Fill in table III for logic circuit III. Use 0's and 1's instead of L's and H's.

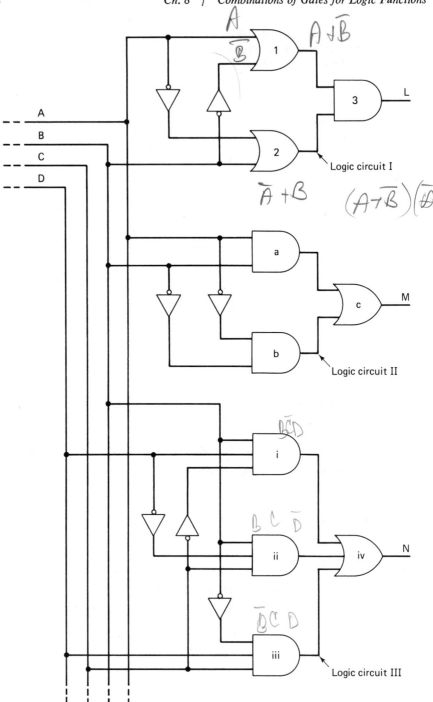

Fig. 8-4.

Table I

1	2		3	4	5
Inputs	Outputs of inverters		Output of OR gate 1	Output of OR gate 2	Output of AND gate 3
A B	$\bar{A}$	$\bar{B}$	$A + \bar{B}$	$\bar{A} + B$	L
L L					
L H					
H L					
H H					

Table II

1	2		3	4	5
Inputs	Outputs of inverters		Output of AND gate a	Output of AND gate b	Output of OR gate c
A B	$\bar{A}$	$\bar{B}$	AB	$\bar{A}\bar{B}$	M
0 0					
0 1					
1 0					
1 1					

Table III

1	2			3	4	5	6
Inputs	Outputs of inverters			Output of AND gate i	Output of AND gate ii	Output of AND gate iii	Output of OR gate iv
B C D	$\bar{B}$	$\bar{C}$	$\bar{D}$	$\bar{B}CD$	$B\bar{C}D$	$BC\bar{D}$	N
0 0 0							
0 0 1							
0 1 0							
0 1 1							
1 0 0							
1 0 1							
1 1 0							
1 1 1							

Fig. 8-5.

8-2 Logic Circuit Combinations with NAND Gates and NOR Gates

ICs with AND gates and OR gates are not so readily available as are ICs with NANDs and NORs. Therefore, most logic circuit combinations consist of NAND gates or NOR gates. For example, the NAND gate combination in Fig. 8-6(A) performs an exclusive OR function. Boolean expressions are shown at the outputs of the individual gates. That is, the inputs A and $\bar{B}$ to NAND gate 1 are ANDed (results in column 5 of the table) and inverted, resulting in an output $\overline{A\bar{B}}$ (column 6). Similarly, inputs $\bar{A}$ and B applied to NAND gate 2 are ANDed (results in column 7) and inverted, causing an output $\overline{\bar{A}B}$ (column 8). These outputs of gates 1 and 2 are then applied to the inputs of NAND gate 3 in which they are ANDed (results in column 9) and

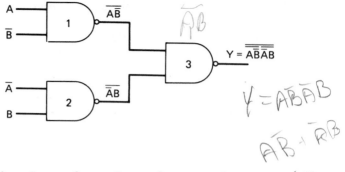

Y = $\overline{\overline{A\overline{B}}\,\overline{\overline{A}B}}$

(handwritten) $\overline{A\overline{B}}$

(handwritten) $Y = \overline{\overline{A\overline{B}}\,\overline{\overline{A}B}}$

(handwritten) $Y = \overline{A\overline{B}}\,\overline{\overline{A}B}$

(handwritten) $A\overline{B} + \overline{A}B$

1	2	3	4	5	6	7	8	9	10
A	B	$\overline{A}$	$\overline{B}$	$A\overline{B}$	$\overline{A\overline{B}}$	$\overline{A}B$	$\overline{\overline{A}B}$	$\overline{A\overline{B}}\,\overline{\overline{A}B}$	$\overline{\overline{A\overline{B}}\,\overline{\overline{A}B}}$
L	L	H	H	L	H	L	H	H	L
L	H	H	L	L	H	H	L	L	H
H	L	L	H	H	L	L	H	L	H
H	H	L	L	L	H	L	H	H	L

(A) Logic circuit with NAND gates
and its functional table

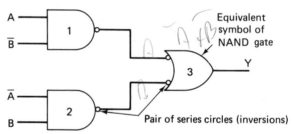

(B) Logic circuit with its output NAND gate
drawn in OR-form

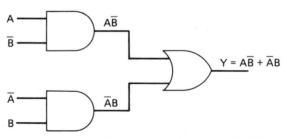

Y = $A\overline{B} + \overline{A}B$

(C) After series inversions (circles) are removed, the circuit of NAND gates
is shown to be equivalent to this one of AND gates and an OR.

Fig. 8-6.

inverted, resulting in the cumbersome expression for Y shown on the circuit and in column 10 of the table. While functional tables obviously can be written for such circuits, we shall avoid doing so. We shall, instead, resketch the circuit to a form that is simpler to analyze. For example, the circuit in Fig. 8-6(A) can be redrawn as the circuit in Fig. 8-6(B). Note that NAND gate 3, shown in AND-form in the circuit in (A), has been replaced with an OR-form equivalent in the circuit in (B). In the circuit in (B), the circle at the output of NAND gate 1 works into a circled input on NAND gate 3. These circles can be viewed as being equivalent to two series inverters which have no overall effect on the logic signal passing through them. Of course, then, the two circles between NAND gates 2 and 3 can be viewed the same way. We can therefore remove these pairs of series circles and not affect the circuit's overall function. That is, we can resketch the circuit in (B) to the equivalent shown in (C). This equivalent circuit in (C) is identical to the one in Fig. 8-1, discussed previously. Its functional table is much easier to sketch (also shown in Fig.8-1). If we compare the final output column 6 in the table of Fig. 8-1 with the final output column 10 in Fig. 8-6(A), we see that they are identical, which means that the circuits represented by these tables have identical logic functions.

A logic circuit of NOR gates only is shown in Fig. 8-7(A). As the functional table beside it shows, the inputs of each NOR are first ORed and then inverted. That is, NOR gate 1 ORs its inputs (column 5) and inverts them (column 6). Similarly, the inputs of NOR gate 2 are ORed (column 7) and inverted (column 8). Finally, the inputs to NOR gate 3 are ORed (column 9) and inverted (column 10). Obviously, this process is somewhat tedious. More easily, the function of this circuit can be determined by sketching its simpler equivalent before plotting its table. This can be done by first replacing NOR gate 3 with its AND-form equivalent. This results in pairs of circles between gates 1 and 3 and between gates 2 and 3, as shown in Fig. 8-7(B). As before, each pair of circles has no overall effect on the logic passing through them, and therefore they can be removed, as in Fig. 8-7(C). The fact that the circuits in Figs. 8-7(A) and (B) perform the same function can be proved by plotting a functional table for this last equivalent [Fig. 8-7(C)]. Then the last column of this table can be shown to be identical to column 10 in Fig. 8-7(A). Since the outputs of the circuits of Fig. 8-7 are always logically opposite to the outputs of the exclusive OR circuit (Fig. 8-1), the latter circuits are called exclusive NORs.

Summary

1. NAND gates and NOR gates are more available on ICs than are AND gates and OR gates.

2. Logic circuits with NAND gates only can be redrawn into, usually simpler to analyze, equivalents of AND and OR gates. This is done by replacing the output NAND gate (the gate NANDing the outputs of the other NANDs) with an OR-form equivalent. This enables us to remove pairs of series circles (inversions) and thus obtain a simpler equivalent circuit to analyze.

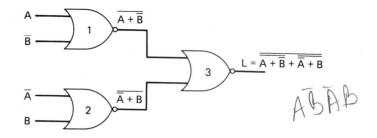

$$L = \overline{\overline{A + \overline{B}} + \overline{\overline{A} + B}}$$

ABAB

1	2	3	4	5	6	7	8	9	10
A	B	$\overline{A}$	$\overline{B}$	$A + \overline{B}$	$\overline{A + \overline{B}}$	$\overline{A} + B$	$\overline{\overline{A} + B}$	$\overline{A + \overline{B}} + \overline{\overline{A} + B}$	$\overline{\overline{A + \overline{B}} + \overline{\overline{A} + B}}$
L	L	H	H	H	L	H	L	L	H
L	H	H	L	L	H	H	L	H	L
H	L	L	H	H	L	L	H	H	L
H	H	L	L	H	L	H	L	L	H

(A) Logic circuit with NOR gates
and its functional table

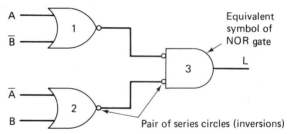

Equivalent
symbol of
NOR gate

Pair of series circles (inversions)

(B) Logic circuit of NOR gates with
its output NOR drawn in AND-form

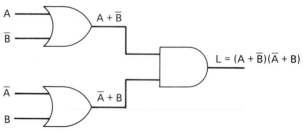

$$L = (A + \overline{B})(\overline{A} + B)$$

(C) After series circles are removed, the circuit of NOR gates is shown to
be equivalent to this one of OR gates and an AND.

Fig. 8-7.

130

3. Logic circuit with NOR gates only can also be redrawn into, usually simpler, equivalents of AND gates and OR gates. In this case, the output NOR gate is redrawn into an equivalent in AND-form. This causes pairs of series circles to appear, which can then be removed to give us a simpler circuit to analyze.

Problems 8-2

1. Sketch a simpler equivalent circuit of Fig. 8-8 by first replacing NAND gate 5 with its OR-form equivalent, and then remove all pairs of series circles.

2. Referring to Problem 1, sketch a functional table from your simplified circuit.

3. Sketch a simpler equivalent circuit of Fig. 8-9 by first replacing NOR gate 5 with its AND-form equivalent, and then remove all pairs of series circles.

4. Sketch a functional table of the simplified equivalent circuit you found in Problem 3.

5. How do the signal outputs of NOR gate 5 in the circuit of Fig. 8-8 compare with the outputs of the AND gate in the circuit of Fig. 8-3?

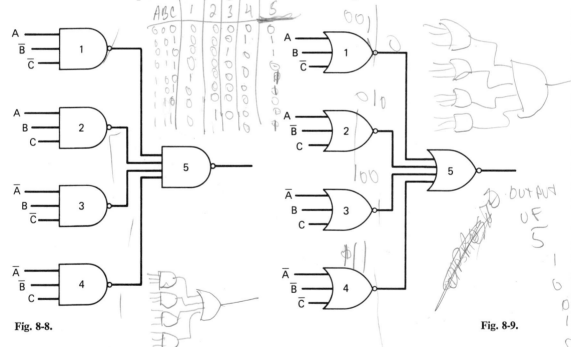

Fig. 8-8.   Fig. 8-9.

8-3 Applications of Logic Combinations

Logic gates can be used in any number of combinations to perform practical decision-making functions. We shall examine a few practical combinations in this section which will pave the way to our understanding others that are discussed in later chapters and occur in actual digital systems. For example, Fig. 8-10 shows a system used to test laboratory rats for their ability to learn to work cooperatively. In this system, three rats are placed in separate adjacent cages, shown in Figs. 8-10(A) and (B). Each of these rats, call them Alfred, Brenda, and Charlie, has his or her own pushbutton. Alfred's pushbutton is A, Brenda's is B, and Charlie's is C. The timer, shown in Fig. 8-10(C), closes the switch Sw for a few seconds every hour. When closed, switch Sw applies a HIGH F.L. (feed light) signal to the relay that turns on a feed light and to one input of each AND gate 1 through 7. These AND gates are thus *enabled* for a few seconds each hour, which means that they can respond to logic signals on their other inputs. To put it another way, AND gates 1 through 7 are *disabled* by a LOW F.L. signal, which causes them to ignore all logic signals on their other inputs. When the F.L. signal is LOW, the outputs of AND gates 1 through 7 are held LOW regardless of the levels of the input signals. The rats have been previously taught to press their individual pushbuttons to get fed when the feed light is on. Now they must learn to push their buttons one at a time to get fed. That is, Alfred gets a food pellet if he pushes his button A before or after Brenda and Charlie push their buttons. Brenda gets her food pellet when she pushes button B before or after Alfred and Charlie. Likewise, Charlie must request his food, with button C, before or after Alfred and Brenda. When Alfred only pushes his button A, the signal F_A out of AND gate 1, in Fig. 8-10(C), goes HIGH, which activates food dispenser A. When Brenda only pushes her button B, the signal F_B out of AND gate 2 goes HIGH and causes food dispenser B to drop a food pellet. Similarly, when only Charlie is pushing his button C, the signal F_C, out of AND gate 3, goes HIGH, which energizes food dispenser C. If they greedily push their buttons simultaneously, none of them gets fed.

The logic circuit of Fig. 8-10 also lights a *busy lamp* when any one of of the rats pushes its button. This serves to tell the two waiting rats that the food mechanism is busy. This is accomplished by ORing the outputs of AND gates 1, 2, and 3. That is, the BUSY signal, out of OR gate 8, goes HIGH if any *one* of its inputs goes HIGH.

If two rats press their buttons at the same time, a bell rings. This serves to warn the rats that they are not cooperating sufficiently and will not get fed. The bell logic consists of AND gates 4, 5, and 6 that work into OR gate 9. When enabled by a HIGH F.L. signal, the output of one of these AND gates will go HIGH if *two* of its inputs A, B, or C are HIGH simultaneously. Of course, then, a HIGH from any one of these AND gates causes a HIGH output BELL signal, via OR gate 9. This signal energizes the bell relay and causes the bell to ring.

If all three rats press their buttons at the same time, an annoyingly loud buzzer activates, which serves to discourage greediness or overanxious button pushing. The output of AND gate 7, when HIGH, activates the buzzer.

The table of Fig. 8-10(D) illustrates how the logic circuit in (C) works. The four inputs F.L., A, B, and C have 16 possible combinations, as shown. Actually, only the last 8 combinations (rows 9 through 16) illustrate the possible circuit behavior during the rats' feeding time. The circuit is disabled by the LOW F.L. signal in the first 8 input combinations shown, forcing all outputs to inactive LOWs.

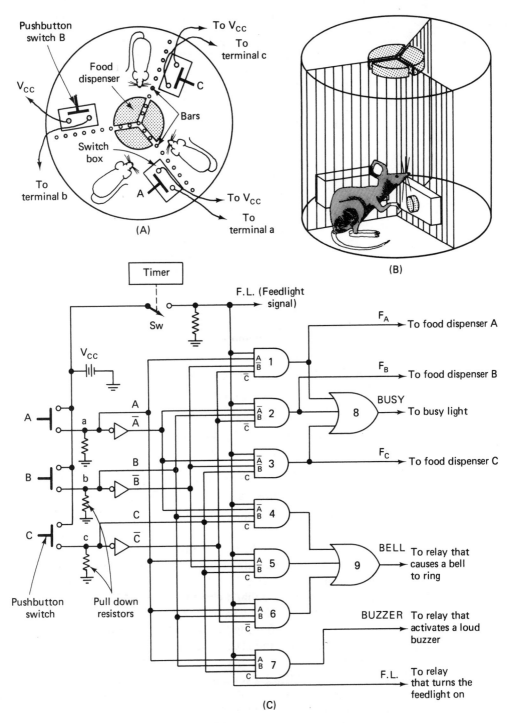

Fig. 8-10. (A) Top view of cage; (B) skewed view of cage; (C) logic circuit using AND gates and OR gates.

	Feed light (F.L.)	A	B	C	F_A	F_B	F_C	BUSY	BELL	BUZZER
1	L	L	L	L	L	L	L	L	L	L
2	L	L	L	H	L	L	L	L	L	L
3	L	L	H	L	L	L	L	L	L	L
4	L	L	H	H	L	L	L	L	L	L
5	L	H	L	L	L	L	L	L	L	L
6	L	H	L	H	L	L	L	L	L	L
7	L	H	H	L	L	L	L	L	L	L
8	L	H	H	H	L	L	L	L	L	L
9	H	L	L	L	L	L	L	L	L	L
10	H	L	L	H	L	L	H	H	L	L
11	H	L	H	L	L	H	L	H	L	L
12	H	L	H	H	L	L	L	L	H	L
13	H	H	L	L	H	L	L	H	L	L
14	H	H	L	H	L	L	L	L	H	L
15	H	H	H	L	L	L	L	L	H	L
16	H	H	H	H	L	L	L	L	L	H

All input combinations   All outputs

Fig. 8-10. (Cont.) (D) functional table for the above logic circuit.

In summary,

$F_A = A\bar{B}\bar{C}$ (Alfred only requesting food)

$F_B = \bar{A}B\bar{C}$ (Brenda only requesting food)

$F_C = \bar{A}\bar{B}C$ (Charlie only requesting food)

BUSY $= A\bar{B}\bar{C} + \bar{A}B\bar{C} + \bar{A}\bar{B}C$ (Alfred only, or Brenda only, or Charlie only requesting)

BELL $= \bar{A}BC + A\bar{B}C + AB\bar{C}$ (Any two rats at a time requesting food)

BUZZER $= ABC$ (All three rats requesting simultaneously)

As mentioned previously, IC logic circuits are more apt to be constructed of NAND gate and NOR gate combinations than of AND and OR gate combinations. Therefore, the logic circuit for the rat-conditioning system would more likely be built as in Fig. 8-11. Note that gates 1 through 9 in Fig. 8-10 have been replaced with NAND gates 1 through 9 in Fig. 8-11. If we compare the circuit of Fig. 8-10 with the one in Fig. 8-11, we can see that a circle has been added to the output of each AND gate and to each input of the OR gates. The resulting *pairs* of circles (inversions) have no effect on the signals flowing through them, and the circuit works exactly as before insofar as the BUSY and BELL signals are concerned. However, the signals at the outputs of NAND gates 1, 2, 3, and 7 have passed through one inversion and are therefore shown as the $\overline{F_A}$, $\overline{F_B}$, $\overline{F_C}$, and $\overline{\text{BUZZER}}$ signals. In many cases, such signals could be used to drive ACTIVE LOW relays to activate food dispensers and the buzzer. But if the same ACTIVE HIGH relays that were used in the system of Fig. 8-10 must be used with the circuit of Fig. 8-11, then the inverters shown must be added.

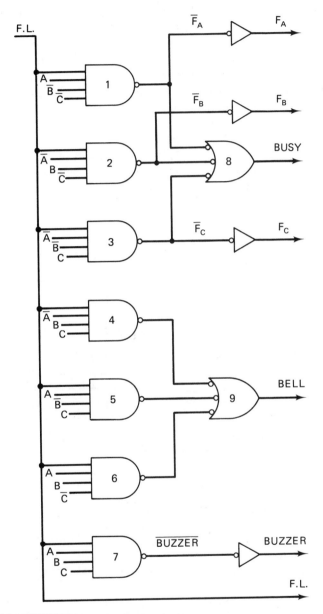

Fig. 8-11. Logic circuit used NAND gates and inverters; NAND gates 1 through 7 are drawn in AND-form, NAND gates 8 and 9 are drawn in OR-form.

The rat-conditioning logic of Fig. 8-10 can also be performed with a circuit of NOR gates. The NOR gate equivalent of the circuit in Fig. 8-10 can be found by first redrawing it as in Fig. 8-12. Note in this circuit that each of the AND gates, 1 through 7, in Fig. 8-10 has been redrawn in its equivalent OR-form. Also, OR gates 8 and 9 in Fig. 8-10 have been replaced with NORs followed by inverters in the redrawn version of Fig. 8-12. These changes do not affect the overall logic being performed.

As yet we do not have a logic circuit of only NOR gates in Fig. 8-12. We can, however, convert this circuit to an equivalent of NORs by removing all the circles at the inputs of AND gates 1 through 7 while at the same time reversing the logic at each input. This has been done in the circuit of Fig. 8-13. Note that the input gates thus become NORs. This circuit consists of NOR gates and inverters. Even the inverters can be replaced with NORs if all inputs are tied together to form a single input or if only one input is used while all the unused inputs are grounded. In the

Fig. 8-12. Rat-conditioning logic circuit with its AND gates redrawn in OR-form and its OR gates replaced with NOR/inverter combination.

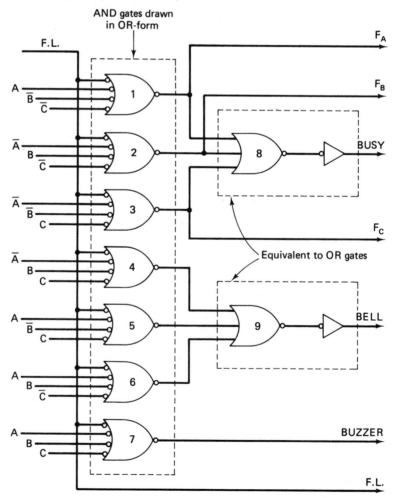

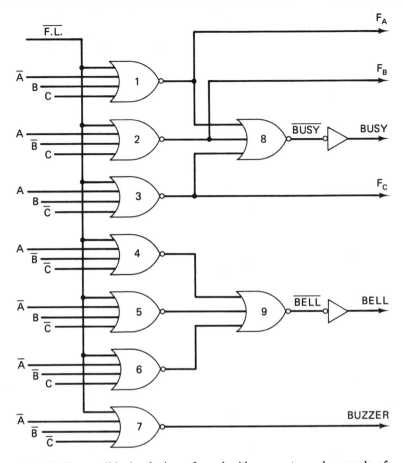

Fig. 8-13. Rat-conditioning logic performed with NOR gates and a couple of inverters.

circuit of Fig. 8-13, it is interesting to note that now the feed light signal $\overline{\text{F.L.}}$ is ACTIVE LOW. That is, this circuit is enabled for a few seconds each hour by a LOW $\overline{\text{F.L.}}$ signal, whereas HIGH F.L. signals enable the circuits of Figs. 8-10, 8-11, and 8-12.

Because the $\overline{\text{F.L.}}$ input signal in Fig. 8-13 is ACTIVE LOW and because the output signals F_A, F_B, F_C, and BUZZER are ACTIVE HIGH, the input NOR gates are typically drawn as in Fig. 8-14. Note in this case that the timer *opens* switch Sw for a few seconds each hour, which pulls the $\overline{\text{F.L.}}$ signal down (LOW) to ground potential through the pull-down resistor. In this circuit, the AND-forms of the input NOR gates better describe what the circuit is doing. This circuit more clearly illustrates the fact that if the inputs $\overline{\text{F.L.}}$, $\overline{A}$, B, and C, to NOR gate 1, are all LOW simultaneously, as is the case when Alfred only pushes button A at feeding time, the output F_A goes HIGH. In other words, an AND-form of NOR gate 1 shows more clearly that it ANDs LOW input signals; that is, when its inputs $\overline{\text{F.L.}}$ *and* $\overline{A}$ *and* B and C are LOW, the output F_A goes HIGH to activate Alfred's food dispenser. Similarly, signals $\overline{\text{F.L.}}$, A, $\overline{B}$, and C, into NOR gate 2 must all be LOW before this gate's output F_B goes HIGH. Of course, these inputs are all LOW when Brenda only pushes button B during feeding time. The other input NOR gates can be analyzed similarly.

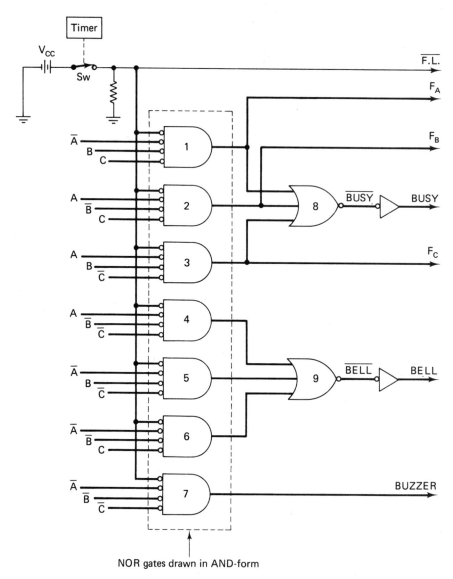

NOR gates drawn in AND-form

Fig. 8-14. Rat-conditioning circuit of NORs and inverters with the gate symbols selected to indicate whether their output, or input, signals are ACTIVE HIGH or ACTIVE LOW.

Summary

1. A logic circuit of AND gates and OR gates can be replaced with an equivalent of NAND gates. This can be done by adding circles at the outputs of AND gates that are in AND-form and at the inputs of OR gates that are in OR-form. This converts

all gates into NANDS. If two circles in series result in some leads, they have no effect on the circuit's overall logic function and therefore require no further modifications. If this converting of ANDS and ORS into NANDS causes a single circle to appear at an output or input, an inverter must be added to the output or the signal logic level must be inverted at the affected input.

2. A logic circuit of AND gates and OR gates can be replaced with an equivalent of NOR gates. This is done by adding circles at the outputs of the OR gates that are in OR-form and at the inputs of the AND gates that are in AND-form. Any resulting pairs of circles in series require no further modification. If this results in single circles appearing at inputs and outputs, the input signal logic levels must be inverted and inverters must be placed at the affected outputs.

Problems 8-3

1. Show how the function of the circuit of Fig. 8-15 can be performed with NAND gates only.

2. Show how the circuit of Fig. 8-15 can be replaced with one of NOR gates. If one or more inverters must be added, use one or more NOR gates that are wired to work as inverters instead.

3. Show a circuit of NOR gates that will perform the same function as the circuit of Fig. 8-16.

4. Show a circuit of AND gates that will perform the same function as the circuit of Fig. 8-16. If one or more inverters must be added, use one or more NAND gates that are wired to work as inverters instead.

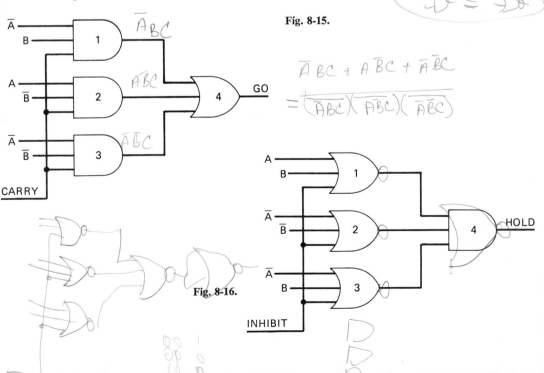

Fig. 8-15.

Fig. 8-16.

Experiment 8-1 Combinations of Gates

Purpose

To gain proficiency in tracing through logic circuits containing combinations of gates. To be able to predict what the output will be for every possible input combination.

Equipment

Digital breadboard kit
7408 quad two-input AND
7432 quad two-input OR

Procedure

1. Before building the logic circuit, examine the diagrams of Figs. L 8-1(A) and (B). Decide which gates you want to use and write the pin numbers of the chip on the diagram of Fig. L 8-1(C). Then write the Boolean expression for the output of each gate right on the figure, as was done in Fig. 8-1(A).

2. Next, write the expression for the output of gate 1 at the heading of column 1 in the table of Fig. L 8-1(D). Then fill in the table for that column. Repeat for column 2 and for the output Y in column 3. (A 1 represents a logical HIGH, and a 0 represents a logical LOW input.)

3. Now wire the circuit of Fig. L 8-1(C) and check your output table by connecting input signals to inputs A, B, and C by means of toggle switches. (*Note:* Be sure to connect V_{CC} and ground.) Start with all inputs LOW (000). If the output (Y) of gate 3 agrees with your truth table, put a check in row 1 of column 4. Then switch the C input HIGH (001) and compare the circuit output to your truth table for that input combination. Again, if they agree, put a check in row 2 of column 4. Repeat for all combinations in the table. If your circuit works as you predicted, go on to the next step. If not, go back to step 1 and start over. Also be sure to check your circuit wiring.

4. Examine the circuit of Fig. L 8-1(E) and write the Boolean expression for the output of each gate on the figure, as you did before.

5. Fill in columns 1 and 2 in the table in Fig. L 8-1(F) for the circuit of Fig. L 8-1(E).

6. Wire the circuit and check the output condition for each input combination. Place a check in each row of column 3 of the table if the output at Y agrees with column 2. If they do not agree, recheck your table and your wiring.

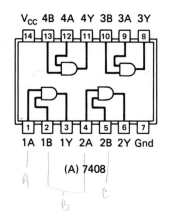

Vcc 4B 4A 4Y 3B 3A 3Y

14 13 12 11 10 9 8

1 2 3 4 5 6 7

1A 1B 1Y 2A 2B 2Y Gnd

(A) 7408

A

B

C

Quad two-input OR gate

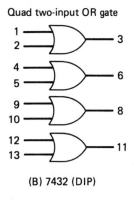

(B) 7432 (DIP)

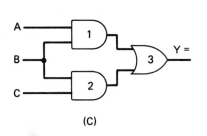

Y =

(C)

A B C	1	2	3	4 Check
0 0 0	○	○	○	
0 0 1	○	○	○	
0 1 0	○	○	○	
0 1 1	○	1	1	
1 0 0	○	○	○	
1 0 1	○	○	○	
1 1 0	1	○	1	
1 1 1	1		1	

(D)

$$AB + BC = B(A+C)$$

$$(A+C)B = BA + BC$$

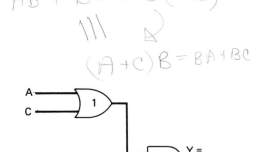

Y =

(E)

A B C	1	2	3. Check
0 0 0	○	○	
0 0 1	1	○	
0 1 0	○	○	
0 1 1	1		
1 0 0	1	○	
1 0 1	1	○	
1 1 0	1	1	
1 1 1	1	1	

(F)

Fig. L 8-1.

141

Quiz for Experiment 8-1

1. A logic circuit with three inputs has ____8____ possible input combinations.

2. If the circuit input is a 0, you must (leave that input unconnected, ground that input).

3. The table in Fig. L 8-1(D) shows that the output will be HIGH if any two, but not all three, inputs are HIGH (true, false).

4. The table in Fig. L 8-1(D) shows that the output will be HIGH if input *B* and at least one other input are HIGH (true, false).

5. A truth table shows the output condition for *every* possible input combination (true, false).

6. Comparing the tables in Figs. L 8-1(D) and L 8-1-(F), the outputs are *identical* for *every* possible input combination (true, false).

7. If two circuits have identical output tables, they are logically equivalent (true, false).

8. In an application where the circuit of Fig. L 8-1(C) is used, you could use the circuit of Fig. L 8-1(E) instead and it will perform logically the same (true, false).

Experiment 8-2 AND/OR/Invert Gate

Purpose

To gain more experience in logic circuit tracing. To become familiar with the AND/OR/INVERT (AOI) gate, a very versatile combinational logic chip.

Equipment

Digital breadboard kit
7450 AND/OR/INVERT
7404 hex inverter

Procedure

1. As you did in Experiment 8-1, write the Boolean expression for the output of each gate on the diagram of Fig. L 8-2(C). [Notice that the AOI chip shown in Fig. L 8-2(A) actually shows a NOR gate output, whereas Fig. L 8-2(C) shows an OR gate followed by an inverter. This is done simply to make the circuit tracing easier. The circuits are logically the same.]

2. Next, fill in the table in Fig. L 8-2(D).

3. Now wire the circuit and apply signals to inputs A and B for all combinations shown in the table. You will need to use two inverters from the 7404 chip, shown in Fig. L 8-2(B). If output Y agrees with the predicted value, place a check in each row in the column provided. If your circuit works as you predicted, go on to the next step. Otherwise, recheck your wiring, go back to step 1, and start over.

4. Examine the circuit of Fig. L 8-2(E) and write the outputs of each gate on the figure as before.

5. Fill in the table in Fig. L 8-2(F) for this circuit as you did for the last circuit.

6. Then wire the circuit and check its operation, putting a check in the space provided if the circuit operates as you predicted. Recheck if it does not agree.

Quiz for Experiment 8-2

1. The output Y of the circuit of Fig. L 8-2(C) is HIGH only if the two inputs are (the same, different, HIGH, LOW).

2. The circuit of Fig. L 8-2(C) is logically equivalent to that of Fig. 8-1 (true, false).

143

3. The circuit of Fig. L 8-2(C) can be used as an EXCLUSIVE OR (true, false).

4. The output of the circuit of Fig. L 8-2(E) is HIGH only if the two inputs are (the same, different, HIGH, LOW).

5. The circuit of Fig. L 8-2(E) can be called an EXCLUSIVE OR (true, false).

6. The circuit of Fig. L 8-2(E) can be called an EXCLUSIVE NOR (true, false).

7. The circuit of Fig. L 8-2(E) can be called a logic comparator because its output will be (HIGH, LOW) whenever both inputs are (HIGH, identical).

Fig. L 8-2.

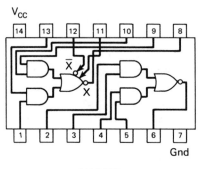

(A) 7450

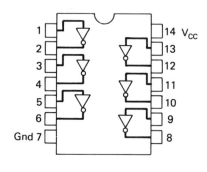

(B) 7404

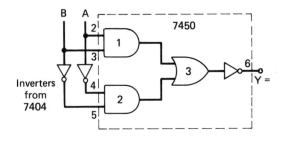

(C)

A B	$\bar{A}$	$\bar{B}$	1	2	3	Y =	Check
0 0	1	1	6	1	1	6	
0 1	1 0		0	0	0	1	
1 0	0 1		0	0	0	1	
1 1	0 0		1	0	1	0	

(D)

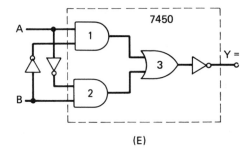

(E)

A B	$\bar{A}$	$\bar{B}$	1	2	3	Y =	Check
0 0	1 1		0	0	0	1	
0 1	1 0		0	1	1	0	
1 0	0 1		1	0	1	0	
1 1	0 0		0	0	0	1	

(F)

Experiment 8-3   Logic Circuits with NAND Gates

Purpose

To see how NAND gates can be used in place of AND gates, OR gates, and inverters.

Equipment

> Digital breadboard kit
> 7400 quad two-input NAND

Procedure

1. Examine the diagram of Fig. L 8-3(A). Simplify the circuit by replacing gate 3 with its OR-form equivalent. Draw your circuit in the blank space provided in Fig. L 8-3(B). (Refer to Fig. 8-6(B) for a similar figure.)

2. Next, simplify the circuit even further by removing any pairs of series inversions (bubbles). [See Fig. 8-6(C).] Draw the final simplified circuit in the blank space of Fig. L 8-3(C).

3. Then write the Boolean expression at the output of each gate of Fig. L 8-3(C).

Fig. L 8-3.

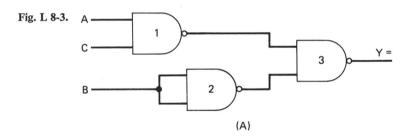

(A)

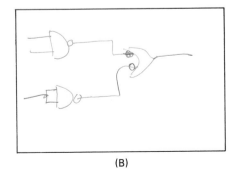

(B)

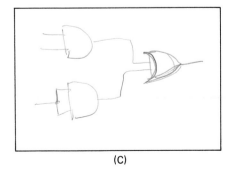

(C)

145

4. Fill in the table in Fig. L 8-3(D).

5. Now wire the circuit exactly as shown in Fig. L 8-3(A). Apply inputs to points *A*, *B*, and *C* by means of toggle switches for all possible combinations listed in the table in Fig. L 8-3(D). Put a check in each row if the circuit operates as you predicted.

Inputs A B C	Output gate 1	Output gate 3	Self check
0 0 0		○	○
0 0 1	○	○	○
0 1 0	○		
0 1 1	○		
1 0 0	○	○	○
1 0 1		○	
1 1 0	○		
1 1 1			

(D)

Fig. L 8-3. (Cont.)

Quiz for Experiment 8-3

1. In its final equivalent circuit, gate 1 of Fig. L 8-3(A) is replaced with an (AND, OR, inverter).

2. Gate 2 is being used as an (AND, OR, inverter).

3. In its final equivalent circuit, gate 3 is replaced with an (AND, OR, inverter).

4. Compare the circuit of this experiment to those of Experiment 8-1. The circuits (are, are not) logically equivalent.

5. In its simplest form, Fig. L 8-3(C) looks like Fig. L 8-1(E) (true, false).

Experiment 8-4   Logic Circuits with NOR Gates

Purpose

You will now try your hand at designing a circuit to perform a specific function using only NOR gates to replace AND gates, OR gates, and inverters.

Equipment

Digital breadboard kit
7402 quad two-input NOR

Procedure

1. Examine the circuit of Fig. L 8-4(A). This is the same as the circuit in Fig. L 8-1(E) of Experiment 8-1. Your task here is to design a circuit which is logically equivalent to Fig. L 8-4(A) using only NOR gates. In the blank space provided in Fig. L 8-4(B), draw the NOR equivalent circuit of Fig. L 8-4(A).

2. As you did in previous experiments, write the Boolean expression for the output of gate 1 and gate 2 of Fig. L 8-4(A) on the figure. Then fill in the appropriate columns in the table of Fig. L 8-4(C).

3. Now wire your circuit and check its output for each set of inputs. Place a check in each row if your circuit has the same output as Fig. L 8-4(A). If not, back to the drawing board.

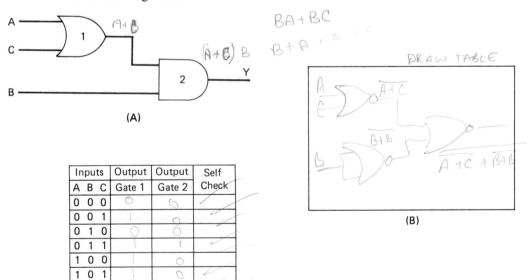

Inputs	Output	Output	Self
A B C	Gate 1	Gate 2	Check
0 0 0	0	0	✓
0 0 1	1	0	✓
0 1 0	0	0	✓
0 1 1	1	1	✓
1 0 0	1	0	✓
1 0 1	1	0	✓
1 1 0	1	1	✓
1, 1 1	1	1	

(C)

Fig. L 8-4.

147

9

Binary Numbers and Their Applications

Introduction

All digital circuits work with signals that represent quantities or values. Quantities or values, however, can accurately be accounted for only with numbers. Therefore, numbers are continually being processed by digital and computer systems. In this chapter we shall learn number systems that are commonly used with digital circuits. We shall also become familiar with ICs that were specifically developed to work with such numbers. Becoming familiar with the terms, and the language in general, in this chapter is especially important. It is another step in our "firming up" the foundation on which we are building a communications link with the legions of technicians, engineers, and manufacturers that serve the digital electronics industry.

9-1 Binary and Decimal Numbers Compared

Our familiar number system, which uses the 10 characters 0 through 9, is called the *decimal* or *base-10* number system. It is generally assumed that this system evolved because early man naturally started counting by 10s with his fingers. A system with 10 characters, however, is not particularly suited for modern electrical and electronic calculating machines. An electrical signal, like a voltage, would require 10 levels or values to represent the 10 characters in our decimal number system. Such a scheme would be far less reliable than one that requires only two levels that could easily be obtained with switches. In previous chapters, we observed that transistors and FETS are easily turned on and off, and thus they serve as very reliable switches. Therefore, a number system that is far more suitable for *transistor* and FET circuits is the *binary* or *base-2* number system. This system has only two characters, 1 and 0. The 1 and 0 can be represented by the HIGH and LOW signals in a typical logic circuit. A portion of the binary number system, with its equivalent decimal values, is shown in Fig. 9-1. Obviously, the binary number system has the disadvantage of generally using more characters, which are called *bits*, to represent a given value than does the decimal system. This disadvantage, however, is insignificant when compared to the many advantages of the binary system for problem solving in modern computer-type circuits.

Often, when decimal (base-10) and binary (base-2) numbers are likely to appear together, their bases are shown in subscript to avoid confusing the two. For exam-

Binary numbers	Decimal numbers
0	0
1	1
10	2
11	3
100	4
101	5
110	6
111	7
1000	8
1001	9
1010	10
1011	11
1100	12
1101	13
1110	14
1111	15
10000	16
10001	17
10010	18
10011	19
10100	20
⋮	⋮
1001011	75
1001100	76
⋮	⋮
1100011	99
1100100	100

Fig. 9-1. List of binary numbers and their decimal equivalents.

ple, the number 11 might be interpreted as eleven in decimal or as three in binary if it is not more clearly defined. We can more specifically show that 11_{10} represents eleven in decimal and that 11_2 represents three in binary.

9-2 Binary-to-Decimal Conversions

The binary number system is *weighted*. This means that a character 1, in a binary number, represents a greater or lesser part of the number's value depending on its position in the number. The weight distribution of binary numbers is shown in Fig. 9-2. If not otherwise shown, a *binary point* is assumed to be at the far right of a binary number, just as decimal points are often assumed to be at the far right of decimal numbers. The first binary bit to the left of the binary point carries a weight of 2^0 or 1. The second bit to the left of the binary point carries a weight of 2^1 or 2. Similarly, the third bit carries a weight of 2^2 or 4. Generally, then, as we move left from bit to bit, the weight of each bit doubles. The far-right bit of a binary number is called the least significant bit (LSB). The last 1 to the left is called the most significant bit (MSB).

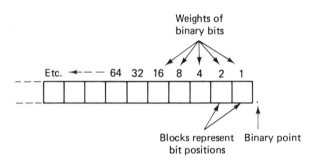

Fig. 9-2. Weight distribution of binary number; weight doubles with each bit position to the left.

By knowing the distribution of weights in binary numbers, we are able to find the decimal equivalents of such numbers. For example, several binary numbers are converted to their equivalent decimal numbers in Fig. 9-3. The weights are shown above each bit. The weights that are above 1's in the binary number are simply added to give the decimal equivalent of this number. More binary numbers and their decimal equivalents are given in Fig. 9-4. The reader can verify these equations for practice.

Weight distribution

(A) Binary number → $\overset{4}{1}$ $\overset{2}{1}$ $\overset{1}{1}$ = 4 + 2 + 1 = 7; thus, $111_2 = 7_{10}$

Weights
over 1's
added

(B) Binary number → $\overset{8}{1}$ $\overset{4}{0}$ $\overset{2}{1}$ $\overset{1}{0}$ = 8 + 2 = 10; thus, $1010_2 = 10_{10}$

Weights
over 1's

(C) Binary number → $\overset{16}{1}$ $\overset{8}{0}$ $\overset{4}{1}$ $\overset{2}{0}$ $\overset{1}{0}$ = 16 + 4 = 20; thus, $10100_2 = 20_{10}$

Weights
over 1's

(D) Binary number → $\overset{32}{1}$ $\overset{16}{0}$ $\overset{8}{1}$ $\overset{4}{0}$ $\overset{2}{0}$ $\overset{1}{1}$ = 32 + 8 + 1 = 41; thus, $101001_2 = 41_{10}$

Weights
over 1's

(E) Binary number → $\overset{64}{1}$ $\overset{32}{0}$ $\overset{16}{0}$ $\overset{8}{0}$ $\overset{4}{0}$ $\overset{2}{0}$ $\overset{1}{0}$ = 64; thus, $1000000_2 = 64_{10}$

Fig. 9-3. Examples of how binary numbers are converted to their decimal equivalents.

(A) $11000_2 = 24_{10}$ (F) $111111_2 = 63_{10}$
(B) $11100_2 = 28_{10}$ (G) $1000110_2 = 70_{10}$
(C) $11111_2 = 31_{10}$ (H) $1100110_2 = 102_{10}$
(D) $100110_2 = 38_{10}$ (I) $1111111_2 = 127_{10}$
(E) $111001_2 = 57_{10}$ (J) $10101010_2 = 170_{10}$

Fig. 9-4. Binary numbers and their decimal equivalents.

9-3   Decimal-to-Binary Conversions

Decimal numbers can be converted into their binary equivalents by a *successive division by 2* process. Figure 9-5 shows how binary equivalents of a few decimal numbers are found with this method. In Fig. 9-5(A), 35_{10} is converted to its binary equivalent by first dividing it by 2. As shown, the result is 17 with a remainder of 1. The remainder is written off to the right and eventually becomes the LSB of the binary equivalent number. The 17 is moved down and, in turn, also divided by 2. Note that the result is 8, which is moved down for the next division by 2, and the remainder 1 is written off to the right. The result of dividing 8 by 2 is 4 with a remainder 0. As before, the quotient 4 is brought down for further division, and the remainder 0 is shown to the right. The last step in this process *always* results in 1 divided by 2. Of course, 2 divides into 1 zero times with a remainder of 1. This last remainder 1 is the MSB of the binary equivalent number. That is, as shown, the remainders read upwards become the binary equivalent as written from left to right. All the examples in Fig. 9-5 can similarly be analyzed. The reader, as an exercise, should work for each equivalent binary number of the decimal numbers given in Fig. 9-4.

(A) Convert 35_{10} to its binary
equivalent.

Solution:
$35 \div 2 = 17 \rightarrow 1$
$17 \div 2 = 8 \;\; \rightarrow 1$
$8 \div 2 = 4 \;\; \rightarrow 0$
$4 \div 2 = 2 \;\; \rightarrow 0$
$2 \div 2 = 1 \;\; \rightarrow 0$
$1 \div 2 = 0 \;\; \rightarrow 1$

Thus, $35_{10} = 100011_2$

(B) Convert 235_{10} to its
binary equivalent.

Solution:
$235 \div 2 = 117 \rightarrow 1$
$117 \div 2 = 58 \;\; \rightarrow 1$
$58 \div 2 = 29 \;\; \rightarrow 0$
$29 \div 2 = 14 \;\; \rightarrow 1$
$14 \div 2 = 7 \;\; \rightarrow 0$
$7 \div 2 = 3 \;\; \rightarrow 1$
$3 \div 2 = 1 \;\; \rightarrow 1$
$1 \div 2 = 0 \;\; \rightarrow 1$

Thus, $235_{10} = 11101011_2$

(C) Convert 1492_{10} to its
binary equivalent.

Solution:
$1492 \div 2 = 746 \rightarrow 0$
$746 \div 2 = 373 \rightarrow 0$
$373 \div 2 = 186 \rightarrow 1$
$186 \div 2 = 93 \;\; \rightarrow 0$
$93 \div 2 = 46 \;\; \rightarrow 1$
$46 \div 2 = 23 \;\; \rightarrow 0$
$23 \div 2 = 11 \;\; \rightarrow 1$
$11 \div 2 = 5 \;\; \rightarrow 1$
$5 \div 2 = 2 \;\; \rightarrow 1$
$2 \div 2 = 1 \;\; \rightarrow 0$
$1 \div 2 = 0 \;\; \rightarrow 1$

Thus, $1492_{10} = 10111010100$

Fig. 9-5. Examples of how decimal numbers are converted into their equivalent binary numbers.

Summary

1. The binary number system is much more suitable for electronic problem-solving circuits than is the decimal system.

2. The binary number system has only two characters, 1 and 0, which can easily be represented by ON or OFF transistors or FETs or by closed or open switches.

3. A binary number consists of a series of 1's or 0's, each of which is called a bit. Later we shall see that a series of binary bits is commonly called a *binary word*.

4. The binary number system is a weighted system, which means that each bit carries more or less of the number's value depending on its position relative to the binary point.

5. The decimal equivalent of a binary number is found by adding the weights of the 1 bits in the number.

6. The far-right bit of a binary number is called the LSB (least significant bit), while the far-left bit is called the MSB (most significant bit).

7. The binary equivalent of a decimal number is found by using a successive division by 2 method.

8. The decimal number system consists of characters 0 through 9. Later we shall see that these characters are commonly called *digits*.

Problems 9-1

512 256 128 64 32 16 .8 .4 .2 .1.

1. Find the decimal equivalent of each of the following binary numbers:

(a) 11110   30
(b) 10111   23
(c) 110111   55
(d) 111010   58

(e) 11001100   204
(f) 10010011   147
(g) 11101110   238
(h) 11110011   243

(i) 100000000   256
(j) 111000111
(k) 110101101   429
(l) 111111111   511

2. Find the binary equivalents of each of the following decimal numbers:

(a) 36   100100
(b) 79
(c) 92   1011100
(d) 127   1111111

(e) 128) 10000000
(f) 160
(g) 255   11111111
(h) 256

(i) 260   100000100
(j) 324
(k) 511
(l) 512

$512 \div 2 = 256 + 0$
$256 \div 2 = 128 + 0$
$128 \div 2 = 64 + 0$
$64 \div 2 = 32 + 0$
$16 + 0$
$8 + 0$
$4 + 0$
$2 + 0$
$1 + 0$
$0 + 1$

1000000000

9-4   The Four-Bit Binary Decoder IC

Having become familiar with the binary number system, we would naturally like to see and become familiar with existing hardware that is able to accept and interpret inputs of binary numbers. The 4-bit binary decoder IC,* shown in Fig. 9-6, is

*Four-bit binary decoders are available from several manufacturers under various names and numbers such as the "9311 one-of-sixteen decoder" by Fairchild, the "74154 four-line to sixteen-line decoder" by Signetics and Texas Instruments, to name a few.

an example of such hardware. It has four inputs that accept binary numbers, A_0, A_1, A_2, and A_3, and two enabling (controlling) inputs, $\overline{E_0}$ and $\overline{E_1}$. Its outputs are $\overline{0}$ through $\overline{15}$. As in previous chapters, overbars are used to identify ACTIVE LOW input and output names when they are shown outside the logic symbols. Four-bit binary numbers (words) are applied to the A_3 through A_0 inputs. A LOW or L input represents a binary bit 0, while a HIGH or H input represents a binary bit 1. As shown in the table of Fig. 9-6(B), there are 16 combinations of 4-bit binary words. Binary 0 is represented by the 4-bit word LLLL. Similarly, binary 10 and 1000 are represented by the words LLHL and HLLL, respectively. Obviously, A_3 is the MSB and A_0 is the LSB of each 4-bit input. Only one or none of the 16 outputs can be LOW at a time. If either enabling input, $\overline{E_0}$ or $\overline{E_1}$, is HIGH (inactive), the decoder is disabled, which means that it ignores all inputs applied to A_3 through A_0 and all outputs remain HIGH (inactive). If *both* $\overline{E_0}$ and $\overline{E_1}$ are pulled ACTIVE LOW, this IC is enabled, and it decodes the binary word on its A_3 through A_0 inputs. When decoding a binary input word, *one* of this IC's 16 outputs goes ACTIVE LOW. For example, if the signals on A_3, A_2, A_1, and A_0 are L, L, L, and L, the $\overline{0}$ output goes LOW because this 4-bit binary word is equal to decimal 0. Likewise, then, binary words LLHL or HLLL, applied to the A_3 through A_0 inputs, force output $\overline{2}$ or output $\overline{8}$ LOW, respectively. We can note that generally the decimal equivalent number of each 4-bit binary input identifies the output name that goes LOW. In the logic diagram we can see that this decoder consists mainly of inverters and NAND gates. Although tedious, it would not be difficult for us to analyze this logic diagram and verify that it indeed works as the table indicates.

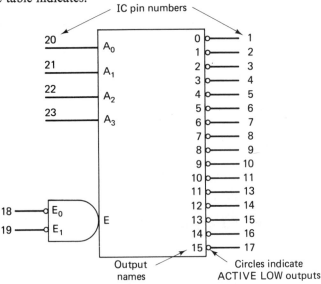

(A) Logic symbol; ACTIVE LOW output names are identified without overbars when shown inside the symbol and with overbars when shown outside the symbols

Fig. 9-6. The four-bit binary decoder, also known as the "9311 one-of-sixteen decoder" and the "74154 four-line to sixteen-line decoder."

Binary numbers	Equivalent 4-bit binary input words	Output names
0	LLLL	$\overline{0}$
1	LLLH	$\overline{1}$
10	LLHL	$\overline{2}$
11	LLHH	$\overline{3}$
100	LHLL	$\overline{4}$
101	LHLH	$\overline{5}$
110	LHHL	$\overline{6}$
111	LHHH	$\overline{7}$
1000	HLLL	$\overline{8}$
1001	HLLH	$\overline{9}$
1010	HLHL	$\overline{10}$
1011	HLHH	$\overline{11}$
1100	HHLL	$\overline{12}$
1101	HHLH	$\overline{13}$
1110	HHHL	$\overline{14}$
1111	HHHH	$\overline{15}$

↑

Outputs that go LOW
only when the 4-bit input
word to its left is applied
while $\overline{E}_0$ and $\overline{E}_1$ are LOW

(B) Functional table

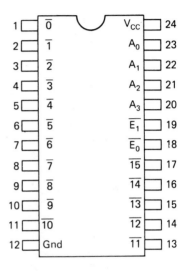

(C) DIP package (top view)

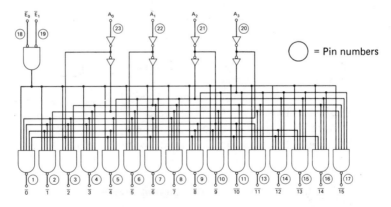

(D) Logic diagram showing equivalent gate arrangement in IC package

Fig. 9-6. (Cont.)

155

9-5 The Four-Bit Binary Decoder for Combinational Logic

The rat-conditioning logic that we analyzed in the previous chapter can be performed with the help of a 4-bit binary decoder.* The circuit of Fig. 9-7 shows how this can be done. The timer, as before, allows feeding for only a few seconds each hour. During feed time, the switch Sw is closed. This pulls the $\overline{E_0}$ and $\overline{E_1}$ signals ACTIVE LOW, which "enables" the 4-bit binary decoder and also turns on the feed light. When enabled, this decoder can respond to binary words on inputs A_3 through A_0. When Sw is open, the decoder is disabled, which means that all its outputs remain HIGH (INACTIVE) regardless of the signals on the A_3 through A_0 inputs. The switch Sw is assumed closed in the remaining discussion of this section.

When Alfred only pushes button A, the signals on inputs A_3 through A_0 are LLLH and the output $\overline{1}$ goes ACTIVE LOW. The ACTIVE LOW output $\overline{1}$ activates the food dispenser A and also drives an input of NAND gate 3. The resulting ACTIVE HIGH out of this NAND gate turns on the busy light. (Remember that if any one of the NAND gate's inputs goes LOW, its output goes HIGH.)

When Brenda only pushes button B, the A_3 through A_0 inputs are LLHL. This causes output $\overline{2}$ to go ACTIVE LOW, which activates her food dispenser by causing the F_B signal to go ACTIVE HIGH via gate 2. Of course, the ACTIVE LOW $\overline{2}$ signal causes the BUSY signal to become ACTIVE HIGH via gate 3, and this turns on the busy light.

When Charlie only pushes button C, the A_3 through A_0 inputs are LHLL, and this forces the $\overline{4}$ output ACTIVE LOW, which drives the F_C output ACTIVE HIGH. Again, the busy light turns on because the BUSY signal becomes ACTIVE HIGH.

If Alfred, Brenda, or Charlie push their buttons two at a time, a warning bell rings. The BELL output signal, when ACTIVE HIGH, causes this bell to ring. This BELL signal becomes ACTIVE HIGH if either of the decoder's output signals $\overline{3}$, $\overline{5}$, or $\overline{6}$ goes ACTIVE LOW. The $\overline{3}$ signal becomes ACTIVE LOW if inputs A_3 through A_0 are LLHH, which occurs if Alfred and Brenda request food at the same time. When Alfred and Charlie request food simultaneously, the A_3 through A_0 inputs are LHLH, causing output $\overline{5}$ to go ACTIVE LOW. Similarly, then, when Brenda and Charlie push buttons B and C at the same time, inputs A_3 through A_0 are LHHL, and the decoder's output $\overline{6}$ goes ACTIVE LOW.

Finally, if all three rats request food at the same time, inputs A_3 through A_0 are LHHH. This, of course, is equivalent to binary 7, and therefore the output $\overline{7}$ of the decoder goes ACTIVE LOW. Via gate 6, this drives the BUZZER signal ACTIVE HIGH, which turns on a loud buzzer to warn the rats that they are getting greedy.

Problems 9-2

1. Identify the pull-down resistor(s) in Fig. 9-7.

2. Identify the pull-up resistor(s) in Fig. 9-7.

3. Redraw the circuit of Fig. 9-7 with the input A_3 input connected to V_{CC} instead of ground. Show what changes in connections must consequently be made on the outputs of the 4-bit binary decoder.

*Review summary in Section 8-3 as needed.

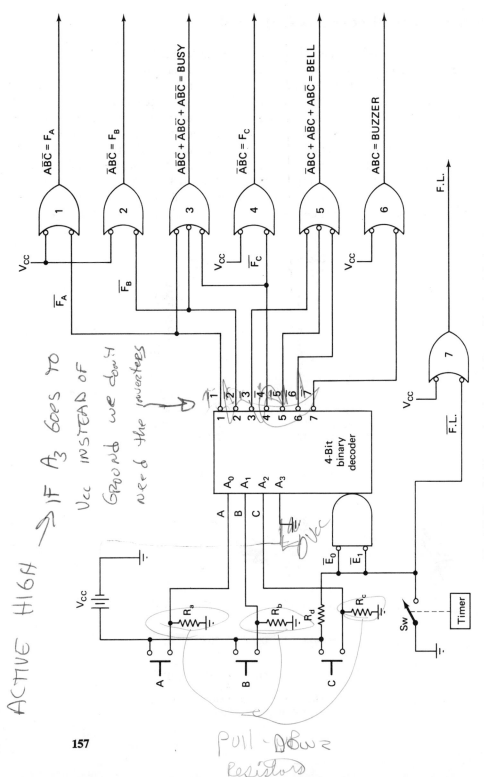

Fig. 9-7. Four-bit binary decoder used in combinational logic circuit; NAND gates 1, 2, 4, 6 and 7 are wired to work as inverters, NAND gates 3 and 5 perform three-input NAND functions.

157

9-6 Binary-Coded Decimal (BCD) Numbers

A commonly used numbers system in digital electronics is the *binary-coded decimal (BCD)* system. This BCD system is related to the binary system. Decimal numbers and their equivalent BCD values are shown in Fig. 9-8. Note that *each* decimal character is represented by a 4-bit word. That is, if a decimal number consists of two or three characters, its equivalent BCD value consists of two or three 4-bit words, respectively. Like binary, this BCD system is weighted. The weight distribution of each 4-bit BCD word is exactly the same as in 4-bit binary words. Thus, from left to right, the weights of the 4 bits, of each BCD word, are 8421, just as they are in 4-bit binary words. However, a 4-bit BCD word, unlike a 4-bit binary word, *never* represents a value greater than 9. For values greater than 9, more than one 4-bit BCD word must be used. As shown in Fig. 9-8, therefore, the largest 4-bit

Decimal numbers	Equivalent BCD 8421		
0			0000
1			0001
2			0010
3			0011
4			0100
5			0101
6			0110
7			0111
8			1000
9			1001
10		0001	0000
11		0001	0001
12		0001	0010
13		0001	0011
.			
.			
25		0010	0101
26		0010	0110
.			
38		0011	1000
39		0011	1001
.			
43		0100	0011
.			
99		1001	1001
.			
123	0001	0010	0011
.			
256	0010	0101	0110

Fig. 9-8. Decimal numbers and their equivalent BCD numbers.

BCD word is 1001. Figure 9-9(A) shows how a few decimal numbers are converted into their BCD equivalents, and Fig. 9-9(B) shows how a few BCD numbers are converted into their decimal equivalents. Generally, it is quite easy to convert BCD values to their decimal equivalents or decimal values to the BCD equivalents.

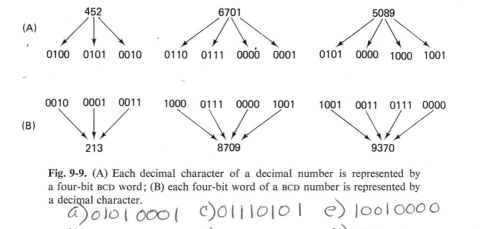

Fig. 9-9. (A) Each decimal character of a decimal number is represented by a four-bit BCD word; (B) each four-bit word of a BCD number is represented by a decimal character.

a) 0101 0001   c) 0111 0101   e) 1001 0000
b) 0110 1001   d) 1000 0100   f) 0101 0000 0001
h) 0110 0011 0010   i) 0111 1000 0111   j) 1000 1001 0101

Problems 9-3

1. Convert the following decimal numbers to their BCD equivalents:

    (a) 51   (b) 69   (c) 75   (d) 84   (e) 90   (f) 378   *0011 0111 1000*

    (g) 501   (h) 632   (i) 747   (j) 895   (k) 987 *1001 1000 0111*   (l) 5280 *0101 0010 1000 0000*

2. Convert the following BCD numbers to their decimal equivalents:

    (a) 1001 0111 *97*   (b) 0100 0010 *42*   (c) 0101 0111 *57*   (d) 0110 0000 *60*

    (e) 0101 1001 0100 *594* (f) 0111 0011 0001 *731* (g) 0110 0000 1000 *608*

    (h) 1000 1001 0111 *897*   (i) 0011 0100 0010 *342*   (j) 1001 0000 1000 0001 *9081*

9-7 BCD Decoders and Seven-Segment Displays

BCD numbers must often be converted to their decimal equivalents. For example, after an electronic calculator performs arithmetic in binary, BCD, or a similar type of system, the final answer must be converted to decimal so that the operator of the calculator can easily interpret it. Likewise, an electronic clock or watch runs (counts time) in binary, BCD, or a related number system, but it must display the time in decimal. Hardware used to convert BCD numbers into their equivalents in decimal is shown in Fig. 9-10. The circuit in this figure consists of two ICs: a BCD-to-7-segment decoder (7447-type IC) and a 7-segment LED (light-emitting diode) display.* If the L.T. (light test) and RBI (ripple blanking input) inputs are HIGH or

---

*This 7-segment display is available from several manufacturers that give it different identifying numbers, such as MAN 1 by Monsanto and TIL 302 by Texas Instruments.

open, as they normally are during decoder operation, various outputs $\bar{a}$ through $\bar{g}$ are pulled ACTIVE LOW. These outputs are connected to LEDs in the 7-segment display. If output $\bar{a}$ is pulled ACTIVE LOW, the two series LEDs in segment a conduct current. When conducting, these LEDs illuminate their segment. Similarly, then, ACTIVE LOW decoder outputs $\bar{b}$, $\bar{c}$, . . . , $\bar{g}$ cause segments b, c, . . . , g, respectively, to become lighted. As shown in the table of Fig. 9-10, all decoder outputs except $\bar{g}$ must be ACTIVE LOW to illuminate a 0. ACTIVE LOW $\bar{b}$ and $\bar{c}$ signals display a 1. Similarly, all segments except $\bar{c}$ and $\bar{f}$ must be ACTIVE LOW to display a 2, etc. The decoder is designed to provide the appropriate logic levels on its outputs $\bar{a}$ through $\bar{g}$ that will display a decimal character equivalent to the 4-bit BCD word in its A through D inputs.

The individual segments of the 7-segment display illuminate with more or less brilliance depending on the value of the resistor R. The $R = 120 \, \Omega$, shown in Fig. 9-10, is about as small as we should go to get good brilliance and reasonably long life from this display device. Larger values of R will cause dimmer displays but longer display life. If this resistor R is too small, the 7-segment display can be ruined. Figure 9-11 shows how separate resistors of about 220 Ω each can be used between the decoder and display unit instead of the single resistor R between the display and V_{CC}. The latter arrangement gives a much more consistent brilliance of each segment.

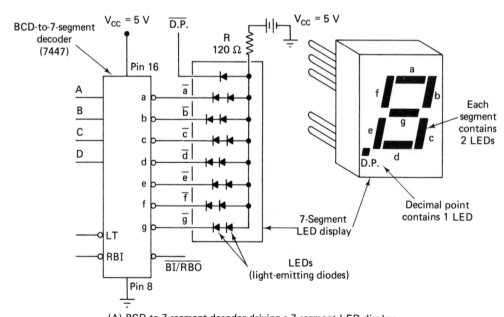

(A) BCD to 7-segment decoder driving a 7-segment LED display

Fig. 9-10.

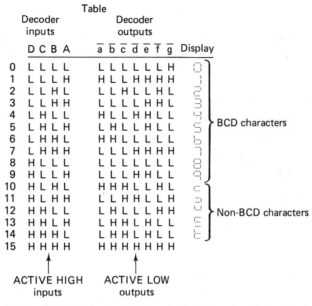

Table

	Decoder inputs				Decoder outputs							Display
	D	C	B	A	$\bar{a}$	$\bar{b}$	$\bar{c}$	$\bar{d}$	$\bar{e}$	$\bar{f}$	$\bar{g}$	
0	L	L	L	L	L L L L L L H							0
1	L	L	L	H	H L L H H H H							1
2	L	L	H	L	L L H L L H L							2
3	L	L	H	H	L L L L H H L							3
4	L	H	L	L	H L L H H L L							4
5	L	H	L	H	L H L L H L L							5
6	L	H	H	L	H H L L L L L							6
7	L	H	H	H	L L L H H H H							7
8	H	L	L	L	L L L L L L L							8
9	H	L	L	H	L L L H H L L							9
10	H	L	H	L	H H H L L H L							
11	H	L	H	H	L L H H L L H							
12	H	H	L	L	L H L L L H H							
13	H	H	L	H	L H H L H L L							
14	H	H	H	L	L H H L H L L							
15	H	H	H	H	H H H H H H H							

BCD characters (rows 0–9)

Non-BCD characters (rows 10–15)

ACTIVE HIGH inputs

ACTIVE LOW outputs

(B) Functional table showing how the 7-segment decoder's outputs respond to all possible 4-bit input words

Fig. 9-10. (Cont.)

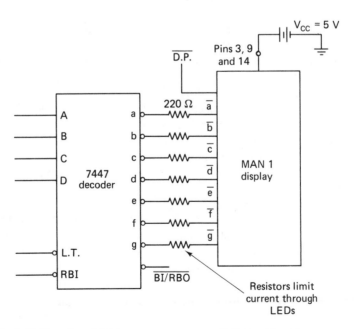

Fig. 9-11. Decoder driving a seven-segment display with separate current limiting resistors for each segment.

161

On the decoder, the $\overline{\text{L.T.}}$ (light test) input can be used to check the display. When $\overline{\text{L.T.}}$ is pulled ACTIVE LOW (grounded), all segments of the display should normally light. The $\overline{\text{RBI}}$ input and the $\overline{\text{BI/RBO}}$ output are used in systems where some decimal characters that are not significant figures are not to be displayed. When grounded or ACTIVE LOW, the $\overline{\text{RBI}}$ input disables the 7-segment display unit; that is, it turns off all segments. An ACTIVE LOW or grounded $\overline{\text{D.P.}}$ signal illuminates the decimal point on the display.

9-8   A BCD Encoder

A BCD encoder can be a circuit that accepts signals, one at a time, from 10 pushbutton switches and converts them to BCD equivalents. The keyboard on an electronic calculator requires an encoder. A simple encoder is shown in Fig. 9-12. The pushbutton switches shown, "0" through "9," can be typical calculator keyboard pushbuttons. When each numbered pushbutton is depressed, an equivalent 4-bit BCD word appears at the encoder's outputs A through D. Typically, these 4-bit words might be loaded into a register. Descriptions and purposes of registers are discussed in later chapters. In this case, the BCD outputs of the encoder are shown working into a decoder to illustrate how 4-bit words can be generated and processed.

When none of the pushbutton switches is depressed, the $\overline{\text{INHIBIT}}$ signal is ACTIVE LOW, being held at ground potential by the pull-down resistor R_5. This disables the decoder and 7-segment display by holding the decoder's $\overline{\text{RBI}}$ input ACTIVE LOW and all the display's segments remain dark. The term ACTIVE, in this case, refers to the way the circuit acts to *prevent* any character from being displayed before a pushbutton is depressed.

If we depress pushbutton "0," the V_{CC} supply is applied to the $\overline{\text{INHIBIT}}$ line, causing it to go HIGH (inactive). This releases the decoder and allows it to respond to its A through D inputs and to drive the 7-segment display. While "0" is depressed, the A through D encoder outputs are held LOW by pull-down resistors R_1, R_2, R_3, and R_4. The LOW A through D inputs to the decoder cause all its outputs except $\bar{g}$ to go ACTIVE LOW, and all the segments on the display, except g, become illuminated.

When we depress switch "1," the V_{CC} supply is applied to resistor R_1 through the forward-biased diode D_1. This pulls the encoder's output signal A HIGH while its B, C, and D signals remain LOW. Simultaneously, the $\overline{\text{INHIBIT}}$ signal is HIGH, which enables the decoder to decode the A through D signals. In this case, the decoder's $\bar{b}$ and $\bar{c}$ outputs go ACTIVE LOW, causing segments b and c on the display to illuminate.

The effects of pushing the other buttons can similarly be analyzed. For example, by pushing "7," diodes D_{10}, D_{11}, and D_{12} become forward biased, and V_{CC} pulls encoder outputs A, B, and C HIGH. Output D remains LOW. The $\overline{\text{INHIBIT}}$ output is also HIGH, which enables the decoder to respond to the H, H, H, and L signals on its A, B, C, and D inputs, respectively. The responding decoder's $\bar{a}$, $\bar{b}$, and $\bar{c}$ outputs go LOW, causing display segments a, b, and c to light.

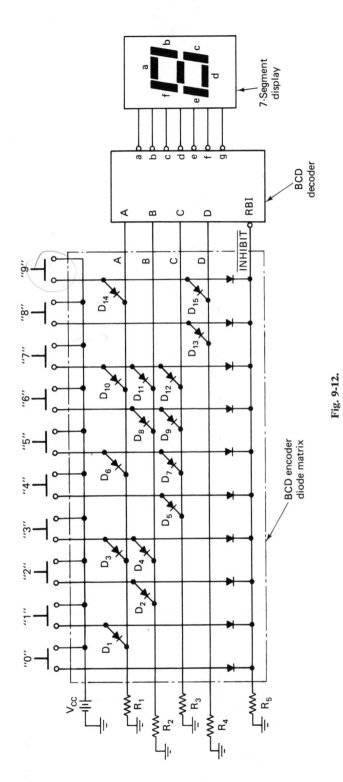

Fig. 9-12.

Problem 9-4

1. In the table of Fig. 9-13, indicate which diodes become forward biased (conductive) and which display inputs become ACTIVE LOW as each pushbutton is depressed. The answers when pushbuttons "0," "1," and "7" are depressed are given as examples.

Pushbuttons being depressed	Encoder diodes that become conductive	Display inputs that become ACTIVE LOW
0	None	$\bar{a}, \bar{b}, \bar{c}, \bar{d}, \bar{e}$, and $\bar{f}$
1	D_1	$\bar{b}$ and $\bar{c}$
2	D_2	$A\, \bar{b}\, \bar{d}\, \bar{e}\, \bar{g}$
3	$D_3 \quad D_4$	$\bar{A}\, \bar{b}\, \bar{c}\, \bar{d}\, \bar{g}$
4	D_5	$A\, \bar{b}\, \bar{c}\, \bar{e}\, \bar{g}$
5	$D_6 \quad D_7$	$A\, \bar{c}\, \bar{d}\, \bar{f}\, \bar{g}$
6	$D_8 \quad D_9$	$\bar{c}\, \bar{d}\, \bar{e}\, \bar{f}\, \bar{g}$
7	D_{10}, D_{11}, D_{12}	$\bar{a}, \bar{b},$ and $\bar{c}$
8	D_{13}	$\bar{A}\, b\, c\, d\, e\, f\, g$
9	$D_{14} \quad D_{15}$	$A\, b\, c\, e\, f\, g$

Fig. 9-13.

9-9 Addition in Digital Systems

As in our more familiar decimal number system, arithmetic must frequently be performed in the binary system. Arithmetic, such as addition, is particularly simple. Examples of several binary numbers being added are shown in Fig. 9-14. The addition process starts at the far right, that is, with the LSBs. The 0 and 1, in the LSB column, added give the sum of 1 as shown. The next column over adds 0 and 0, and their sum is 0. Next, 1 and 0 are added, and again the sum is 1. Until now, no carries have been required. Adding the 1 and 1 in the fourth column to the left results in a binary sum of 10 (equivalent to 2 in decimal). The 0 of this 2-bit word is placed in the answer row of the fourth column, and the 1 becomes a *carry* into the fifth column. Therefore, this 1 carry must add to the two 1's already in the fifth column, resulting in a binary sum of 11 (equivalent to 3 in decimal). The right bit, a 1 in this case, of this answer is placed in the fifth column of the answer row. The left bit is carried over to the sixth column. Since there are no sixth column bits in the binary numbers being added, the 1 carry into the sixth column simply becomes the MSB of the answer. The remaining examples in Fig. 9-14 can similarly be analyzed. The answer of each example can be verified by converting its binary numbers to decimal equivalents.

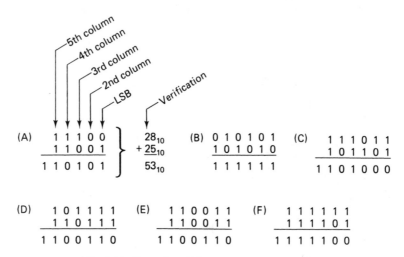

Fig. 9-14. Examples of binary numbers being added.

Problems 9-5

1. Add the following pairs of binary numbers:

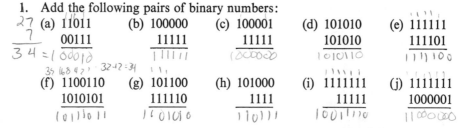

(a) 11011
    00111

(b) 100000
    11111

(c) 100001
    11111

(d) 101010
    101010

(e) 111111
    111101

(f) 1100110
    1010101

(g) 101100
    111110

(h) 101000
    1111

(i) 1111111
    11111

(j) 1111111
    1000001

2. Verify your answers in Problem 1 by reworking each problem in decimal.

9-10   Binary Addition with Combinational Logic

The logic circuit of Fig. 8-2, discussed in the previous chapter, performs a *summing* function of three binary bits. Additional gates, as shown in Fig. 9-15, can be used to perform the *carry* function. This circuit, with its three inputs and SUM and CARRY outputs, is called an *adder* or sometimes a *full adder*. The *A* and *B* inputs of this circuit can be bits, in the same column, of two binary numbers being added. The

C input can be a carry from a preceding (adjacent right-hand) column. For example, if the 2 bits to be added are 0 and 0 and if the carry from the adjacent column is also 0, row 1 of the table in Fig. 9-15 indicates the appropriate adder circuit inputs. Note that this circuit's resulting SUM and CARRY outputs are LOW. This is consistent with the adding techniques we learned in the previous section. That is, if we add three binary 0's, their sum is zero and there is no carry.

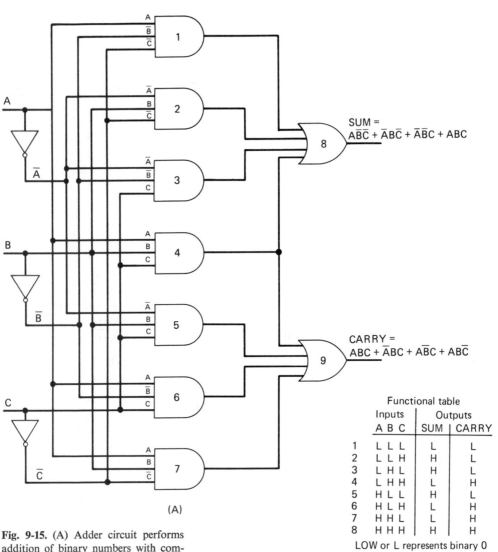

$$\text{SUM} = \overline{A}\overline{B}C + \overline{A}B\overline{C} + A\overline{B}\overline{C} + ABC$$

$$\text{CARRY} = ABC + \overline{A}BC + AB\overline{C} + A\overline{B}C$$

(A)

Fig. 9-15. (A) Adder circuit performs addition of binary numbers with combinational logic; (B) functional table for the adder circuit.

Functional table

	Inputs A B C	Outputs SUM	CARRY
1	L L L	L	L
2	L L H	H	L
3	L H L	H	L
4	L H H	L	H
5	H L L	H	L
6	H L H	L	H
7	H H L	L	H
8	H H H	H	H

LOW or L represents binary 0
HIGH or H represents binary 1

(B)

Rows 2, 3, and 5 of the table in Fig. 9-15 show how the adder's outputs, SUM and CARRY, respond if one of the three inputs is HIGH while the other two are LOW. As shown in this table, the SUM output is HIGH but the CARRY output is LOW. This, too, fits the facts we learned in the previous section. By adding three binary bits, two 0's and one 1, the sum is 1, which has no carry.

Rows 4 and 7 show what happens to the SUM and CARRY outputs if two of the adder's inputs are HIGH while one is LOW. As shown, the SUM output goes LOW while output CARRY is HIGH. This, of course, represents addition of two binary 1's and a 0. The answer is binary 10. That is, the resulting sum is 0 (right bit) and the carry must be 1 (left bit of answer).

That last row in the table of Fig. 9-15 shows that if all three inputs are HIGH, the resulting SUM and CARRY output signals are HIGH. This covers addition of three input 1's, two 1's from the binary numbers being added plus a 1 carry from the right-hand column. The answer, of course, is binary 11. The SUM output, therefore, must be HIGH to represent the right 1 of this answer. The CARRY output must be HIGH, too, to carry the left 1 to the left-hand column of bits being added. The procedure of how each carry *from* the right-hand column and how each carry *into* the left-hand column are handled is discussed further in the next section.

Adder circuits are available in ICs. The 74183-type IC, shown in Fig. 9-16, contains two full adders. The inputs $1A$, $1B$, and $1C_n$ are for one of the adders. Its outputs are $1S$ (output sum) and $1C_{n+1}$ (output carry). Therefore, the other adder's inputs are $2A$, $2B$, and $2C_n$ with outputs $2S$ and $2C_{n+1}$.

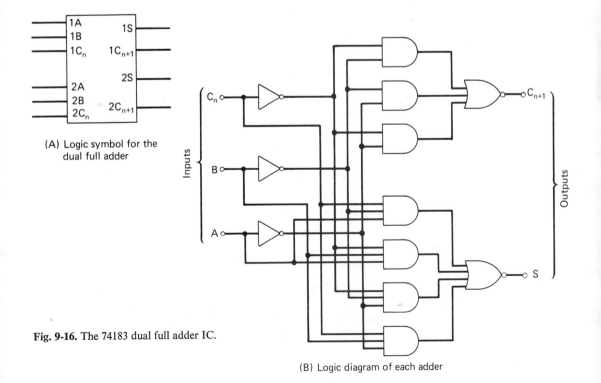

(A) Logic symbol for the dual full adder

(B) Logic diagram of each adder

Fig. 9-16. The 74183 dual full adder IC.

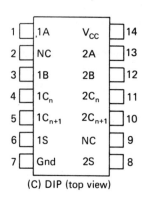

(C) DIP (top view)

Truth table

Inputs			Outputs	
C_n	B	A	S	C_{n+1}
L	L	L	L	L
L	L	H	H	L
L	H	L	H	L
L	H	H	L	H
H	L	L	H	L
H	L	H	L	H
H	H	L	L	H
H	H	H	H	H

(D) Truth table for each adder

Fig. 9-16. (Cont.)

9-11 Parallel Addition of Binary Words

Adder circuits can be interconnected as in Fig. 9-17 to add two 4-bit binary words. Each block represents an adder circuit. The A_3 through A_0 inputs represent one 4-bit binary word, A_0 being the LSB. The B_3 through B_0 inputs represent another 4-bit word that is to be added to the A_3 through A_0 word. Of course, B_0 is the LSB. The sum of the A_3 through A_0 word and the B_3 through B_0 word appears at the S_4 through S_0 outputs. Note that the carry output C_{n+1} of each adder becomes the carry input C_n of the next (more significant) adder. Also, the last (MSB) adder's carry output is the S_4 bit of the sum. Since the LSB adder receives no input carries, its carry input lead is *hardwired* to ground.

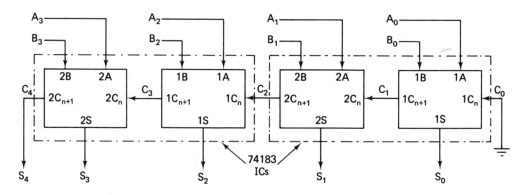

Fig. 9-17. Parallel addition of two four-bit binary words.

Examples of a few sets of input words and their resulting output sums are shown in Fig. 9-18. In Fig. 9-18(A), the LSB adder's inputs A_0, B_0, and C_0 are 0, 1, and 0, respectively. Its resulting sum S_0 and carry C_1 outputs are 1 and 0, respectively. Note that this output carry is the input carry to the next, more significant, adder.

The next adder's inputs, in Fig. 9-18(A), are $A_1 = 1$, $B_1 = 1$, and $C_1 = 0$. This causes outputs $S_1 = 0$ and $C_2 = 1$. In this case, obviously, a 1 is carried into the next more significant adder.

The next more significant adder's inputs A_2, B_2, and C_2 therefore are 0, 0, and 1, respectively. Its resulting outputs, as shown, are $S_2 = 1$ and $C_3 = 0$.

Finally, the MSB adder receives $A_3 = 1$, $B_3 = 1$, and $C_3 = 0$, and therefore its S_3 and C_4 outputs are 0 and 1, respectively. As a check, we can add the A_3 through A_0 word (1010) with the B_3 through B_0 word (1011) on paper to verify that indeed their sum is the S_4 through S_0 word (10101). The reader should similarly analyze the examples in Figs. 9-18(B) and (C) to get a better "feel" for the way sum and carry outputs are generated and how the carry outputs *ripple* into more significant positions.

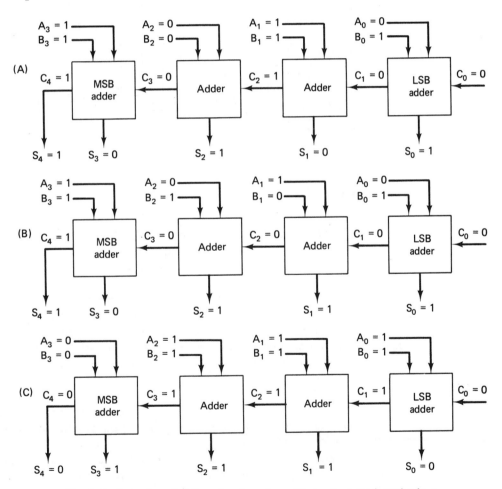

Fig. 9-18. Examples of various inputs and resulting outputs and carries in a four-bit binary parallel adder.

Problem 9-6

1. Referring to the table of Fig. 9-19, the A_3 through A_0 and the B_3 through B_0 inputs represent inputs to the 4-bit parallel adder of Fig. 9-17. Working one row at a time, indicate all the resulting sum and carry outputs.

	Inputs								Sum and Carry Outputs							
	A_3	A_2	A_1	A_0	B_3	B_2	B_1	B_0	C_4	S_3	C_3	S_2	C_2	S_1	C_1	S_0
1	1	0	1	0	0	1	0	1	0	1	0	1	0	1	0	1
2	1	0	1	0	1	0	1	0	1	0	0	1	1	0	0	0
3	0	0	1	1	0	0	1	1	0	0	0	1	1	1	1	0
4	0	0	1	1	0	1	1	1	0	1	1	0	1	1	1	0
5	0	1	1	0	0	1	1	1	0	1	1	1	1	0	0	1
6	1	0	1	1	1	0	0	1	1	0	0	1	0	0	1	0
7	1	0	0	0	1	0	0	0	1	0	0	0	0	0	0	0
8	1	1	1	1	1	1	1	1	1	1	1	1	1	1	1	0

Fig. 9-19.

9-12 Multiplexers

Logic symbols and diagrams of two common types of IC multiplexers are shown in Fig. 9-20. As shown in Fig. 9-20(A), the 4-input multiplexer has four data inputs D_0 through D_3. The logic signal on any *one* of these data inputs can be made to flow, internally through the IC, directly to the output Y. Thus, four separate signals can be on inputs D_0 through D_3 but only one of them can be passed on to output Y, provided that the $\overline{\text{STROBE}}$ input is ACTIVE LOW. When the $\overline{\text{STROBE}}$ input is HIGH, the IC is disabled and the output Y remains LOW regardless the other inputs. A 2-bit binary address on inputs A_1 and A_0 determines which of the four data inputs is passed on to output Y through the IC, A_0 being the LSB of each 2-bit address. For example, when inputs A_1 and A_0 are 0 and 0 (equivalent to decimal 0), the data or signal on input D_0 is passed on to output Y. When A_1 and A_0 are 0 and 1, respectively (equivalent to decimal 1), the data on input D_1 appear at output Y. Similarly, with an input address of 10 (equivalent to decimal 2) on A_1 and A_0, the data on input D_2 can be observed at output Y. Obviously, then, the decimal equivalent of each 2-bit address indicates the number of the observed (addressed) data input.

The 8-input multiplexer, shown in Fig. 9-20(B), works much as does the 4-input type. In this case, *one* of *eight* data inputs D_0 through D_7 is *addressed* by a 3-bit binary word on inputs A_3 through A_0, provided that the $\overline{\text{STROBE}}$ input is ACTIVE LOW. As before, the decimal equivalent of the input address indicates the number of the data input that becomes internally connected to the Y output. For example, input address 011 or 101, on inputs A_3 through A_0, causes data on D_3 or D_5 to flow through the IC to its output Y.

Fig. 9-20.

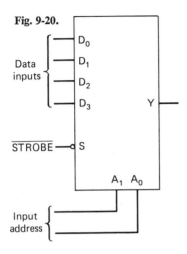

(A) Logic symbol for half of
a 74153 4-input multiplexer

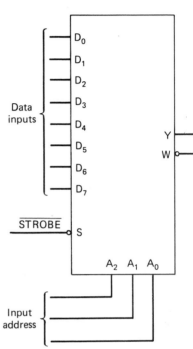

(B) Logic symbol for the 74151
8-input multiplexer

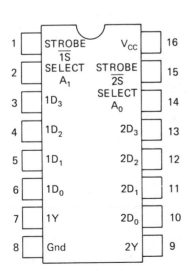

(C) Connection diagram DIP
(top view) of 74153 IC

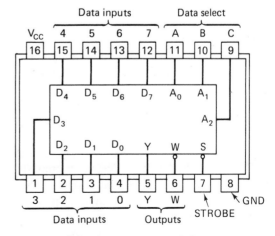

(D) Connection diagram DIP
(top view) of 74151 IC

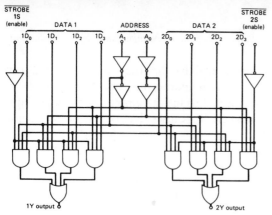

(E) Logic diagram of the 74153

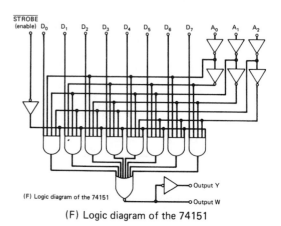

(F) Logic diagram of the 74151

Fig. 9-20. (Cont.)

(F) Logic diagram of the 74151

9-13 Multiplexers for Combinational Logic

Some digital circuits or systems are *synchronous*. For the present, we can assume that a system, or circuit, is synchronous if it has repetitive or regularly recurring signals. Multiplexers can also be used in synchronous or *asynchronous* (nonsynchronous) systems. The rat-conditioning logic circuits of the preceding chapter are asynchronous circuits. This rat-conditioning logic can be performed with 4-input multiplexers, as shown in Fig. 9-21.

As in the circuits of Figs. 8-10 through 8-14, the signal A, B, or C is HIGH if rat Alfred, Brenda, or Charlie pushes his(her) individual feed button. In this case, the $\overline{F.L.}$ signal is applied to the $\overline{S}$ inputs and is pulled ACTIVE LOW for a few seconds each hour. This enables the multiplexers to respond to signals on their data and address inputs. When $\overline{F.L.}$ is HIGH, the multiplexers are disabled, and all Y outputs remain LOW (inactive).

The multiplexer in Fig. 9-21(A) has an ACTIVE HIGH F_A (feed Alfred) signal if Alfred only pushes his button. That is, if Brenda and Charlie do not push their buttons, the B and C signals are both 0's. This addresses the multiplexer in Fig. 9-21(A) to its D_0 input, which allows Alfred's signal A to become the F_A output signal. Note that unused inputs are *hardwired* to ground (0 or LOW logic levels) so that the F_A output is LOW (inactive) with all other combinations of inputs B and C.

172

The F_B signal out of the multiplexer in Fig. 9-21(B) is ACTIVE HIGH if Brenda only pushes her feed button. In this case, the $B = 1$ and $C = 0$ signals address the multiplexer to its D_2 input. Thus the $\bar{A}$ input signal becomes the F_B output signal. Of course, if $A = 0$, then $\bar{A} = 1$, and the F_B output goes ACTIVE HIGH.

The multiplexer in Fig. 9-21(C) has an F_C output that goes ACTIVE HIGH when $A = 0$, $B = 0$, and $C = 1$, that is, when Charlie only is requesting food. These B and C inputs address the multiplexer D_1 input. The $\bar{A}$ signal thus becomes the F_C output.

As in the previous rat-conditioning logic circuits, the BUSY signal in Fig. 9-21 is ACTIVE HIGH if one and only one rat is requesting food at any instant in the feed-time period. Thus the BUSY signal must be ACTIVE HIGH if inputs A, B, and C are

Fig. 9-21. Four-input multiplexers used to perform combinational logic.

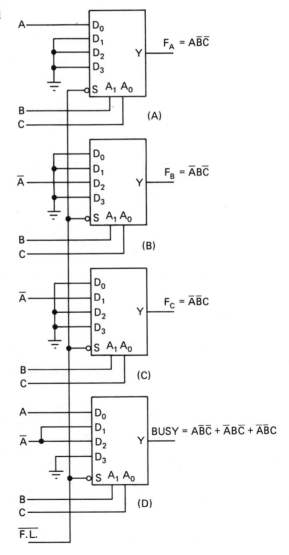

1, 0, and 0, or if they are 0, 1, and 0, or if they are 0, 0, and 1. In the first case, when B and C are both 0's, the multiplexer in Fig. 9-22(D) is addressed to its D_0 input, and therefore the A signal applied to this input appears at the output. Thus if $A = 1$, BUSY $= 1$. In the case when B and C are 0 and 1, respectively, this multiplexer's D_1 input is addressed, allowing the applied $\bar{A}$ signal to become the output. Thus if $A = 0$, causing $\bar{A} = 1$, the output BUSY $= 1$. Finally, when B and C are 1 and 0, the D_2 input is addressed, and again the $\bar{A}$ signal becomes the BUSY output. Of course, then, BUSY $= 1$ when $A = 0$. Obviously, the unused data inputs of each multiplexer must be wired to ground in this system.

Problem 9-7

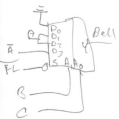

1. The system of Fig. 9-21 is not the complete rat-conditioning logic circuit discussed in the previous chapter. Methods of obtaining the BELL and BUZZER signals are not shown. Indicate how two more 4-input multiplexers can be wired to give us the appropriate BELL and BUZZER signals. Place the B and C signals on the address inputs A_1 and A_0, respectively. Also show the $\overline{\text{F.L.}}$ signal *strobing* the multiplexers. Indicate exactly how A or $\bar{A}$ is wired into appropriate data inputs. Show how unused inputs are handled.

9-14 Dot-AND/OR Connections

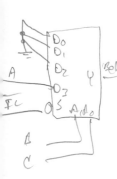

In a previous chapter we learned that some ICs are built with open collector outputs that can be used with pull-up resistors and that such outputs are able to give higher HIGH outputs than can be obtained from devices with totem-pole outputs. In this section, we shall see how the outputs of open collector ICs can be directly wired together to reduce the number of gates required to perform some types of logic functions. Direct wiring of open-collector outputs is called a dot-AND/OR connection. As shown in Fig. 9-22, each dot-AND/OR connection requires a pull-up resistor.

In Fig. 9-22(A) we should note that the output transistors, of the two open collector gates, are in parallel. Therefore, if either or both of these transistors turns on, the output $\bar{Y}$ goes LOW. Of course, then, the output $\bar{Y}$ goes HIGH only if both transistors are off. Likewise in Fig. 9-22(B), $\bar{Y}$ is HIGH only if both gates driving this output are HIGH.

The circuits in Figs. 9-22(C) and (D) show two ways that a pair of 7412 NAND gates, in dot-AND/OR connection, can be drawn. The circuit in Fig. 9-22(C) could be used to emphasize that the output signal LET is ACTIVE HIGH. That is, the direct connection, at the LET output, ANDS HIGH outputs of the two gates driving it. Thus, LET is ACTIVE HIGH only if the outputs of gates 1 and 2 are both HIGH. Since each gate's output is HIGH if either or both of its inputs are LOW, the Boolean expression for this circuit's output can be shown as LET $= (\bar{A} + \bar{B})(\bar{C} + \bar{D})$. The circuit in Fig. 9-22(D) better emphasizes an ACTIVE LOW output $\overline{\text{LET}}$. In this case, a LOW out-

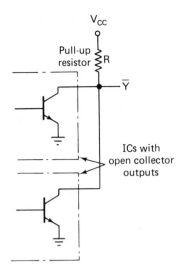

(A) Open collector outputs can be
directly connected to a single
pull-up resistor

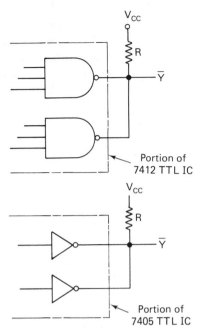

(B) Examples of open collector
ICs shown with outputs in
dot-AND/OR connection

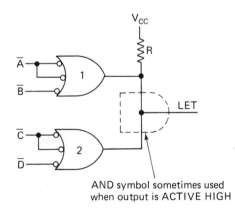

AND symbol sometimes used
when output is ACTIVE HIGH

(C) NAND gates of the 7412 used to
perform the logic function
LET = $(\overline{A} + \overline{B})(\overline{C} + \overline{D})$

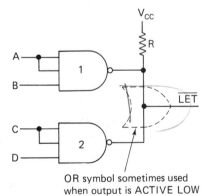

OR symbol sometimes used
when output is ACTIVE LOW

(D) NAND gates of the 7412 used to
perform $\overline{LET} = \overline{AB} + \overline{CD}$

Fig. 9-22.

$\overline{AB} + \overline{CD}$

put from either gate will pull the output $\overline{\text{LET}}$ ACTIVE LOW. Since both inputs on either gate must be HIGH before its output goes LOW, the Boolean expression for this circuit's function can be shown as $\overline{\text{LET}} = AB + CD$.

Some types of gates, in logic families other than TTL, have internal pull-up resistors. These can often be dot-AND/OR connected too but, do not require external pull-ups (Fig. 9-23).

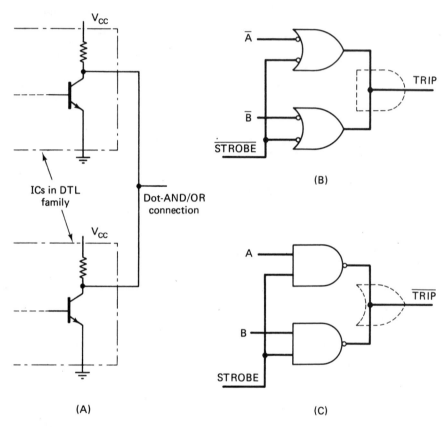

Fig. 9-23. (A) DTL IC's wired in dot-AND/OR connection; (B) Dot-AND/ORed DTL's ACTIVE HIGH output; (C) dot-AND/ORed DTL's with ACTIVE LOW output.

Summary

1. A 4-bit binary decoder has 16 separate outputs, one and only one of which can go ACTIVE LOW with each of the 16 possible combinations of 4-bit binary inputs.

2. A 4-bit binary decoder has two enabling inputs, both of which must be LOW to enable this IC to respond to 4-bit input words.

3. There are 16 combinations of 4-bit binary words, but there are only 9 combinations of 4-bit BCD words.

4. When converting decimal to BCD, each decimal digit is represented with a 4-bit binary word.

5. The BCD-to-7-segment decoder accepts 4-bit BCD input words. Its resulting outputs provide appropriate current paths to ground for the LEDs in the 7-segment display.

6. By grounding appropriate inputs on the 7-segment display, any decimal digit can be displayed.

7. An encoder is able to accept inputs representing individual decimal digits and encode (convert) them into equivalent BCD words.

8. The binary adder circuit, known also as the full adder, consists of combinational logic circuitry. Its function is to add 2 binary bits and a carry input and therefore to provide a sum and carry output.

9. Adder circuits are available in ICs, and therefore several can easily be wired to accept and add multibit binary words simultaneously.

10. ICs with open collector outputs can be wired in dot-AND/OR connections.

11. In a dot-AND/OR connection, the open collector outputs of individual gates are connected together and to a pull-up resistor.

12. Some types of ICs, with outputs other than totem-pole transistors, can also be dot-AND/ORed, but external pull-ups are not required.

Problems 9-8

1. Fill in the truth table for the circuit of Fig. 9-24(A). Write a Boolean expression for the output function *K*.

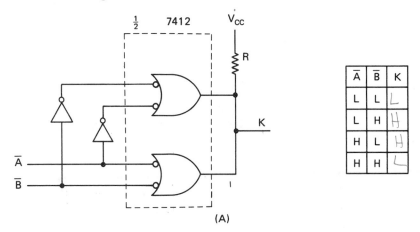

(A)

Fig. 9-24. NAND gates with dot-AND/OR connected outputs.

2. Fill in the truth table for the circuit of Fig. 9-24(B), and write a Boolean equation for its output $\bar{L}$.

3. What logic function, discussed previously, does the circuit of Fig. 9-24(A) perform? $K = (\bar{A} + B)(A + B)$

4. What logic function, discussed previously, does the circuit of Fig. 9-24(B) perform? EXCLUSIVE OR

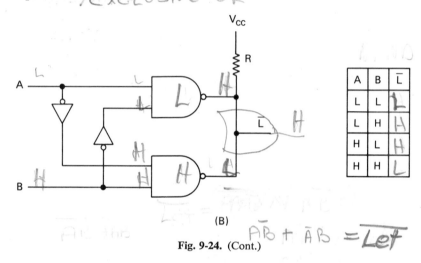

A	B	$\bar{L}$
L	L	L
L	H	H
H	L	H
H	H	L

(B)

$\bar{A}B + \bar{A}B = \bar{L}$ L or

Fig. 9-24. (Cont.)

5. The circuit of Fig. 9-25 has two output terminals, Y_L or Y_H and Z_L or Z_H. When the switch Sw is down in the L position, the two outputs are called Y_L and Z_L. On the other hand, when Sw is up on the H position, the outputs are called Y_H and Z_H. When Sw is down, indicate the resulting output logic levels of Y_L and Z_L on the table of this figure for each set of inputs shown.

6. Referring to Fig. 9-25 again, show the resulting outputs Y_H and Z_H when Sw is up in the H position. Work with one row of inputs at a time.

7. With reference to the circuit of Fig. 9-12, what character will be displayed if the following pushbuttons are depressed:
    (a) "0" and "5"?   9
    (b) "1" and "3"? None   — BlAwk DISPlAy
    (c) "7" and "9"? 7

8. With reference to the circuit of Fig. 9-12, what character will be displayed if the following pushbuttons are depressed at the same time:
    (a) "1" and "9"?   9
    (b) "7" and "8"? NOTHING
    (c) "2" and "5"? 7

9. The waveforms shown in Fig. 9-26 are applied to the inputs of the adder in Fig. 9-16. Sketch the resulting $1S$ and $1C_{n+1}$ outputs on the scales provided in this figure.

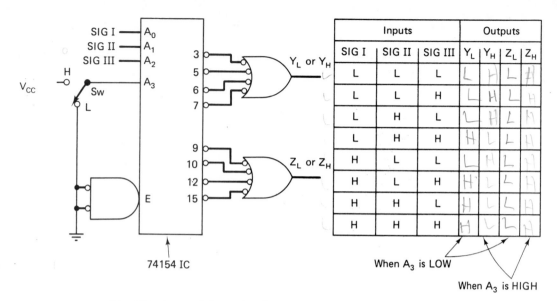

Inputs			Outputs			
SIG I	SIG II	SIG III	Y_L	Y_H	Z_L	Z_H
L	L	L	L	H	L	H
L	L	H	L	H	L	H
L	H	L	L	H	L	H
L	H	H	H	L	L	H
H	L	L	L	H	L	H
H	L	H	H	L	L	H
H	H	L	H	L	L	H
H	H	H	H	L	L	H

V_{CC}

SIG I — A_0
SIG II — A_1
SIG III — A_2

A_3

Sw

E

74154 IC

Y_L or Y_H

Z_L or Z_H

When A_3 is LOW

When A_3 is HIGH

Fig. 9-25. A one-of-sixteen decoder used to perform combinational logic.

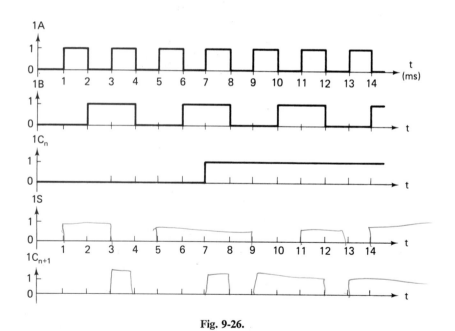

1A

1B

$1C_n$

1S

$1C_{n+1}$

t (ms)

Fig. 9-26.

179

10. The table in Fig. 9-27 lists all possible combinations of inputs to the 74153 multiplexer shown. Indicate the resulting Y output with each set of inputs.

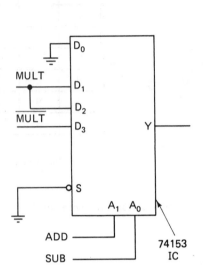

Inputs				Outputs
MULT	$\overline{\text{MULT}}$	SUB	ADD	Y
0	1	0	0	
0	1	0	1	
0	1	1	0	
0	1	1	1	1
1	0	0	0	
1	0	0	1	1
1	0	1	0	
1	0	1	1	

Fig. 9-27.

Experiment 9-1 LED Readout

Purpose

To become familiar with the MAN-1 7-segment readout device and the 7447 decoder driver.

Equipment

        Digital breadboard kit
        MAN-1 (or equivalent 7-segment readout)
        7447
        220-Ω, $\frac{1}{4}$-W $\pm 5\%$ resistor   *234*
        120-Ω, $\frac{1}{4}$-W $\pm 5\%$ resistor   *12 1*

Procedure

To become familiar with how each segment lights, you will now determine which pins of the MAN-1 control each segment.

1. Insert the MAN-1 into the socket strip. Connect +5 V dc to the anode connections, pins 3, 9, and 14, through a single 220-Ω resistor, as shown in Fig. L 9-1(A). (No ground pin is used on this device.)

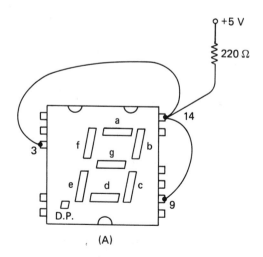

(A)

Fig. L 9-1.

181

2. Next, connect one end of a wire to ground and carefully touch each pin, one at a time, with the other end. You should see each segment lighting separately. Write in the segment letters corresponding to the pin numbers in the spaces below:

Pin

1 _A_

2 _f_

3 ANODE

4 NC

5 NC

6 _D.P._

7 _e_

Pin

8 _d_

9 ANODE

10 _c_

11 _G_

12 NC

13 _b_

14 ANODE

3. Wire the circuit of Fig. L 9-1(B). Connect the outputs of the 7447 to the appropriate input pins of the 7-segment readout. Starting with all input switches in the 0 (LOW) position, flip the switches as required and fill in the table below:

Switch Positions DCBA		Numeral Lit
0000		0
0001		1
0010		2
0011		3
0100		4
0101		5
0110		6
0111		7
1000		8
1001		9
1010		⊏
1011		⊐
1100		U
1101	⊏	
1110	⌊	
1111	Nothing	

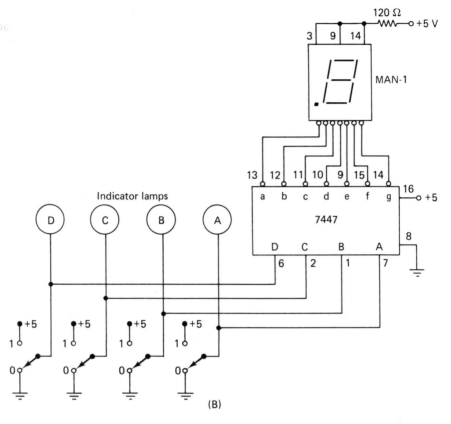

Fig. L 9-1. (Cont.)

Quiz for Experiment 9-1

1. The 7-segment readout consists of many LEDs which must be (forward, back) biased to light up.

2. Each segment is lit by driving its appropriate pin (LOW, HIGH).

3. List the pins that must be LOW to produce the numeral 4. _____ F GBC = 15,14, 11,12

4. List the pins that must be LOW to produce the numeral 6. F,G,ED C 15,14,9, 10,11

5. Explain why the 7447 is called a BCD-to-7-segment decoder rather than a binary-to-7-segment decoder.
    Because # 0-9 1001
    0000 are decoded to the
    7 segment which
    can display only
    9 # 5

183

Experiment 9-2 Decimal-to-BCD Encoder

Purpose

We shall now design a system for *encoding* decimal numbers into a BCD code. Such an encoder is used on keyboards of pocket calculators. When you press a decimal key, say the number 5, the encoder changes the decimal 5 into its BCD equivalent 0101 and then feeds these binary data into the actual calculator chip.

Materials

> Digital breadboard kit
> (Twelve) (about) diodes
> 100-Ω, $\frac{1}{4}$-W $\pm 10\%$ resistor

Procedure

Refer to Fig. L 9-2. Notice the terminal strip with nine insulated terminals. The terminals on the digital breadboard kit can be used. Terminals 1, 2, 4, and 8 are directly wired to indicator lamps *A*, *B*, *C*, and *D*, respectively. This is slightly different from the circuit of Fig. 9-12. The terminals represent switches on a calculator keyboard. Touching the clip lead to terminal 2, for example, is equivalent to depressing key 2. Since the clip lead is connected to the $+V_{CC}$ supply through a small resistance, indicator lamp *B* will light. The other lamps will remain out. The

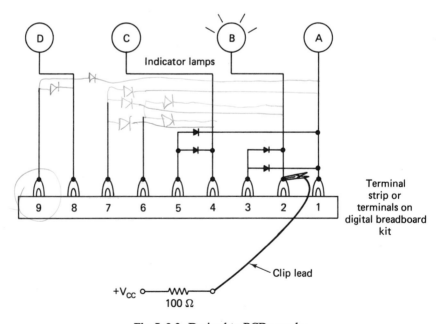

Fig. L 9-2. Decimal to BCD encoder.

lamps, then, represent the BCD code equivalent of the decimal 2, namely 0010—and similarly for the numbers 1, 4, and 8.

But when you depress the digit key 3, the BCD equivalent is 0011; that is, lamps *A* and *B* should *both* light. They cannot be shorted together with a wire; otherwise both lamps would light every time you pressed key 1 or key 2.

The problem is solved by connecting diodes from terminal 3 to each of the two lamps. This way, when key 3 is pressed, both lamps *A and B* will light. But if either key 1 or key 2 alone is pressed, one of the diodes will be back biased and isolate the other lamp.

Similarly, terminal 5, representing key 5, has diodes to lamps *A* and *C* so that the code 0101 will be present when terminal 5 is made high.

Your job in this experiment is to design the remainder of the encoder. That is, you decide where the diodes should be connected for lines 6, 7, and 9. Then draw them on Fig. L 9-2. Finally, build the circuit to prove your design.

Experiment 9-3 Binary Addition

Purpose

To check out the 74183 dual full adder chip.

Equipment

Digital breadboard kit
74183

Procedure

1. Build the circuit of Fig. L 9-3(A).

2. Use toggle switches connected to inputs 1A, 1B, and 1C_n to provide the appropriate inputs, and fill in the table below:

Inputs C_n B A	Outputs S	C_{n+1}
0 0 0	0	0
0 0 1	1	0
0 1 0	1	0
0 1 1	0	1
1 0 0	1	0
1 0 1	0	1
1 1 0	0	1
1 1 1	1	1

3. Compare your table with that of Fig. 9-16(D). If it is identical, go on to the next step; otherwise, recheck your wiring and try again.

4. Next, build the circuit of Fig. L 9-3(B). Notice that the CARRY output of the first adder is connected to the CARRY input of the second adder. This circuit is the same as the two least significant adders of Fig. 9-17 in the text.

5. Using toggle switches, apply inputs for all combinations shown in Fig. L 9-3 (C). Fill in the blanks with 1's or 0's corresponding to the state of the indicator lamps S_2, S_1, S_0.

186

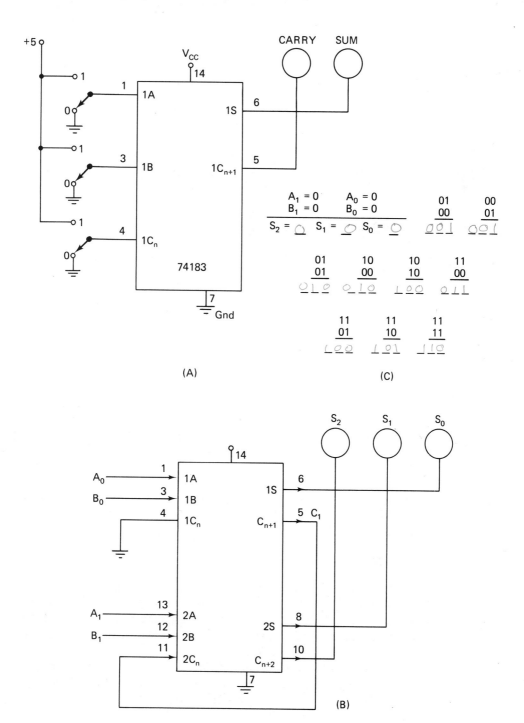

(A)

$A_1 = 0$ $A_0 = 0$
$B_1 = 0$ $B_0 = 0$
$S_2 =$ $S_1 =$ $S_0 =$

01	00
00	01

001 001

01	10	10	11
01	00	10	00

010 010 100 011

11	11	11
01	10	11

100 101 110

(C)

(B)

Fig. L 9-3.

10

Square-Wave Generators
for Digital Circuits

Introduction

Much as the heart pulses life into a living animal, square-wave generators serve to pump life and action into some types of digital systems. A *synchronous* type of digital system uses one or more square-wave generators. Such generators are commonly called *oscillators* or *clocks*, and their square-wave outputs are called oscillations or clock pulses. Therefore, the term clock or *digital clock*, as used in computer terminology, is not likely a device that tells time. The variety of circuits that provide square-wave outputs is numerous. A few of the more popular types are discussed in this chapter.

10-1   The Astable Multivibrator

The astable multivibrator, shown in Fig. 10-1, is a common and reliable circuit that generates square waves. A square wave is available off either collector with respect to ground. This circuit's transistors alternately turn on and off and thus produce the square voltage waveforms. That is, when transistor Q_1 is turned on, Q_2 is off, and when Q_1 is off, Q_2 is on.*

The frequency of an astable multivibrator's output is determined by the values of its base resistors R_{B_1} and R_{B_2} and the capacitors C_1 and C_2. If $R_{B_1} = R_{B_2}$ and $C_1 = C_2$, then the output waveforms are symmetrical, as shown in Fig. 10-2(A), and the time period of each cycle is

$$T \cong 1.4R_{B_1}C_1 \quad \text{or} \quad T \cong 1.4R_{B_2}C_2 \qquad (10\text{-}1)$$

*When the astable multivibrator's transistors are switching on and off, the circuit is said to be *oscillating*.

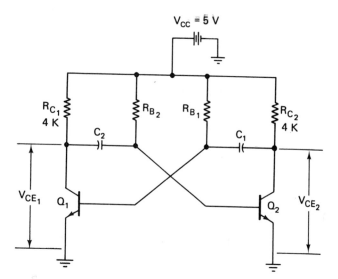

Fig. 10-1. The astable multivibrator works as a square wave generator.

Therefore, the frequency of the outputs is

$$f \cong \frac{1}{T} \quad \text{or} \quad f \cong \frac{1}{1.4 R_{B_1} C_1} \quad \text{or} \quad f \cong \frac{1}{1.4 R_{B_2} C_2} \tag{10-2}$$

The significance of these equations is that the output frequency decreases with larger values of base resistances or capacitances.

The collector resistors R_{C_1} and R_{C_2} do not affect the output frequency of the astable multivibrator, and their values are not critical. Generally, smaller values of R_{C_1} and R_{C_2} cause their respective transistors to switch faster, which often is desirable. On the other hand, larger collector resistors drain less current from the V_{CC} supply, also a desirable feature. Circuit designers then *trade off* one desirable feature, more or less, for the other depending on which is more important for the application. The astable multivibrator will not work reliably if its base resistors are much larger than the collector resistors. Typically, R_{B_1} is selected to be in the range of about 20 to 50 times larger than R_{C_1}. Of course, then, R_{B_2} is about 20 to 50 times larger than R_{C_2}.

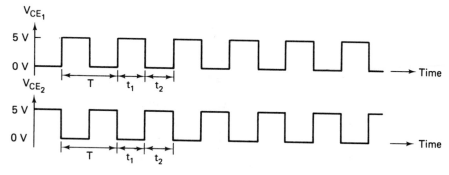

(A) Waveforms when $R_{B_1} = R_{B_2}$ and $C_1 = C_2$; that is, when the product $R_{B_1}C_1$ is equal to the product $R_{B_2}C_2$

Fig. 10-2. Typical waveforms from the astable multivibrator.

If the product $R_{B_1}C_1$ is *unequal* to the product $R_{B_2}C_2$, the square-wave output of the astable circuit is *asymmetrical* (not symmetrical). Asymmetrical waveforms are shown in Fig. 10-2(B). These waveforms appear as outputs if R_{B_1} is half the value of R_{B_2} while C_1 and C_2 are equal or if R_{B_1} and R_{B_2} are equal while C_1 is half the capacitance of C_2.

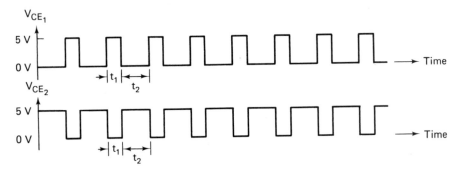

(B) Waveforms when $2R_{B_1}C_1 = R_{B_2}C_2$

Fig. 10-2. (Cont.)

10-2 The Schmitt NAND Gate

The astable multivibrator is not the only circuit used to generate square waves. An IC device, called the Schmitt NAND, also serves to generate square waves when used with a couple of externally wired components. Logic symbols for the Schmitt NAND gate are shown in Fig. 10-3(A). Each Schmitt NAND works somewhat like an

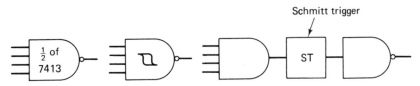

(A) Logic symbols used to represent the Schmitt NAND gate

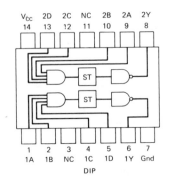

(B) Dual Schmitt NAND (7413) package

Fig. 10-3.

ordinary NAND gate in that its output goes LOW only when all its inputs are HIGH. The Schmitt NAND differs in that it has relatively precise input *threshold* voltages at which its output switches. For example, the Schmitt NANDs in Fig. 10-4 are wired to work much like inverters. That is, if the input voltage V_{in} goes HIGH, the output voltage V_o goes LOW. Of course, then, a LOW V_{in} causes a HIGH V_o. The Schmitt NAND, however, typically recognizes an input V_{in} as HIGH if its value is 1.7 V or higher. On the other hand, V_{in} is typically recognized as a LOW input if its value drops to 0.9 V or less. Therefore, typically the upper threshold is 1.7 V, and the lower threshold is 0.9 V. A significant and notable feature of a Schmitt NAND is that the difference in the HIGH and LOW input thresholds is quite precisely 0.8 V. Thus if a certain Schmitt NAND has an upper threshold of 1.9 V (higher than typical), we can depend on its lower threshold being 1.1 V. Similarly, if the upper

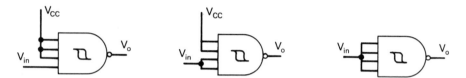

Fig. 10-4. Schmitt NANDs wired to work with one input.

threshold is 1.5 V, we can expect 0.7 V as the lower threshold. Figure 10-5 shows how a typical Schmitt NAND responds to varying V_{in} signals. This kind of output switching caused by upper and lower input thresholds is called *hysteresis*. A typical output vs. input characteristic of a Schmitt NAND gate is shown in Fig. 10-6. Such a V_o vs. V_{in} characteristic curve is commonly called a *transfer function*. It can also be referred to as a hysteresis curve.

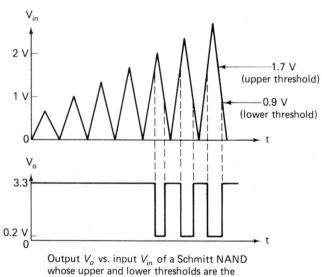

Output V_o vs. input V_{in} of a Schmitt NAND whose upper and lower thresholds are the typical 1.7 and 0.9 V, respectively

Fig. 10-5. Voltage waveforms of Schmitt NANDs wired as in Fig. 10-4.

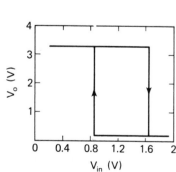

Fig. 10-6. Typical output verses input characteristic (hysteresis) curve; called a transfer function.

The Schmitt NAND will work as a square-wave generator when wired as shown in Fig. 10-7(A). Its V_{in} and V_o waveforms are shown in Fig. 10-7(B). Initially, when the supply voltage is applied, the voltage across the capacitor C, which is the V_{in} voltage, is 0 V. This LOW V_{in} drives the output V_o HIGH, which is typically to about 3.3 V* when a 5-V V_{CC} supply is used. This HIGH 3.3 V output causes the capacitor C to begin charging through the 330-Ω resistor R. Therefore, V_{in} proceeds to rise until it reaches the upper threshold voltage V_{th}. At V_{th}, the Schmitt NAND switches; that is, its output quickly goes LOW to about 0.2 V. The capacitor C now proceeds to discharge causing V_{in} to decay. When V_{in} decays to the lower threshold voltage V_{th}', the Schmitt NAND's output quickly switches back to a HIGH state, which starts another cycle. The time of each cycle depends on the value of C. The time constant

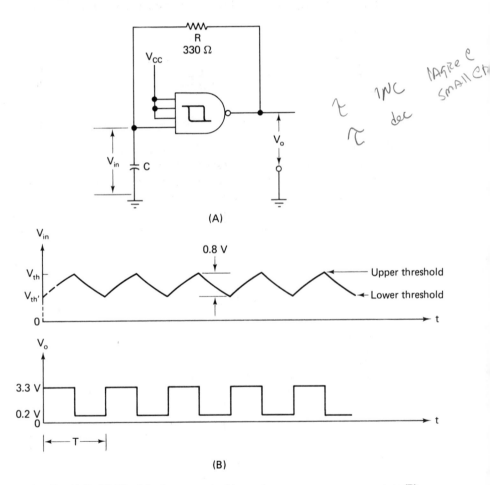

(A)

(B)

Fig. 10-7. (A) The Schmitt NAND wired to work as a square wave generator; (B) waveforms associated with the Schmitt NAND square wave generator.

*The 7413 is a TTL device with totem-pole outputs; therefore, its output HIGHS are noticeably less than the V_{CC} supply.

is increased or decreased with larger or smaller capacitance C, respectively. Consequently, T can be varied from 0.1 μs to 10 s, which means that this circuit's output frequency f can be varied from 10 MHz to 0.1 Hz by selecting smaller or larger values of C.

10-3 CMOS Gates in Square-Wave Generators

Two CMOS gates, such as the two-input NORs of the 4001 IC, can be wired as in Fig. 10-8(A) to work as a square-wave generator. Its waveforms are shown in Fig. 10-8(B). While this circuit is generating square waves, its capacitor C_T is continually charging and discharging through R_T. As with the previously discussed astable circuits, this circuit's output frequency is determined by its time constant. Therefore, its output frequency can be increased by decreasing either R_T or C_T.

This CMOS circuit's action can be described as follows: At the *instant* V_o out of gate 2 goes HIGH, essentially the same positive voltage appears at the left-hand side of C_T, which is shown as the feedback voltage V_f in Fig. 10-8. This HIGH V_f voltage is applied to the input of gate 1, causing its output, which is V_{in} to gate 2, to go LOW. This LOW V_{in} voltage holds gate 2's output V_o HIGH. With time, C_T becomes charged, causing V_f to decay; see the V_f waveform in Fig. 10-8(B). The

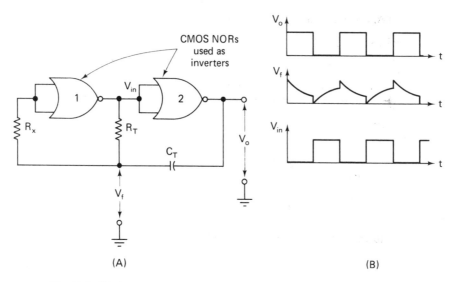

Fig. 10-8. (A) A CMOS square wave generator, and (B) its voltage waveforms.

charge path is shown in Fig. 10-9(A). Eventually, V_f decays to a voltage that is interpreted as a LOW input by gate 1, and its output promptly switches to a HIGH level. This HIGH V_{in} to gate 2 drives its output V_o to a LOW level. After this instant, C_T proceeds to discharge and recharge in the opposite polarity; note the current path in Fig. 10-9(B). Consequently, the voltage V_f rises positively as shown on waveform V_f in Fig. 10-9(B). Thus, in time, V_f rises to a value that is interpreted as a HIGH input by gate 1. Its output then quickly switches back LOW. This LOW V_{in} to gate 2 drives its output V_o HIGH again to start another cycle.

Modern CMOS ICs are made with diodes in parallel with their inputs. These diodes go into conduction and thus serve to protect the CMOS's input FETs if excessive positive or negative input voltages are applied. The resistor R_x in the circuit of Fig. 10-8 limits the current through such diodes.

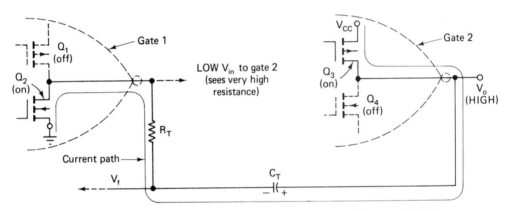

(A) Capacitor's current path when gate 1's output is LOW and gate 2's output is HIGH

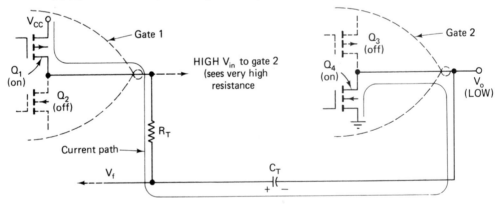

(B) Capacitor's current path when gate 1's output is HIGH and gate 2's output is LOW

Fig. 10-9.

Frequently, a digital clock must run or stop when commanded to do so. In such cases, the CMOS generator can be modified as shown in Fig. 10-10. When the controlling input signal $\overline{RUN}$ goes ACTIVE LOW, this clock proceeds to generate square waves. When $\overline{RUN}$ is HIGH, NOR gate 1 is disabled and the clock stops.

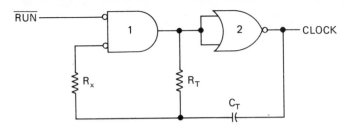

Fig. 10-10. Gated CMOS square wave generator.

10-4 Signal-Squaring Circuits

Often sine-wave voltage sources are readily available where square waves for digital circuits are needed. Here we shall see how, with just a few components, a sine-wave voltage can be converted into a square wave.

The transistor circuit (RTL inverter) in Fig. 10-11(A) works as a sine-to-square-wave converter when larger values of sine-wave input voltages are applied. Sine waves, or other input signal waveforms, of about 0.2 V peak to peak or greater cause the transistor to alternately swing between *saturation* and *cutoff*. Larger varying input signals yield squarer output waveforms. When used in this way, this transistor circuit is called an overdriven amplifier.

We learned previously (Section 2-5) that the circuit of Fig. 10-11 is an inverter. We can reason, therefore, that any logic inverter can be used as a signal-squaring device. Figure 10-12 shows a circuit used for this purpose.

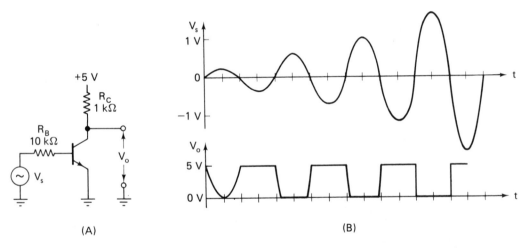

Fig. 10-11. (A) Simple RTL inverter; (B) output V_o versus input V_s waveforms of the RTL inverter.

Fig. 10-12. One-sixth of TTL inverter serves as a signal squaring circuit.

The circuit of Fig. 10-13 can also convert sine waves to square waves. The additional TTL inverter and feedback resistor R_F makes this circuit work like a Schmitt trigger. That is, compared to the circuit of Fig. 10-12, the circuit of Fig. 10-13 has more precise threshold voltages, which are the input voltages that are recognized as HIGHs or LOWs; see the typical output vs. input waveforms in Fig. 10-13(B). This circuit also has faster (shorter) output rise and fall times; that is, this Schmitt trigger's output can change from HIGH to LOW or from LOW to HIGH very quickly. Short rise and fall times are often necessary or desirable in digital systems.

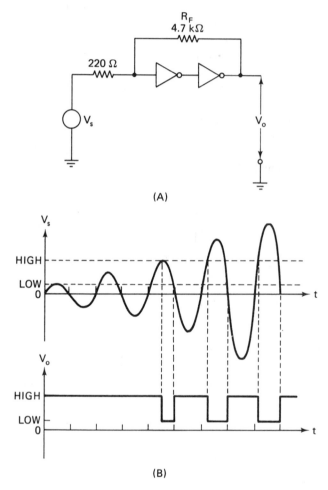

Fig. 10-13. (A) Two TTL inverters wired to work as a signal squaring circuit with much more precise threshold voltages, and (B) typical output V_o versus input V_s waveforms.

10-5 Square Waves from an IC Timer

An integrated circuit, called the 555 timer, is a very flexible device that is used to perform a variety of logic circuit functions. This timer is available in eight-pin packages, shown in Fig. 10-14, and at a relatively low cost, considering the complexity of its inner circuitry. With a few externally wired components, as shown in Fig. 10-15, the 555 IC works as a variable frequency square-wave generator.

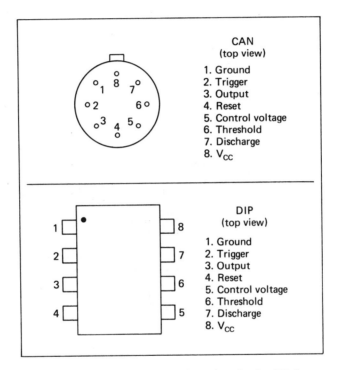

CAN
(top view)

1. Ground
2. Trigger
3. Output
4. Reset
5. Control voltage
6. Threshold
7. Discharge
8. V_{CC}

DIP
(top view)

1. Ground
2. Trigger
3. Output
4. Reset
5. Control voltage
6. Threshold
7. Discharge
8. V_{CC}

Fig. 10-14. Packages and pin configurations for the 555 timer.

Although the details of the 555's inner circuitry is not shown in Fig. 10-15, a block diagram of its relevant circuitry is. When the 5-V supply voltage is applied, the capacitor C proceeds to charge through R_A and R_B (dotted-line path). Initially, while this capacitor's voltage is small, the output of the level-sensing circuit is LOW. This LOW cuts off the transistor and, via the inverting buffer, causes a HIGH output V_o at pin 3. As the capacitor C charges and reaches $\frac{2}{3}$ of the V_{CC} voltage, 3.3 V in this case, the level-sensing circuit's output goes HIGH. This turns the transistor Q

on, which provides a discharge path to ground for C through R_B (dashed-line path). When C discharges to $\frac{1}{3}$ of the V_{CC} voltage, 1.67 V in this case, the level-sensing circuit's output goes LOW again, which starts another cycle. See the capacitor's voltage V_c and output voltage V_o waveforms in Fig. 10-15(B). Since R_B is variable, the resistance of the charge and discharge paths can be varied. Therefore, the output frequency of this circuit can be selected by adjustments of R_B.

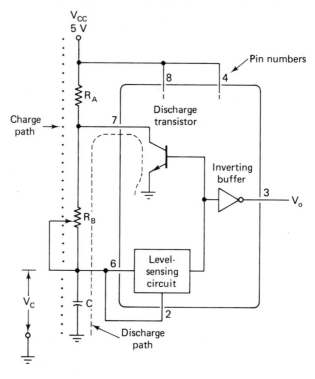

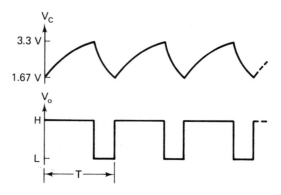

Fig. 10-15. (A) The 555 timer wired to work as a variable square wave generator, and (B) its capacitor and output voltage waveforms.

Summary

1. A clock in a digital system is a square-wave generator.

2. Clocks are used in synchronous digital systems.

3. The square waves from a clock are called clock pulses.

4. An astable *multivibrator* is commonly used as a clock.

5. An astable multivibrator can be constructed with two transistors, a couple of capacitors, and a few resistors.

6. An IC called the 7413 Schmitt NAND can be wired with external components to also work as an astable circuit (square-wave generator).

7. Two CMOS gates will work as a square-wave generator when wired with appropriate external components.

8. An overdriven amplifier can be used to convert sine waves, or other slowly changing waves, to square waves.

9. A sine wave, or other slowly changing waveform, of sufficient amplitude applied to the input of an IC inverter produces a square wave at the inverter's output.

10. The popular and flexible 555 timer can be used as an adjustable square-wave generator.

Problems 10-1

1. With reference to the Schmitt NAND of Fig. 10-4, what kind of output waveform V_o can we expect if we apply a sinewave V_{in} of 3 V rms? $V_o = 3 V$ rms INVERTED SINE-WAVE

2. If in the circuit of Fig. 10-1, $R_{B_1} = R_{B_2} = 100$ kΩ and $C_1 = C_2 = 1$ uF, what output frequency can we expect? $f = \dfrac{1}{1.4\,(100K)(1u)}$

3. With reference to the previous problem, if we exchange R_{B_1} with 200 kΩ but do not change the other components, what will happen to the output frequency and waveform as viewed at the collector of Q_1?   SQUARE WAVE WILL BE ASYMMETRICAL   *less current drain*

4. How does the 7413 Schmitt NAND differ from an ordinary NAND gate?   A SCHMITT NAND HAS PRECISE INPUT THRESHOLD VOLTAGES

5. If three inputs of the Schmitt NAND are tied to ground and V_{in}, shown in Fig. 10-5, is applied to the fourth input, what kind of output waveform V_o can we expect?   called hysteresis   pg 191

6. What purpose would a trimmer (variable) capacitor serve in place of the fixed C in the circuit of Fig. 10-7?   Could inc. or dec. time constant

7. What change(s) can be made on the circuit of Fig. 10-9 to increase its output frequency?   decrease R_T or C_T

8. With reference to the circuit of Fig. 10-15, if we must extend the time t_1 of each HIGH portion of the output V_o but not affect the time t_2 of the LOW portions, what change(s) can we make on this circuit?   Change C or/and R_B

9. Again with reference to the circuit of Fig. 10-15, what single change can we make to cause a lower output frequency but not affect the output waveform (ratio of t_1/t_2)?   ADJUST R_B

Experiment 10-1 Transistor Astable Multivibrator

Purpose

The transistor astable multivibrator has been used for years as a square-wave generator in many digital applications. It is still used not only in discrete component systems but also in conjunction with ICs, as, for example, in many pocket calculators. You will now learn how to design and modify this versatile circuit.

Materials

Digital breadboard kit
Oscilloscope
(Two) *NPN* transistors—any switching type
(Two) capacitors, 25 μF
(Three) capacitors, 0.025 μF
(Two) resistors, 2-K, $\frac{1}{4}$W $\pm 5\%$
(Two) resistors, 56-K, $\frac{1}{4}$W $\pm 5\%$
(One) resistor, 20-K, $\frac{1}{4}$W $\pm 5\%$

Procedure

1. Construct the circuit of Fig. L 10-1 and apply power. If the circuit is working properly, the lamps should be blinking on and off. Does each lamp stay lit for

approximately the same time? _____ What is the approximate period of

the oscillation? $T =$ _____.

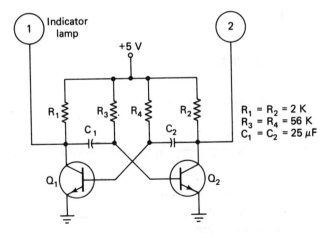

Fig. L 10-1. Astable multivibrator.

$R_1 = R_2 = 2$ K
$R_3 = R_4 = 56$ K
$C_1 = C_2 = 25\ \mu$F

2. With the circuit still oscillating, connect a 20-K resistor in parallel with R_3. Explain what you observe that is different from step 1. _____

_____

3. Now shut off the power and replace C_1 and C_2 with 0.025-μF capacitors. Leave R_3 and R_4 each 56 K. Observe the collector of Q_2 with a scope. (If your circuit is working properly, you should see a square wave.) Is the waveform reasonably symmetrical? _____ What is the approximate period of the square wave? _____ How does this compare with the period observed in step 1?

_____ What is the peak-to-peak value of the square wave? _____

4. Again with the oscillator running, connect a 20-K resistor in parallel with R_3. Explain what you see on the scope as compared to the waveform of step 3.

_____

_____

5. Next remove the 20 K from across R_3 and shunt R_4 with the 20 K. Explain what you see compared to the waveform of step 4. _____

_____

6. With R_3 and R_4 both 56 K again, bridge C_1 with another 0.025-μF capacitor. Explain what you observe at the collector of Q_2.

Quiz for Experiment 10-1

1. The transistors in the astable multivibrator are alternately being driven into cutoff and saturation. When a transistor is cut off, its collector current is (zero, maximum) and its collector voltage is (zero, V_{cc}).

2. In the circuit of Fig. L 10-1, lamp 2 is lit when Q_2 is (saturated, cut off).

3. Decreasing R_3 in step 2 (increased, decreased) the time that Q_2 was cut off, as seen by lamp 2 being on for a (shorter, longer) time than lamp 1.

4. Besides making the waveform nonsymmetrical, decreasing R_3 also (increased, decreased) the period of the square wave.

5. Observing the square wave in step 3, the maximum value of the waveform

    was _____ V, occurring when Q_2 was (cut off, saturated). The minimum value of voltage at the collector of Q_2 was _____ V, occurring when Q_2 was (cut off, saturated).

6. In step 6, bridging C_1 with another capacitor (increased, decreased) the period of oscillation by (increasing, decreasing) the length of time Q_2 was held cut off.

7. In general we can say about astable multivibrators that decreasing the value of the biasing resistors, R_3 and R_4, (speeds up, slows down) the oscillator, and increasing the value of these resistors (speeds up, slows down) the oscillator.

8. Increasing the value of the cross-coupling capacitors, C_1 and C_2, (speeds up, slows down) the oscillator and vice versa.

Experiment 10-2 Integrated Circuit Astable Multivibrator

Purpose

To study a commonly used IC square-wave generator.

Materials

Digital breadboard kit
Oscilloscope
7413 dual Schmitt NAND
1-K pot
330-Ω $\frac{1}{4}$W $\pm 5\%$ resistor
1-μF capacitor

Procedure

1. Construct the circuit of Fig. L 10-2(A). Start with the pot slider at ground ($V_{in} = 0$). What is the state at the output (HIGH, LOW)?

2. Now very slowly increase the setting of the pot while measuring V_{in} with a voltmeter. At what value of V_{in} does the output logic level switch? $V_{in} = $ __1.7 V__.

3. Continue increasing V_{in} all the way up to V_{CC}. Does any further change take place in the output?   __NO__

4. Now gradually decrease the setting of the slider back toward ground. At what value of V_{in} does the output logic level change?   __1.0 V goes High__
[Repeat the above steps; that is, move the slider up and down a few times to see that the values of switching (threshold) voltages remain the same.]

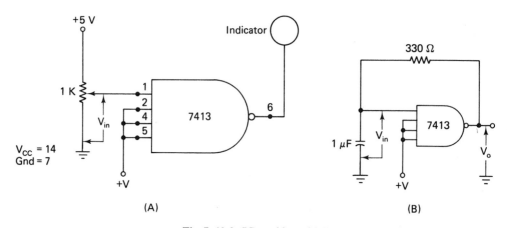

(A)   (B)

Fig. L 10-2. IC astable multivibrator.

5. Next, assemble the circuit of Fig. L 10-2(B). Apply power and observe V_{in} and V_0 with a scope. Describe what you see. _____

_____

V_{IN} ⟍⟋⟍⟋⟍ 1.4v

15.5

1 2 sec/div

V_0 _____

Quiz for Experiment 10-2

1. Since the 7413 is a NAND gate, all inputs must be (HIGH, LOW) for the output to be LOW.

2. As the pot slider was moved upward from ground, the voltage at pin _____ became sufficiently positive to act as a (HIGH, LOW) input.

3. Then as the slider was made more positive, the output (remained LOW, became gradually higher).

4. Finally, when the slider was returned to ground, the output switched back to HIGH when the input (was HIGH, was zero, became LOW enough).

5. In the circuit of Fig. L 10-2(B), assume V_{in} was 0 when power was first applied. How did V_{in} get HIGH enough to cause the output to switch LOW?
   The 1μF cap charged through the 330Ω Resis

6. Once the output switched LOW, (capacitor C began to charge more positive, capacitor C began to discharge through R).

7. Then, eventually, the output switched HIGH again when (the voltage across C dropped LOW enough, the voltage across C got HIGH enough).

8. To increase the frequency at which the output switched HIGH and LOW, you could (increase R, decrease R, increase C, decrease C).

Experiment 10-3 Astable Multivibrator Using CMOS

Purpose

CMOS multivibrators are very efficient oscillators with excellent temperature stability. In this experiment, you will become familiar with one of the most popular types using a common quad two-input NOR gate.

Materials

Digital breadboard kit
Oscilloscope
CD 4001A quad two-input NOR
3-MΩ, $\frac{1}{4}$-W $\pm 5\%$ resistor
1.5-MΩ, $\frac{1}{4}$-W $\pm 5\%$ resistor
1-MΩ, $\frac{1}{4}$-W $\pm 5\%$ resistor
470-kΩ, $\frac{1}{4}$-W $\pm 5\%$ resistor
(2) 0.5-μF capacitors

Procedure

1. Build the circuit of Fig. L 10-3(A) and apply power. If your circuit is working properly, the indicator lamp should be blinking. What is the approximate time period T of the output cycle? $T =$ _1.5 sec_

2. With the circuit generating square waves (oscillating), connect another 0.5-μF capacitor in parallel with C_T. What is the effect on the period of oscillation?
   Doubles   3 sec

3. Remove the extra capacitor and replace R_T with 470 K. What effect do you notice about the period of oscillation? _3.8/10 ≈ .4 sec_
   Replace R_T with 1.5 MΩ again and leave this oscillator assembled for later use.

4. Construct the circuit of Fig. L 10-3(B). With power applied, alternately flip switch S to position A for a few seconds and then to position B for a few seconds. Describe what you observe. _A (low) T = 3.%/10 ~ .4 sec_
   B (High) Non flashing

5. Next, disconnect the switch from pin 8. Connect the output from pin 4 (of the oscillator built previously) to the input of pin 8. Apply power. Explain what you observe. _short flash   long flash_

Current A alternates CRt B between low
& High shor - loug pulso

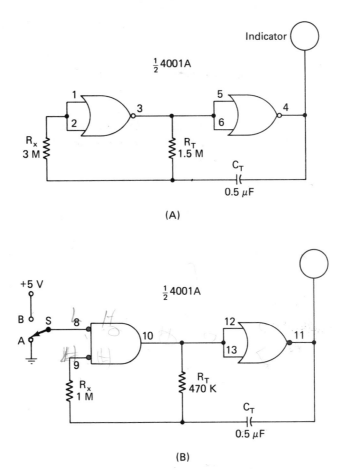

(A)

(B)

Fig. L 10-3. CMOS astable multivibrator.

Quiz for Experiment 10-3

1. Increasing the value of C_T in the oscillator (increases, decreases) the period of oscillation.

2. Decreasing the value of R_T in the oscillator (increases, decreases) the period of oscillation.

3. In the circuit of Fig. L 10-3(B), with switch S in position A, the input to pin 8 was (HIGH, LOW). Therefore the output of the first NOR gate was (always HIGH, always LOW, the opposite of the level at pin 9).

4. With reference to Fig. L 10-3(B), with switch S in position B, the input to pin 8 was (HIGH, LOW). Therefore the output of the first NOR gate was (always HIGH, always LOW, the opposite of the level at pin 9).

5. If the oscillator period was adjusted for 1 ms and if a 100-Hz square wave was applied to pin 8, rather than a switch, the output at pin 11 would be (a 100-Hz wave, a continuous 1-kHz wave, gated bursts of a 1-kHz wave).

Experiment 10-4   Changing Sine Waves into Square Waves

Purpose

You will become familiar with using an inverter as an overdriven amplifier to change sine waves into square waves. Then you will work with a Schmitt trigger circuit, which will produce square waves with very fast rise and fall times.

Materials

Digital breadboard kit
Oscilloscope
Sine-wave generator
NPN transistor (any switching type)
7404 hex inverter
10-K, $\frac{1}{4}$-W $\pm 5\%$ resistor
4.7-K, $\frac{1}{4}$-W $\pm 5\%$ resistor
1-K, $\frac{1}{4}$-W $\pm 5\%$ resistor
220-Ω $\frac{1}{4}$-W $\pm 5\%$ resistor

Procedure

1. Construct the inverter circuit of Fig. L 10-4(A). Adjust the generator to a frequency of 1 kHz at an amplitude of about 0.1 V p-p. Observe the output V_o with a scope. Then gradually increase the generator output up to about 10 V p-p while watching the output V_o. Explain what you observe at small input signal amplitudes and then as V_{in} gets larger and larger. _____ at 2Vp-p

the sine wave begins to turn into the square

wave

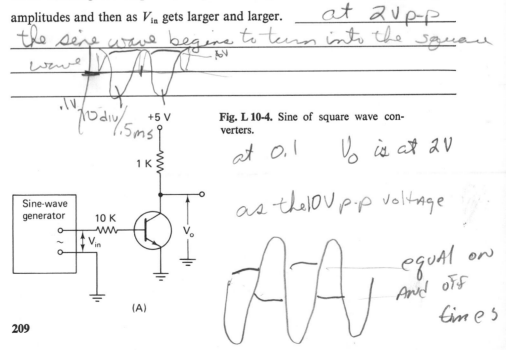

Fig. L 10-4. Sine of square wave converters.

at 0.1 V_o is at 2V

as the 10V p-p voltage

equal on
And off
times

1 K

Sine-wave generator

10 K

V_{in}

V_o

+5 V

(A)

209

The previous circuit used discrete components; now we shall do the same job with ICs.

2. Construct the circuit of Fig. L 10-4(B). The 1 K in series with the input is for protection. Again starting with V_{in} of about 0.1 V p-p, gradually increase V_{in} while observing the output with a scope. How does this circuit compare to that of Fig. L 10-4(A)? *sin & sq. wave grow proportional*

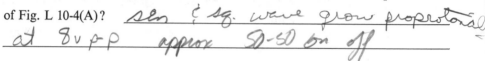

at 8v p-p approx 50-50 on off

In the overdriven amplifiers, or inverters, the rise and fall times are relatively slow. We shall now build a Schmitt trigger to give fast rise and fall times.

3. Build the circuit of Fig. L 10-4(C). Starting with $V_{in} = 0$, gradually increase V_{in} to several volts p-p while watching V_o with a scope. Explain what you see for various values of V_{in}. *.6V output*

at 5Vp-p it begins to trigger

at 6.5 Vp-p the sq & sin are in phase

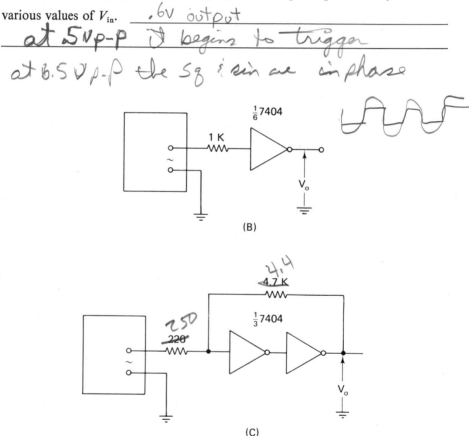

(B)

(C)

Fig. L 10-4. (Cont.)

Quiz for Experiment 10-4

1. In Fig. L 10-4(A), when $V_{in} = 0$, V_o is (V_{CC}, 0, $\frac{1}{2}V_{CC}$).

2. In Fig. L 10-4(A), when the amplitude of the signal V_{in} is large enough, V_o is (V_{CC}, 0, $\frac{1}{2}V_{CC}$, a 5-V p-p square wave).

3. Comparing the Schmitt trigger to the overdriven inverter as a wave-squaring circuit, a/an (inverter, Schmitt trigger) would be better to convert very low-frequency sine waves into square waves.

4. With reference to Problem 3, if fast rise time is not too important, say, for example, when the input frequency is high, a/an (inverter, Schmitt trigger) would be less expensive.

Experiment 10-5 IC Timers

Purpose

The 555 IC timer is one of the most commonly used ICs for generating square waves. Its frequency can be easily varied, and it uses few components. We shall now take a look at this interesting device.

Materials

Digital breadboard kit
555 timer
LED
1-MΩ pot
100-K pot
100-K, $\frac{1}{4}$-W ±5% resistor
240-Ω, $\frac{1}{4}$-W ±5% resistor
27-Ω, $\frac{1}{4}$-W ±5% resistor
Other resistors
8-Ω speaker (small, inexpensive type)
1-μF capacitor
0.1-μF capacitor
0.02-μF capacitor

Procedure

1. Construct the circuit of Fig. L 10-5(A). With R_B adjusted for maximum resistance, what is the frequency of oscillation? $f =$ _____. Next, adjust R_B to its minimum resistance setting. What is the approximate frequency of oscillation? $f =$ _____.

2. Set R_B to its maximum value again. Replace C_T with an 0.1-μF capacitor. What is the approximate frequency of oscillation? $f =$ _____. As you can see, the 555 timer can easily be adjusted to give you a 1-Hz clock. Of course, it is equally useful as a higher-frequency clock. Since the 555 can source or sink up to 200 mA, it can drive several other circuits. It can also be used to generate a low-level audible signal by simply connecting a speaker to the output.

3. Build the circuit of Fig. L 10-5(B). Do not connect the clock to point A yet. Apply power and vary the setting of pot R_B. Explain what happens at various settings. _____

_____

_____

_____

4. Next, connect a 1-Hz clock to point *A*. Explain what you observe.

_____

_____

_____

5. Finally, change R_x to 470 K and apply power. Explain what you observe.

_____

_____

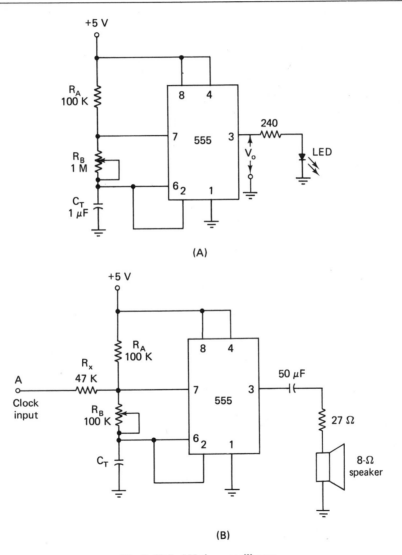

(A)

(B)

Fig. L 10-5. 555 timer oscillators.

Quiz for Experiment 10-5

1. The period of the 555 timer can be increased by increasing (R, C, either R or C).

2. In step 4, when the clock was connected to the tone generator, the tone was keyed on when the clock went (HIGH, LOW).

3. The pitch of the tone was (higher, lower) with the clock connected than in step 3 for the same setting of R_B, because C charged up (faster, slower) with the clock connected than without.

4. In step 5, the two-tone signal resulted because (C could not charge high enough, the charge path for C changed each time the clock went HIGH and LOW).

5. Suppose you replaced R_B in Fig. L 10-5(B) with a photoconductive cell. The pitch of the tone would (remain constant, increase with an increase in light, decrease with an increase in light).   *Note:* A photoconductive cell is a resistor whose resistance decreases with an increase in light falling on it.

11

The Monostable Circuit

Introduction

A circuit occasionally used in digital systems is the *monostable multivibrator*. As its name implies, it has one stable state; "monos" is a Greek word for *one* or *single*. We can understand, therefore, why the monostable multivibrator is also known as a *one-shot* or a *single-shot*. Any one of its names somewhat describes the one-shot's behavior. The one-shot stays in a stable state until a pulse is applied to its input. When triggered by an input pulse, it goes into an unstable state for a specific amount of time and then it returns to its stable state. Thus, when triggered, the one-shot provides an output pulse (shot) of dependable width (time duration).

11-1 General Types of Monostable Multivibrators

One-shot circuits are available on ICs, or can be built with discrete parts, to be either *leading edge triggered* or *trailing edge triggered*. A leading edge-triggered one-shot "does its thing," that is, delivers an output pulse, when a HIGH-going signal is applied to its input. Of course, then, the trailing edge-triggered one-shot provides an output pulse when a LOW-going signal is applied to its input. Depending on the circuit type, the one-shot's output can be either a LOW pulse or a HIGH pulse. For example, the circuit of Fig. L 11-1(A) has two outputs that are complementary. Complementary outputs have opposite logic levels. This circuit's outputs are the collectors of the transistors. When stable, the output at the collector of Q_1 is HIGH and the output at the collector of Q_2 is LOW. When a trigger

215

(appropriate pulse) input is applied, via C_2, this circuit goes into an unstable state; output Q_1 goes LOW and output Q_2 goes HIGH momentarily. After a moment, this circuit automatically returns to its stable state. The point is that output Q_1 pulses LOW but output Q_2 pulses HIGH when the circuit is triggered.

11-2 Applications of Monostable Multivibrators

One-shots find their way into a variety of applications. For example, one-shots can be used in *interface circuitry* between a digital computer and electromechanical relays. The output pulses from the computer might be too short to energize such relays directly. One-shots can easily be triggered by short inputs and in turn can provide the much longer (wider) pulses needed by the relays. One-shots might also be used as time delay devices. In such applications, one-shots are used to slow down the flow of certain logic signals through the digital system.

Logic circuit designers generally try to avoid the use of one-shots. Although they are sometimes necessary, needless use of one-shots tends to make a system unpredictable. One-shots are easily triggered by *glitches* on the dc supply or ground lines. Glitches are sporadic, undesirable pulses that commonly occur in digital systems. Induced noise voltages on the one-shot's output lead can also cause it to trigger. One-shots, thus, can be sources of troublesome pulses that occur at wrong times.

Experiment 11-1 Transistor Monostable Multivibrator

Purpose

In the last chapter you built a transistor astable multivibrator which generated a continuous train of pulses. You will now build a *monostable*, or *one-shot*, multivibrator using a similar circuit, which will generate a *single* pulse each time it is triggered.

Equipment

Digital breadboard kit
Oscilloscope
Square-wave generator (or use a sine-wave generator and a squaring circuit as in Chapter 10).
(Two) *NPN* transistors (any switching type)
(Two) 25-μF capacitors
(One) 0.025-μF capacitor
(One) 0.01-μF capacitor
(One) 0.001-μF capacitor
(Two) 2-K, $\frac{1}{4}$-W $\pm5\%$ resistors
(Two) 56-K, $\frac{1}{4}$-W $\pm5\%$ resistors
(One) 20-K, $\frac{1}{4}$-W $\pm5\%$ resistor
(One) 50-K pot

Procedure

1. Build the circuit of Fig. L 11-1(A). Apply power. With the switch in the L position, which lamp is lit? _____

2. Flip the switch to the H position.

3. After a few seconds, flip the switch back to the L position.

4. Repeat steps 2 and 3 several times while observing both lamps. Describe what you observe. _____

_____

_____

If your circuit is working properly, you should see lamp 2 come ON and lamp 1 go OFF for a short period when the switch goes from H to L. The time that lamp 2 is ON is called the *pulse width*.

5. Q_2 is held cut off by C_1 discharging through R_3. From your previous experience with transistor astable multivibrators, increasing C_1 should cause Q_2 to be

held in cutoff (longer, less). Bridge C_1 with another 25-μF capacitor, making the total capacitance 50 μF. Repeat steps 2 and 3 a few times. Describe what you observe. _____

_____

_____

6. Again from your previous experience, decreasing R_3 should (increase, decrease) the pulse width. Bridge R_3 with a 20-K resistor, and describe what you observe while flipping the switch HIGH and LOW.

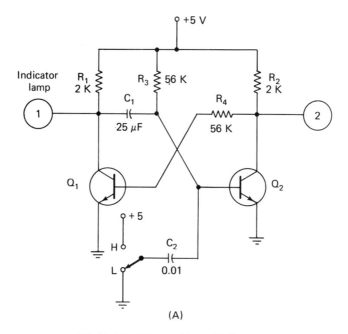

Fig. L 11-1. Monostable multivibrators.

7. Build the circuit of Fig. 11-1(B). Connect a square-wave generator to the input C_2 and adjust the generator output to 5 V peak at a frequency at about 400 Hz. (If you do not have a square-wave generator available, use a sine-wave generator followed by one of the squaring circuits discussed in Chapter 10.)

8. Observe the output at the collector of Q_2 with a scope. Adjust pot R_4 from its maximum to its minimum values several times while watching the output with a scope. Describe what you observe. _____

_____

_____

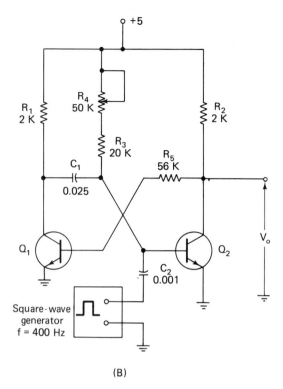

(B)

Fig. L 11-1. (Cont.)

Quiz for Experiment 11-1

The following questions refer to the circuit of Fig. L 11-1(A):

1. In its resting state, which transistor is normally ON?

2. When the switch is flipped to the H position, C_2 (discharges and turns Q_2 OFF, charges up to 5 V).

3. When the switch is flipped back to the L position, C_2 (discharges and turns Q_2 OFF momentarily, charges up to 5 V).

4. When Q_2 turns OFF, its collector voltage (rises positively and turns Q_1 ON, goes to zero and turns Q_1 OFF).

5. Once triggered OFF by C_2, Q_2 remains OFF (permanently, temporarily by C_1 discharging through R_3).

6. Increasing C_1 (increases, decreases) the pulse width.

7. Decreasing R_3 (increases, decreases) the pulse width.

219

8. In step 8 of the experiment we saw that the number of pulses per second, called the *pulse repetition rate* (PRR), was determined by the (setting of R_4, generator frequency).

9. The pulse width in step 8 was controlled by the (setting of R_4, generator frequency).

10. The circuit of Fig. L 11-1(B) is a/an (astable, monostable) multivibrator because it (oscillates at 400 Hz, generates a single pulse of definite width each time it is triggered).

Experiment 11-2   555 Monostable Multivibrator

Purpose

In the previous chapter, you used a 555 timer chip as an astable multivibrator. Now we shall build a pulse generator with this versatile unit.

Equipment

> Digital breadboard kit
> 555 timer chip
> 100-μF capacitor
> (Two) 0.1-μF capacitors
> 500-K pot
> 10-K, $\frac{1}{4}$-W $\pm 5\%$ resistor
> 2-K, $\frac{1}{4}$-W $\pm 5\%$ resistor

Procedure

1. Build the pulse generator circuit of Fig. L 11-2. Adjust the 500-K pot to zero, making $R_T = 10$ K. (R_T is the sum of the 10-K fixed resistor and the 500-K pot.) With the switch in the H position, the output at pin 3 is (HIGH, LOW).

2. Flip the switch down to the LOW position. Wait several seconds and then flip the switch back to HIGH. Repeat switching HIGH and LOW every few seconds while watching the output at pin 3. What do you observe? _____

_____

_____

Fig. L 11-2.

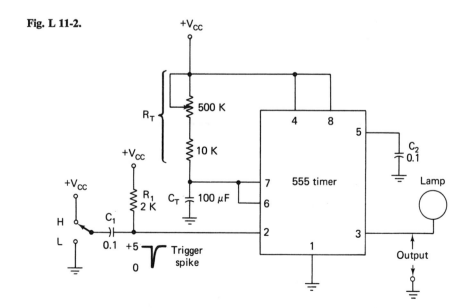

3. Now increase the setting of the 500-K pot to about its midrange. Flip the switch to its LOW position again. What happens to the pulse width? _____

_____

_____

4. Adjust the 500-K pot to its maximum value. Again measure the pulse width. $PW =$ _____ .

Quiz for Experiment 11-2

1. A good use for the circuit of Fig. L 11-2 is as an exposure timer for making photographic prints in a darkroom. The output of the timer is used to turn on the printing lamp, and the exposure time is adjustable by the setting of the 500-K pot. Over what range of exposure times is the circuit adjustable?

2. How could you double the maximum exposure time without changing R_T?

3. When the switch in the circuit is flipped from H to L, capacitor C_1 produces a (positive, negative)-going pulse at pin 2.

4. Resistor R_1 holds pin 2 normally (HIGH, LOW) until a trigger pulse is applied.

5 (optional).   In a previous chapter, you learned how to use a transistor as a lamp driver. Draw a diagram showing how you would wire the circuit of Fig. L 11-2 to control a lamp driver. The lamp to be used draws 0.5 A at 6 V. Assume that the base current of the lamp driver is to be 20 mA when the timer output is HIGH. Also use a momentary pushbutton switch instead of a toggle switch so that the lamp will pulse ON for a specified duration each time the switch is depressed.

12

RS Flip-flops

Introduction

In previous chapters we learned how logic gates are selected to perform required combinational logic functions. Generally, a circuit is a combinational logic circuit if its output goes HIGH or LOW depending on the combination of its logic signal inputs. For example, the circuit of Fig. 8-10 in Chapter 8 is a combinational logic circuit. Its BUZZER output signal goes ACTIVE HIGH if the input combination $A = 1$, $B = 1$, and $C = 1$ is applied. It does not matter in what order these HIGH inputs are applied. Now we shall consider sequential logic circuits. They require a definite order or sequence of inputs before their outputs become ACTIVE. Thus a sequential circuit might require that input A go HIGH first, then input B is to go HIGH next, and finally input C is to go HIGH before the output becomes ACTIVE. Thus if B goes HIGH before A, or if C goes HIGH before either A or B, the output remains inactive. In this chapter we shall study the RS flip-flop, which is the basic building block of some types of sequential logic circuits. The RS flip-flop also serves as a binary memory cell; that is, it can memorize a logic 1 or a 0 when told to do so.

12-1   Set/Reset Flip-flops with ACTIVE LOW Inputs

The set/reset flip-flop, generally known as the RS flip-flop, is often used in sequential circuits. It is able to memorize a logic 1 or a 0 and we shall see what this means in this and the next chapter.

An RS flip-flop can be constructed with two two-input NAND gates, as shown in Fig. 12-1(A). As indicated, its outputs usually are called Q and $\bar{Q}$, which means

that they are complementary. Complementary outputs normally have opposite
logic levels. Normally, therefore, if $Q = 1$, then $\bar{Q} = 0$, and if $Q = 0$, then $\bar{Q} = 1$.

When $Q = 1$ and $\bar{Q} = 0$, the RS flip-flop is said to be in the *set* state. When
its outputs $Q = 0$ and $\bar{Q} = 1$, the RS flip-flop is in the *reset* state. An RS flip-flop
remains in either the set or reset state until acted upon by an appropriate input
signal. Because the RS flip-flop is normally in either of two states, set or reset, it
is also called a *bistable circuit*.

The inputs $\bar{S}$ and $\bar{R}$ on the circuit and symbol of Fig. 12-1 are ACTIVE LOW.
This means that this flip-flop will change states when a momentary LOW is applied
to the appropriate input. Normally, only one of the inputs, $\bar{S}$ or $\bar{R}$, is pulled ACTIVE
LOW at any instant. Generally, a LOW on the $\bar{S}$ (set) input, only, sets the flip-flop,
whereas a LOW on the $\bar{R}$ (reset) input, only, resets the flip-flop. This action will
become clearer as we study this RS flip-flop's functional table and read the following four paragraphs.

In a usual application of the RS flip-flop, with circles at its inputs, both inputs
are not pulled LOW at the same time. If they are, however, as shown in row 1 in the
table in Fig. 12-1, both outputs go HIGH. Forcing both outputs HIGH in this manner
is normally not done because this *is not* a stable state of the RS flip-flop. That is,
both outputs will not stay HIGH if the input signals that caused them to go HIGH
are removed.

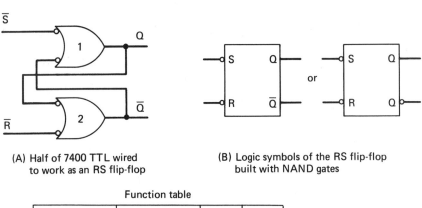

(A) Half of 7400 TTL wired
to work as an RS flip-flop

(B) Logic symbols of the RS flip-flop
built with NAND gates

Function table

	$\bar{S}$	$\bar{R}$	Q	$\bar{Q}$	
1	LOW	LOW	HIGH	HIGH	← Normally not used
2	HIGH (inactive)	LOW (ACTIVE)	LOW	HIGH	
3	LOW (ACTIVE)	HIGH (inactive)	HIGH	LOW	
4	HIGH (inactive)	HIGH (inactive)	No change		

(C)

Fig. 12-1.

As shown in row 2 of the table in Fig. 12-1, a momentary ACTIVE LOW applied to the $\bar{R}$ (reset) input, while $\bar{S}$ is inactive HIGH, will reset this flip-flop, causing its Q output to go LOW. If this flip-flop is in the reset state before $\bar{R}$ is pulled LOW, it remains reset after the LOW is applied to $\bar{R}$.

Row 3 of the table shows that this flip-flop sets (Q goes HIGH, $\bar{Q}$ goes LOW) when its $\bar{S}$ (set) input is momentarily pulled ACTIVE LOW while its $\bar{R}$ input is inactive HIGH. If this flip-flop is in the set state before its $\bar{S}$ input is pulled LOW, it remains set after the LOW on $\bar{S}$ is applied.

As shown in row 4 of the table, the Q and $\bar{Q}$ outputs of this flip-flop do not change (remain stable) when both inputs are HIGH. That is, if this flip-flop is placed in a set state by a momentary ACTIVE LOW applied to input $\bar{S}$, it will remain set even though its $\bar{S}$ input is allowed to return to a HIGH state. Similarly, if this flip-flop is placed in the reset state by an applied ACTIVE LOW on the $\bar{R}$ input, it stays reset even though the $\bar{R}$ input is allowed to become HIGH again.

The waveforms of Fig. 12-2 show how the RS flip-flop, with ACTIVE LOW (circled) inputs, responds to input signals. In this case, output Q is initially LOW, which means that the flip-flop (FF) is in the reset state. At t_1, the input signal on $\bar{S}$ goes ACTIVE LOW, causing this FF to set. Note that though $\bar{S}$ goes HIGH again, the FF stays set and that another LOW-going $\bar{S}$ input, shown at t_2, has no effect. At t_3, the ACTIVE LOW pulse on the $\bar{R}$ input causes the FF to reset. Although $\bar{R}$ rises HIGH again and subsequently pulses LOW at t_4, this FF remains reset. Then at t_5 another LOW-going pulse on $\bar{S}$ sets the FF again. And then at t_6 it is reset again by the LOW-going pulse on $\bar{R}$.

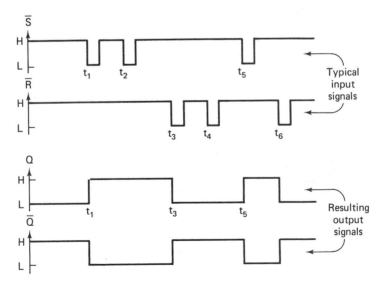

Fig. 12-2. Output waveforms (Q and $\bar{Q}$) resulting from typical ACTIVE LOW inputs ($\bar{S}$ and $\bar{R}$).

The RS flip flop is frequently used in the *bounceless switch* circuit shown in Fig. 12-3. A mechanical switch, such as Sw in this circuit, tends to *bounce* after it is thrown. This means that the switch arm will first strike, but then bounce off, contact *s* after the arm is thrown in the "up" position; note this Fig. 12-2(B). Typically the arm will bounce many times before it finally settles to a good contact with *s*. As we would expect, and as shown in Fig. 12-3(C), the arm of the switch will likewise bounce many times off contact *r* after Sw is thrown into the "down" position. Generally, all mechanical switches tend to bounce and therefore are impractical, for use by themselves, as sources of logic pulses. This is especially true where the number of pulses is important. For example, mechanical switches com-

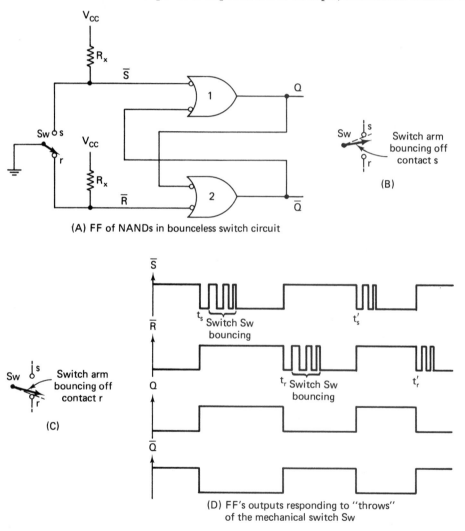

(A) FF of NANDs in bounceless switch circuit

(B)

(C)

(D) FF's outputs responding to "throws" of the mechanical switch Sw

Fig. 12-3.

monly are on the front panel of a digital system. They give the system operator capability to manually feed bits into the system. In such a system, the number of bits from each switch is usually very critical, and therefore switch bouncing could cause a lot of trouble. In such cases, each switch is used with an RS flip-flop, which eliminates the problem of contact bounce.

The waveforms in Fig. 12-3(D) illustrate how the voltages on the circuit in Fig. 12-3(A) respond to "throws" of the switch Sw. Since Sw is initially in the "down" position, it puts an ACTIVE LOW signal on the $\bar{R}$ (reset) input, causing the FF to reset. At the same instant, the $\bar{S}$ input is pulled HIGH (inactive), to the V_{CC} voltage, through the pull-up resistor R_x. At time t_s, Sw is thrown into the "up" position, which pulls the $\bar{S}$ input ACTIVE LOW at the instant the switch arm strikes contact s. At this same instant, the $\bar{R}$ input is pulled HIGH through resistor R_x. The FF is thus commanded to become set, and it responds with a HIGH-going Q output at time t_s. As shown on the waveform for $\bar{S}$, Sw bounces after this time t_s, causing the $\bar{S}$ input to change between HIGH and LOW several times. While the switch Sw is bouncing, the FF is commanded to set each time $\bar{S}$ swings from HIGH to LOW. But the FF was already set at t_s, and therefore it simply remains set.

At time t_r, Sw is thrown into the "down" position. This pulls the $\bar{R}$ input ACTIVE LOW and causes the FF to reset. Simultaneously, the $\bar{S}$ goes HIGH, being pulled up to V_{CC} through R_x. After t_r, the switch is shown bouncing, but the FF remains reset.

At $t_s{}'$, the switch Sw is thrown to its "up" position, causing the FF to set again. Then after a while, at $t_r{}'$, Sw is thrown to its "down" position, causing the FF to reset again. The point to note is that the switch can set or reset the FF, but the switch's bouncing has no effect on the FF's outputs.

12-2 ACTIVE HIGH **Set/Reset Flip-flops**

A pair of two-input NOR gates can be wired to work as an RS flip-flop as shown in Fig. 12-4(A). In this case, the S and R inputs are ACTIVE HIGH; therefore, these inputs are shown without circles on the logic diagram; see this in Fig. 12-4(B). An RS flip-flop with ACTIVE HIGH inputs tends to change states when one or the other of its inputs is pulled HIGH.

The functional table in Fig. 12-4 shows how this FF reacts to each possible combination of inputs. Row 1 shows that if both inputs are pulled down to inactive LOWs, the outputs do not change. This means that a FF in the set state remains set after both S and R inputs are made LOW. On the other hand, if this FF is in the reset state before S and R are pulled LOW, it remains reset after the LOW inputs are applied.

Row 2 shows that if the S input is momentarily pulled ACTIVE HIGH, while the R input is inactive LOW, the Q output goes HIGH; that is, the FF becomes set. If the FF is already in a set state when its S input goes HIGH, it remains set after the HIGH S input is applied.

As indicated in row 3, a momentary ACTIVE HIGH signal on the *R* input, while *S* is held LOW, causes the FF to reset. If this FF is in a reset state before *R* is pulled HIGH, it remains reset after the HIGH on *R* is applied.

In usual applications of this FF, both of its inputs are not pulled HIGH at the same time. As shown in row 4 of the table, this would cause both outputs to go LOW, which is not a stable state. That is, both outputs cannot remain LOW after the input signals causing them to go LOW are removed.

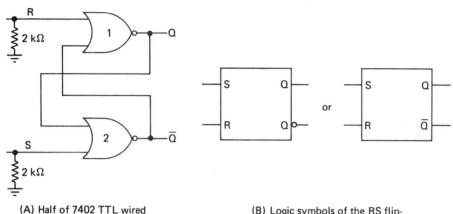

(A) Half of 7402 TTL wired to work as an RS flip-flop

(B) Logic symbols of the RS flip-flop built with NOR gates

Functional table

	S	R	Q	Q̄	
1	LOW (inactive)	LOW (inactive)	No change		
2	HIGH (ACTIVE)	LOW (inactive)	HIGH	LOW	SET
3	LOW (inactive)	HIGH (ACTIVE)	LOW	HIGH	RESET
4	HIGH	HIGH	LOW	LOW	←—Normally not used

(C)

Fig. 12-4.

The ACTIVE HIGH RS flip-flop is commonly used in a bounceless switch circuit as shown in Fig. 12-5(A). In this case, the arm of the switch is wired to V_{CC} instead of ground. Thus when the switch Sw is in the "up" position as shown, the *R*'input is ACTIVE HIGH. At the same time, the *S* input is LOW, being pulled down to about ground potential through the pull-down resistor R_y. The waveforms in Fig. 12-5(B) show how the outputs *Q* and *Q̄* react to various throws of the switch Sw. Times t_s, t'_s, and t''_s are instants when Sw is thrown "down", causing the FF to set. Note that the Sw bounces after each of these instants but that the FF ignores this and remains stable in the set state. Times t_r, t'_r, and t''_r are instants when Sw is thrown "up", causing the FF to reset. Note that though Sw bounces after these instants, the FF remains stable in the reset state.

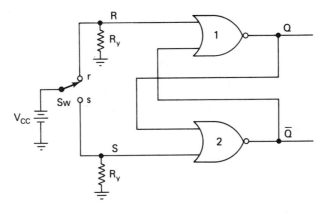

(A) FF of NORs in bounceless switch circuit (use pull-down resistors R_y of about 2 KΩ with TTL NORs)

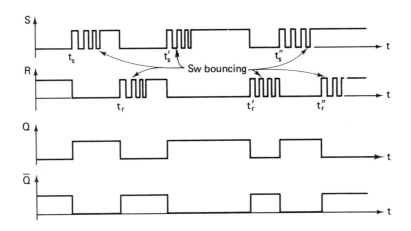

(B) FF's outputs responding to "throws" of mechanical switch Sw

Fig. 12-5.

12-3 A Sequential Application of RS Flip-flops

The rat-conditioning circuit we studied in Chapter 8 allows the rats, Alfred, Brenda, and Charlie, to obtain food if they request it one at a time. Now we shall modify this circuit so that these rats get fed only if they learn to request food in a definite order one at a time. Figure 12-6 shows such a modification. We can assume that the BUSY, BELL, and BUZZER combinational logic circuitry is present, though not shown, and that it works as previously described. Only the feed Alfred F_A, feed Brenda F_B, and feed Charlie F_C logic has been modified. In this case, Alfred must request food first (A goes HIGH first). Then Brenda must request next (B goes HIGH second). Finally, Charlie must request last (C goes HIGH third). If they learn to follow this order, outputs F_A, F_B, and F_C go HIGH and each rat gets a feed pellet. If they request food in any other order, one at a time, none of them gets fed.

In the circuit of Fig. 12-6, the BUSY signal is used to provide enabling inputs to NAND gates 2, 3, and 4. Remember that the BUSY signal is HIGH only if one rat is requesting food at any time during feed time (review Sec. 8-3 if necessary).

When Alfred requests food (*A* is HIGH), NAND gate 1 applies an ACTIVE LOW on the set input of FF I, causing its *Q* output to go HIGH. Thus a HIGH is applied to the top input of NAND gate 2.

Next, when Brenda only requests food (*B* is HIGH, *A* and *C* are LOW), the BUSY signal goes HIGH, causing three HIGHs into NAND gate 2. The resulting ACTIVE LOW out of this NAND sets FF II, which in turn applies a HIGH into the top input of NAND gate 3.

Now when Charlie only requests food (*C* goes HIGH, *A* and *B* are LOW), the BUSY signal goes HIGH, enabling NAND gate 3. Its resulting ACTIVE LOW output sets FF III.

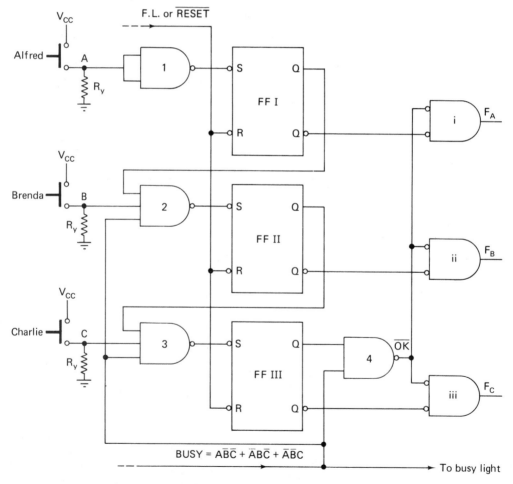

Fig. 12-6. Sequential logic circuit that requires inputs *A*, *B* and *C* to go HIGH in progressive order one at a time before F_A, F_B and F_C can go HIGH.

Now that FF III is set, and while the BUSY signal is HIGH, NAND gate 4 is enabled, causing an ACTIVE LOW $\overline{\text{OK}}$ signal. That is, $\overline{\text{OK}}$ is ACTIVE LOW after the signals A, B, and C have gone HIGH one at a time in progressive order. The LOW $\overline{\text{OK}}$ signal enables NOR gates i, ii, and iii, which allow the $\overline{Q}$ outputs of the three FFs to drive signals F_A, F_B, and F_C ACTIVE HIGH and the rats get fed.

Although not shown, the reset $\overline{R}$ input of each FF can be wired to the feed-light switch Sw so that these FFs reset after each feed-time period. Thus the FFs will all be in the reset state at the beginning of the next feed-time period.

The circuit of Fig. 12-6 works fine as long as the rats request food one at a time. If they persist in requesting food two or three at a time, in spite of the discouraging bell or buzzer that results, we can add the circuit of Fig. 12-7 to the circuit of Fig. 12-6. The circuit of Fig. 12-7 uses a lock-out flip-flop, which, when set, holds FFs I, II, and III in a reset state if two or three rats request food at the same time. That is, the BELL or BUZZER signal goes HIGH if two or three rats press their buttons at the same time; the BELL and BUZZER signals come from combinational logic circuitry such as in Figs. 8-10(C), 8-11, or 8-14. A HIGH BELL or BUZZER signal sets the lock-out FF via NOR GATE iv. The resulting HIGH from the Q output of this FF pulls the $\overline{\text{RESET}}$ line LOW via NOR gate v, which resets the FFs. Thus the F_A, F_B, and F_C signals remain inactive LOW, and the rats are locked out regardless of the buttons they might continue to push. This means that they lose their chance to get fed until the next feed-time period. The F.L. signal resets all four FFs at the end of each feed-time period.

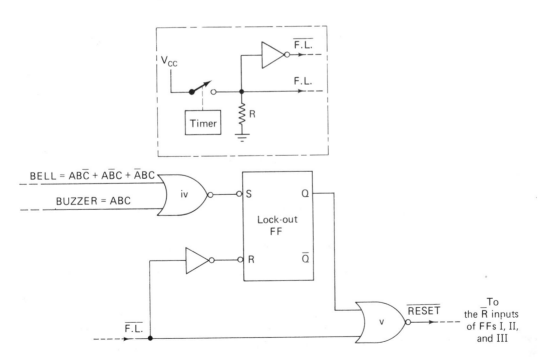

Fig. 12-7. Lockout circuit that can be used to disable the circuit of Fig. 12-6 if two or three of the signals, A, B and C, are HIGH at the same time.

Summary

1. Two NAND gates can be wired to work as an RS flip-flop that has ACTIVE LOW inputs.

2. Two NOR gates can be wired to work as an RS flip-flop that has ACTIVE HIGH inputs.

3. An RS flip-flop has two stable states, the set state and the reset state.

4. Because the RS FF has two stable states, it is also called a bistable multivibrator.

5. When the RS FF is set, its Q output is HIGH. When it is reset, its Q output is LOW.

6. A LOW-going signal on an ACTIVE LOW set $(\bar{S})$ input of an RS FF causes it to go into a set state. After the FF sets, it remains set regardless of the number of additional LOW-going pulses on the $\bar{S}$ input.

7. A LOW-going signal on an ACTIVE LOW reset $(\bar{R})$ input of an RS FF causes it to become reset. After the FF resets, it remains reset regardless of the number of additional LOW-going pulses on the $\bar{R}$ input.

8. A HIGH-going signal on an ACTIVE HIGH S input of an RS FF causes it to become set. Once set the FF remains set even though many additional HIGH going S inputs are applied.

9. A HIGH-going signal on an ACTIVE HIGH R input of an RS FF causes it to become reset. After it is reset, the FF remains reset regardless of the number of additional HIGH-going pulses that are applied to the R input.

10. On the *outside* of the logic symbol for the RS flip-flop, ACTIVE LOW set and reset input are referred to as the $\bar{R}$ and $\bar{S}$ inputs, respectively.

Problems 12-1

1. Figure 12-8 shows a circuit and how its $\bar{S}$ and $\bar{R}$ inputs change as a result of several "pushes" of the switch Sw. Sketch the resulting Q and $\bar{Q}$ outputs on the scale provided.

2. With reference to the circuit of Fig. 12-8, if the ground of the switch Sw is connected to V_{cc} instead, what change(s) can we expect at the outputs Q and $\bar{Q}$ after several "pushes" of this switch? Assume that the FF is initally in a reset state. __FF__ → __ReSET__   __N O   MATTER   WHERE__

    __THE   SWITCH   IS__   __BerAuse__ ^{Both} __INPUTS → HIGH__

3. Figure 12-9 shows a circuit and how its S and R inputs change as a result of several "throws" of the switch Sw. Sketch the resulting Q and $\bar{Q}$ outputs on the scale provided. Assume that this FF is initially in the set state.

4. If the arm of the switch Sw in Fig. 12-9 is connected to ground instead of V_{cc}, what change(s) can we expect at the outputs Q and $\bar{Q}$ after several "pushes" of this switch? Assume that the FF is initially in the set state. _____

FF stay set   No matter where switch is
Both inputs → low

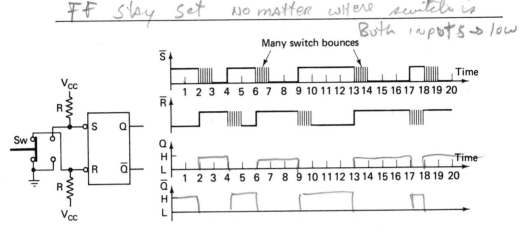

Fig. 12-8.

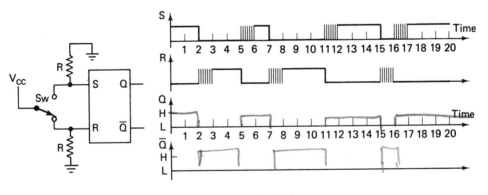

Fig. 12-9.

Experiment 12-1   RS Flip-flops Made with Inverters

Purpose

To learn how to build RS flip-flops using inverters. First you will build one with discrete components and then one with IC inverters.

Equipment

Digital breadboard kit
(Two) silicon transistors
4049 CMOS hex inverter
(Two) 20-K, $\frac{1}{4}$-W $\pm 5\%$ resistors
(Two) 1-K, $\frac{1}{4}$-W $\pm 5\%$ resistors

Procedure

1. Construct the circuit of Fig. L 12-1(A). Notice that transistor Q_1 and resistors R_1 and R_2 form an inverter, like the ones you studied in Chapter 2. Similarly, transistor Q_2 and resistors R_3 and R_4 form another inverter. With the input switch in the LOW (0) position, the output of Q_1 is (HIGH, LOW), and the output of Q_2 is (HIGH, LOW).

2. Flip the input switch to the HIGH (1) position. The output of Q_1 is (HIGH, LOW), and the output of Q_2 is (HIGH, LOW). The output of Q_2 is always the (same as, opposite of) the output of Q_1. The output of Q_2 is always the (same as, opposite of) the *input* to Q_1.

Fig. L 12-1.

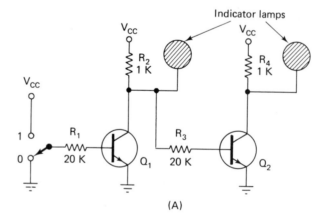

(A)

3. Now disconnect the toggle switch from the input of Q_1, and connect the output of Q_2 to the base resistor of Q_1, as shown in Fig. L 12-1(B). This figure shows the conventional way of drawing an RS flip-flop using discrete components. We can draw the logic symbol as shown in Fig. L 12-1(C).

4. Apply power. If your circuit is wired correctly, one collector should be HIGH, and the other should be LOW. If so, check here _____, and go on to the next step.

5. Connect one end of a clip lead to ground, and momentarily touch the collector of the transistor which has a HIGH output. What happens? _____

---

6. Alternately touch one collector and then the other at intervals of several seconds while observing the outputs. Does grounding a HIGH output always cause the flip-flop to change states? _____ Does grounding a LOW output cause the output to change states? _____ Does the circuit remain in a previous state until you force it to switch? That is, is the circuit *stable* in both states?

---

7. Now we shall build an RS flip-flop with IC inverters. Wire the circuit of Fig. L 12-1(C) using two inverters of the 4049 package, shown in Fig. L 12-1(D). Since the two inverter outputs are always opposite, the flip-flop outputs are usually labeled Q and $\bar{Q}$, as shown in the figure.

8. Momentarily attach a clip lead from ground to Q and $\bar{Q}$ alternately, as you did with the discrete flip-flop. Does it perform the same (yes, no)?

9. There is another way of changing the states of a CMOS RS flip-flop. Connect one end of a clip lead to the Q output. Now momentarily touch it alternately to ground and then to V_{CC}. Explain what you observe.

Fig. L 12-1. (Cont.)

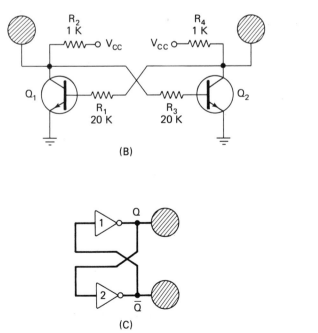

(B)

(C)

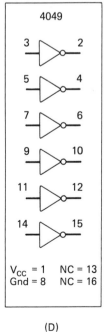

(D)

Quiz for Experiment 12-1

1. The two outputs of an RS flip-flop are always in opposite states (true, false).

2. Once an RS flip-flop is forced into one state, for example, with Q_2 HIGH and Q_1 LOW, it remains in that state until forced into its other state (true, false).

3. The RS flip-flop "remembers" the state it was forced into, so it can be used as a simple binary *memory* cell (true, false).

4. Recalling the circuits you built in Chapter 10, two transistors cross-coupled with two capacitors generated a continuous square wave. The circuit did not remain in either state permanently, so it was called a/an (astable, monostable, bistable) multivibrator.

5. In Chapter 11, you built a circuit to generate a simple pulse when triggered. This circuit preferred to remain in one particular state, so it was called a/an (astable, monostable, bistable) multivibrator.

6. Now in Chapter 12, you built a circuit that can remain in either of two states indefinitely. We call this circuit a/an (astable, monostable, bistable) multivibrator.

7. How many flip-flops can you build with one 4049 chip? _____

8. The technique of forcing the Q output LOW by connecting it to ground and forcing it HIGH by connecting it to V_{CC} is called *jamming*. It is safe to jam the CMOS output HIGH or LOW because the conducting FET has a high enough resistance to limit the current to a safe value. When the collector of Q_2 in Fig. L 12-1(B) is jammed LOW, what component limits the current through the

    clip lead? _____

9. If the collector of Q_2 were jammed HIGH (connected to V_{CC} through a clip lead) while Q_2 was conducting, what might happen? (*Remember, a conducting transistor has a low resistance.*) _____

Experiment 12-2 Back-to-Back NAND Gates as an RS Flip-flop

Purpose

To become familiar with NAND gate flip-flops.

Equipment

Digital breadboard kit
7400 quad two-input NAND

Procedure

1. Wire the circuit of Fig. L 12-2. (See Chapter 6 for the pin numbers on the chip.) If your circuit is wired correctly, the output of one of the gates should be HIGH and the other LOW. Notice that the two inputs are connected to a HIGH level through pull-up resistors, so both inputs are normally (HIGH, LOW) in the absence of a signal.

2. With this circuit, we do not normally jam the outputs HIGH or LOW, but we apply LOW signals to either input to cause the output to switch states. Connect one end of a clip lead to ground, and alternately touch input 1 and then input 2 with the other end of the lead. Repeat this several times until you are sure what happens. Grounding input 1 causes the Q output to go (HIGH, LOW). Grounding input 2 causes the Q output to switch (HIGH, LOW).

3. Show how you would build a bounceless switch with the NAND gate RS flip-flop by drawing an SPDT switch on the diagram of Fig. L 12-2.

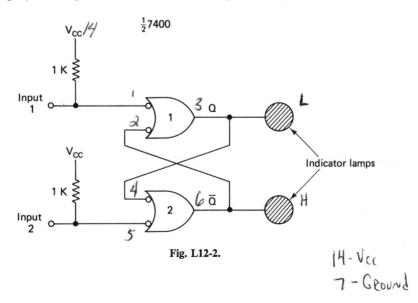

Fig. L12-2.

14 - Vcc
7 - Ground

Quiz for Experiment 12-2

1. When the Q output is HIGH, the flip-flop is set. When the Q output is LOW, the flip-flop is reset. If the Q output is LOW, grounding input (1, 2) will set the flip-flop.

2. If the Q output is HIGH, grounding input (1, 2) will reset the flip-flop.

3. Inputs 1 and 2 are ACTIVE (HIGH, LOW) inputs.

4. If the flip-flop is reset, grounding input 2 will (set, not change) it.

5. If the flip-flop is set, grounding input 1 will (reset, not change) it.

Experiment 12-3   Back-to-Back NOR Gates as an RS Flip-flop

Purpose

To become familiar with NOR gate flip-flops.

Equipment

Digital breadboard kit
CD 4001A quad two-input NOR

Procedure

1. Wire the circuit of Fig. L 12-3. (See Chapter 6 for the pin numbers.) The 1-K resistors at each input hold both inputs normally (HIGH, LOW).

2. Again with this circuit, we shall not jam the outputs HIGH or LOW, but we shall apply signals to inputs 1 and 2. Experiment with the circuit by connecting one end of a clip lead either to ground or to V_{CC} as you think is required and then momentarily touch 1 and 2 alternately until you are sure how the circuit works. Then fill in Table L 12-3 to make sure you have tried all possibilities. Write in either "change" or "no change" under Q.

Table L 12-3

	Q Initially LOW	Q Initially HIGH
LOW signal to input 1	~~Q HIGH~~ NC	NC
LOW signal to input 2	~~Q HIGH~~ NC	NC
HIGH signal to input 1	NC	Q LOW
HIGH signal to input 2	~~F~~ Q HIGH	NC

3. On Fig. L 12-3, show how you would connect an SPDT toggle switch to make a bounceless switch with the two NOR gates.

Fig. L 12-3.

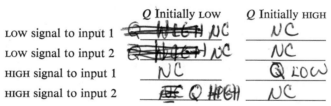

$\frac{1}{2}$CD4001

Input 1

Input 2

1 K

1 K

Q

$\overline{Q}$

Indicator lamps

239

13

D-Type and JK Flip-flops

Introduction

Digital circuits fall into two general classifications, synchronous and asynchronous (nonsynchronous). All the circuits that we have studied so far are asynchronous types. We shall start looking at some synchronous components and circuits here. By far there are more synchronous than asynchronous circuits in the typical digital system. Synchronous circuits require one or more clocks (square-wave generators) to pulse life and action within them. In such circuits, nothing happens if the clock or clocks are not running. Generally, clocked circuits or systems have better stability and reliability than do asynchronous types.

Basic components found in synchronous digital circuits are the D-type and JK flip-flops. These FFs have asynchronous features that make them similar to RS FFs. In addition, JK FFs have synchronous features that are made to work with a clock input. We shall study both features in this chapter. This will pave the way to an understanding of other clocked devices and circuits, such as counters and registers, which are very important items discussed in later chapters.

13-1   The D-Type Flip-flop

The logic symbol and typical IC package for the D-type flip-flop are shown in Fig. 13-1. Note that each FF has four inputs:

1.   The S_D input (also called the direct set, the set, or the preset input),

2.   The C_D input (also called the clear or reset R_D input),

3.   The D input, and

4.   The C_p (clock pulse or the trigger T) input.

As with the RS FF, the two outputs are called Q and $\bar{Q}$.

The $\overline{S_D}$ and $\overline{C_D}$ inputs on the D-type FF work like the $\bar{S}$ and $\bar{R}$ inputs on a RS FF that has ACTIVE LOW inputs. That is, the D-type FF responds to LOW or LOW-going signals on its $\overline{S_D}$ and $\overline{C_D}$ inputs, and they allow us to set or reset the FF asynchronously, which means without a clock input.

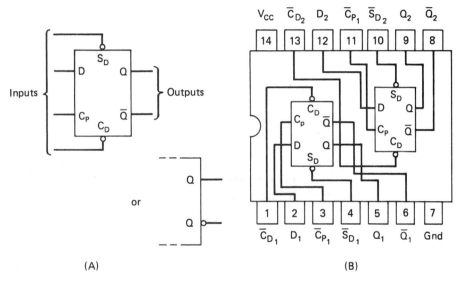

Fig. 13-1. (A) Symbol for the D-type flip-flop; (B) IC package containing D-type flip-flops (TTL/SSI·5474/7474).

The table in Fig. 13-2 shows how the outputs of the D-type FF respond to the four possible combinations on its $\overline{S_D}$ and $\overline{C_D}$ inputs. Row 1 shows that if both $\overline{S_D}$ and $\overline{C_D}$ inputs are LOW, both outputs are driven HIGH. The FF is normally not used in this way because it is not in a stable state when both of its outputs are HIGH. This means that the outputs will remain HIGH only as long as both the $\overline{S_D}$ and $\overline{C_D}$ inputs are held LOW. If we allow one or both of the inputs to become HIGH, the FF will immediately switch to one of its two stable states. The stable states are the set and reset states, just as in the RS FF. We can recall that a FF is set when its Q output is HIGH and its $\bar{Q}$ output is LOW. Of course, then, it is reset when its Q and $\bar{Q}$ outputs are LOW and HIGH, respectively.

As indicated in row 2 of the table in Fig. 13-2, a LOW (ACTIVE) signal on the $\overline{S_D}$ input, while the $\overline{C_D}$ input is HIGH or open, causes the Q output to go HIGH; that is, it sets the FF. If additional LOW-going signals or pulses are applied to the $\overline{S_D}$ input, after it becomes set, the FF remains stable in the set state. On the other hand, when input $\overline{C_D}$ is driven LOW (ACTIVE), while $\overline{S_D}$ is HIGH or open, this FF resets. If additional LOW-going signals or pulses are applied to the $\overline{C_D}$ input, after it resets, this FF remains reset.

Row 4 shows that if both the $\overline{S_D}$ and $\overline{C_D}$ inputs are HIGH or open, the FF's outputs do not change. This means that a D-type FF in a set state will remain set as long as $\overline{S_D}$ and $\overline{C_D}$ remain HIGH. Likewise a D-type FF in a reset state remains reset as long as both inputs are HIGH.

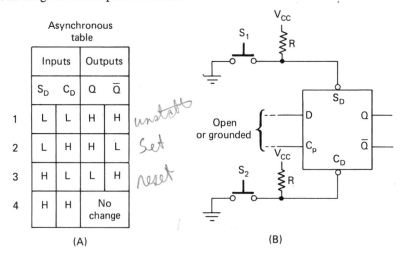

Fig. 13-2. (A) Asynchronous functional table for the D-type flip-flop; (B) D-type flip-flop wired for asynchronous operation.

Summary

1. The D-type FF has four inputs and two outputs.

2. When pulled LOW (to ground potential), the $\overline{S_D}$ input sets the D-type FF. A FF is set when its Q output is HIGH.

3. The $\overline{S_D}$ input is also called the direct set, or the set, or the preset input.

4. When pulled LOW (to ground potential), the $\overline{C_D}$ input resets the D-type FF. A FF is reset when its Q output is LOW.

5. The $\overline{C_D}$ input is also called the direct clear, or the clear, or the reset input.

6. The Q and $\bar{Q}$ outputs of the D-type FF are complementary (opposite logic levels) unless both $\overline{S_D}$ and $\overline{C_D}$ inputs are pulled LOW simultaneously. These inputs are not pulled LOW at the same time in typical applications.

7. After the D-type FF is put in its set state, repetitive LOW $\overline{S_D}$ signals have no effect. An ACTIVE LOW $\overline{S_D}$ signal will affect the FF only if it is in the reset state.

8. After the D-type FF becomes reset, repetitive LOW $\overline{C_D}$ signals have no effect. An ACTIVE LOW $\overline{C_D}$ input signal affects the FF only if it is initially in the set state.

9. Setting or resetting the D-type FF with $\overline{S_D}$ or $\overline{C_D}$ inputs is called asynchronous operation.

Problem 13-1

1. Referring to the D-type FF in Fig. 13-2, indicate its output conditions (HIGH or LOW) for each of the switch input conditions shown in the table of Fig. 13-3. To the far right of each row write *set*, *reset*, or *unstable* to indicate the state of the flip-flop.

Fig. 13-3.   Table

S – set
RES: reset
uns – unstable

Input switches S_1	S_2	Outputs Q	$\overline{Q}$	State of FF
1 CLOSED	CLOSED	H	H	UNS
2 CLOSED	OPEN	H	L	S
3 OPEN	OPEN	H	L	S
4 CLOSED	OPEN	H	L	S
5 OPEN	OPEN	H	L	S
6 CLOSED	CLOSED	H	H	UNS
7 OPEN	CLOSED	L	H	RES
8 OPEN	OPEN	L	H	RES
9 OPEN	CLOSED	L	H	Res
10 CLOSED	OPEN	H	L	S
11 OPEN	CLOSED	L	H	Res
12 CLOSED	CLOSED	H	H	UNS

13-2 Synchronous Operation of the D-Type Flip-flop

During synchronous operation, the D-type FF requires a clock (square-wave) signal applied to its C_p input. The leading edge (LOW to HIGH transition) of the clock signal *can* cause this FF to change states, that is, change from the set to the reset state or from the reset to the set state. Whether or not the FF's state does change depends on the logic level that is on the D input at the instant the leading edge C_p input arrives.

In the following discussion of how the D-type FF behaves during synchronous operation, we can assume that the $\overline{S_D}$ and $\overline{C_D}$ inputs are wired to HIGHs or simply open. A HIGH logic signal applied to the D input of the D-type FF puts it into a set *mode*. This means that this FF will set on the next leading edge of the clock pulse. If the FF is already set while the D input is pulled HIGH, it stays set regardless of the number of incoming clock pulses.

When a LOW logic level is applied to the D input, the D-type FF is in the reset *mode*. This means that it will reset on the next leading edge of the incoming clock pulse. After the D-type FF resets, it stays reset as long as the D input is LOW regardless of the number of clock pulses applied.

A D-type FF working synchronously is shown in Fig. 13-4. In this case, the Q and $\bar{Q}$ outputs are shown to be initially LOW and HIGH, respectively; that is, the FF is initially in the reset state. With the switch S in the down position as shown, the D input is LOW, putting the FF in a reset mode. Since it is already reset, the clock pulses are shown to have no effect on the outputs. Note that this FF remains reset through leading edge pulses 1, 2, and 3.

If we throw the switch S into the up position, the D input goes HIGH. The D-type FF is thus put into its set mode. This does not mean that this FF sets at the instant input D is pulled HIGH. A HIGH D input instructs the FF to set on the next HIGH-going C_p input. Therefore, as shown, the leading edge 4 of the clock pulse causes the FF to become set; that is, its Q output goes HIGH and its $\bar{Q}$ output goes LOW. The next clock pulse 5 is then ignored because the HIGH on the D input holds the FF in the set mode but it already is set.

Just before the sixth clock pulse, the D input is pulled LOW again, as is the case when switch S is placed back into its down position. This FF is again in the reset mode, but it does not reset until the next HIGH-going clock pulse. Note that the Q output goes LOW and that the $\bar{Q}$ output goes HIGH at the instant of the sixth C_p input. Thus reset, this FF ignores pulses 7, 8, and 9 because the LOW D input holds this FF in a reset mode.

Studying Fig. 13-4 further, we see that the D input is pulled HIGH again after clock pulse 9. This puts the FF back into the set mode of operation, causing it to set on the tenth leading edge of the clock pulse. The subsequent pulses 11 and 12 are ignored because the HIGH on the D input holds the FF in its set mode, and it is already set during these pulses.

The synchronous action of the D-type FF is often summarized as in the table of Fig. 13-5. The notation t_n refers to the time before the leading edge of the applied clock pulse. The notation t_{n+1} refers to the time after the clock's leading edge. Therefore, row 1 shows that if the D input is LOW before the clock pulse (time t_n), the outputs Q and $\bar{Q}$ are LOW and HIGH, respectively, after the clock pulse (time t_{n+1}). Row 2 shows that if the D input is HIGH before the clock pulse C_p, the outputs Q and $\bar{Q}$ are HIGH and LOW, respectively, after C_p.

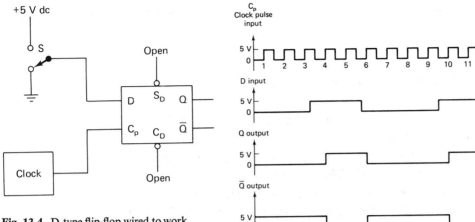

+5 V dc

S

Open

S_D

D   Q

C_p C_D $\overline{Q}$

Open

Clock

C_p
Clock pulse
input

D input

Q output

$\overline{Q}$ output

Fig. 13-4. D-type flip-flop wired to work synchronously with example input and output signal waveforms.

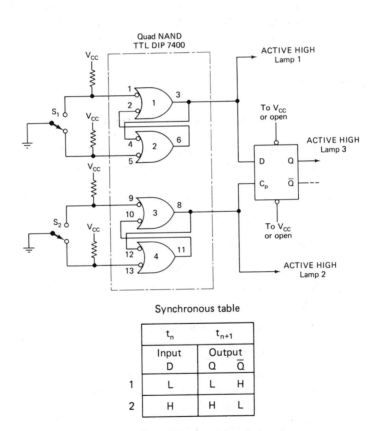

Quad NAND
TTL DIP 7400

V_{CC}

ACTIVE HIGH
Lamp 1

S_1 V_{CC}

To V_{CC}
or open

ACTIVE HIGH
Lamp 3

D   Q

C_p $\overline{Q}$

V_{CC}

S_2 V_{CC}

To V_{CC}
or open

ACTIVE HIGH
Lamp 2

Synchronous table

	t_n	t_{n+1}	
	Input D	Output Q	$\overline{Q}$
1	L	L	H
2	H	H	L

t_n is the time before the positive clock pulse.

t_{n+1} is the time after the positive clock pulse.

Fig. 13-5. The D-type flip-flop operated synchronously, and its synchronous table.

245

Summary

1. Synchronous operation of a D-type FF requires a clock (square wave) applied to its C_p input.

2. The D and C_p inputs of the D-type FF are used during synchronous operation. During synchronous operation, the $\overline{S_D}$ and $\overline{C_D}$ inputs are held HIGH or open.

3. When working synchronously, the Q and $\bar{Q}$ outputs of the D-type FF cannot change until a HIGH-going clock pulse is applied.

4. A HIGH on the D input puts the D-type FF in a set mode, which means that its Q output goes HIGH on the next leading edge C_p input.

5. After the D-type FF is set, it remains set as long as its D input is held HIGH regardless of the number of clock pulse inputs.

6. Generally, the logic level on the D input appears on the Q output after the next HIGH-going C_p input. Therefore, a LOW on the D input causes the Q output to go LOW on the very next leading edge on the C_p input.

Problems 13-2

Answer the following questions by referring to the circuit of Fig. 13-5.

1. When switch S_1 is in the down position, as shown, what condition is lamp L_1 in, lit or not lit?   *Ans.*   _NOT LIT_

2. When switch S_1 is in the down position, what logic level is applied to the D input of the FF, HIGH or LOW?   *Ans.*   _LOW_

3. When S_1 is in the up position, what condition is lamp L_1 in? _LIT_
   What is the logic level on the D input at the same time? _HIGH_

4. When S_2 is in the down position, as shown, lamp L_2 is (lit, not lit), and the logic level on the C_p input is (HIGH, LOW). (Circle the correct answers.)

5. When switch S_2 is in the up position, lamp L_2 is _LIT_ and the logic level on the C_p input is _HIGH_.

6. If the FF is initially in a reset state and S_2 is thrown up and down several times while S_1 is down, the Q output of the FF will (go HIGH, go LOW, stay the same) and lamp L_3 will (light, not light).

7. Now if S_1 is thrown into its up position and S_2 is thrown up and down several times, the Q output will _go High_ and lamp L_3 will _Lit_ .

8. If the switches are initially in positions such as to cause all lamps to be lit, what will happen to L_2 and L_3 if S_1 is thrown to cause L_1 to go out? L_2 will STAY SAME, and L_3 will GO OUT

9. If all lamps are initially lit and S_2 is thrown, causing L_2 to go out, lamp L_1 will STAY lit, and L_3 will STAY lit

10. If initially L_1 and L_3 are lit but L_2 is out, what will happen to L_1 and L_3 when S_2 is thrown, causing L_2 to turn on? L_1 will STAY out, and L_3 will STAY lit

11. If initially L_1 is out but L_2 and L_3 are lit, what will happen to L_1 and L_3 if S_2 is thrown to cause L_2 to go out? L_1 will STAY OUT, and L_3 will STAY lit.

12. If initially L_1 and L_2 are out but L_3 is lit, what will happen to each lamp after S_2 is thrown? L_1 will STAY OUT, L_2 will light, and L_3 will GO OUT

13. If all lamps are initially out, what will happen to each lamp after S_2 is thrown? L_1 will STAY out, L_2 will light, and L_3 will STAY out

13-3 The JK Flip-flop

The logic symbol for the JK flip-flop and IC packages* in which it is available are shown in Fig. 13-6. As shown, this type of FF has five inputs and two outputs. Its controlling inputs for asynchronous operation are the

> $\overline{S_D}$ (direct set, set, or preset) input and the
> $\overline{C_D}$ (direct clear, clear, or reset) input.

The inputs used for synchronous operation are the

> J (jay) input,
> K (kay) input, and the
> $\overline{C_p}$ (clock pulse, trigger T) input.

As with the previously discussed FFs, the outputs are Q and $\bar{Q}$.

The $\overline{S_D}$ and $\overline{C_D}$ inputs of the JK flip-flop work exactly as do the $\overline{S_D}$ and $\overline{C_D}$ inputs of the D-type FF discussed in a previous section. That is, the circles shown in these inputs indicate that they are ACTIVE LOW, and therefore a LOW-going signal

---

*JK flip-flops are available in a number of different type numbers, such as 7476, 7478, 74103, and 74112, to name just a few.

on either the $\overline{S_D}$ or $\overline{C_D}$ input, respectively, will set or reset the FF. The table and circuit of Fig. 13-7 show how the JK FF works and can be used asynchronously.

The JK FF shown in Fig. 13-8 is wired to work synchronously. When used synchronously, the $\overline{S_D}$ and $\overline{C_D}$ inputs of the JK FF are held HIGH or open and a square wave is applied to its $\overline{C_p}$ input. The source of square waves is usually a clock, though a manually operated switch is used in this case. When a mechanical switch, such as S_1, is used to generate clock pulses, a bounceless switch circuit must be used. In this case, when S_1 is down, the $\overline{C_p}$ input is LOW. When S_1 is up, this input is HIGH.

The J and K inputs are controlling inputs. They tell the FF what to do on the next clock pulse. Note that the clock pulse input on the JK FF is circled, which means that it is ACTIVE LOW—not ACTIVE HIGH as the C_p input is on the D-type FF. Thus the clock input never has any effect on the JK FF when rising from a LOW to a HIGH logic level. Instead, the clock input can have effect only when it falls, that is, goes from HIGH to LOW. Because of this feature, this type of JK FF is often called a *trailing edge-triggered* FF.

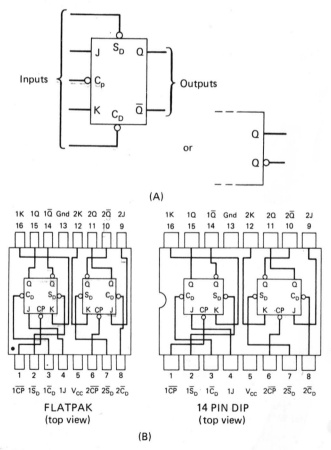

Fig. 13-6. (A) Logic symbol for the JK flip-flop; (B) IC packages containing JK flip-flops (TTL/SSI·5476/7476 Manufacturers' type).

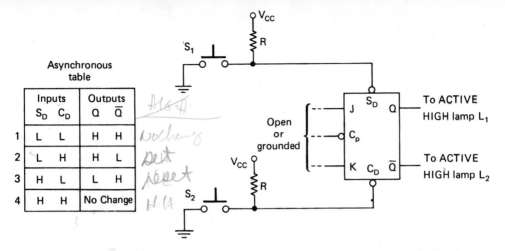

Inputs		Outputs	
S_D	C_D	Q	$\overline{Q}$
1	L	L	H	H
2	L	H	H	L
3	H	L	L	H
4	H	H	No Change	

Handwritten notes: "no change", "Set", "reset"

Fig. 13-7. (A) Table for asynchronous operation of the JK flip-flop; (B) JK flip-flop wired for asynchronous operation.

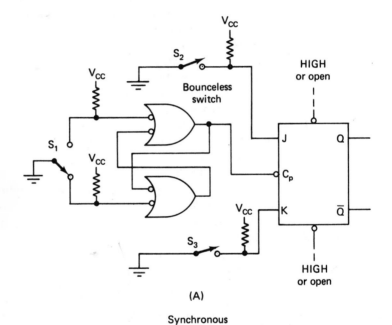

(A)

Synchronous table

	t_n		t_{n+1}		
	Inputs		Outputs		
	J	K	Q	$\overline{Q}$	
1	L	L	No change		Inhibit mode
2	L	H	L	H	Reset mode
3	H	L	H	L	Set mode
4	H	H	Toggle		Toggle mode

Fig. 13-8. (A) JK flip-flop wired to work synchronously; (B) functional table for the JK flip-flop that is working synchronously.

(B)

The functional table in Fig. 13-8 shows how the JK FF behaves synchronously. The term t_n refers to the time before a LOW-going clock pulse is applied. The term t_{n+1} refers to the time after the LOW-going clock pulse.

Row 1 of the table shows that if both the J and K inputs are LOW, the Q outputs of the FF will not change. This is an *inhibit mode* of operation. When in an inhibit mode, the JK FF ignores all incoming clock pulses. Thus if it is in a set state before the J and K inputs are pulled LOW, it will remain set regardless of the number of clock pulses applied. On the other hand, if this FF is initially in a reset state, it will remain reset no matter how many clock pulses are applied as long as the J and K inputs are held LOW.

When the J input is LOW and the K input is HIGH, as shown in row 2 of the table, the JK FF is in a reset mode. This means that if $J = 0$ and $K = 1$ at t_n (time before the LOW-going clock pulse), this FF will be reset at t_{n+1} (time after the LOW-going clock pulse). If it initially is in a reset state, when J is made LOW and K is pulled HIGH, the JK FF stays reset regardless of the number of LOW-going clock pulses applied. Therefore, in the circuit of Fig. 13-8, with S_2 closed and S_3 open, the Q output will be LOW after S_1 is thrown up and down several times.

When the J input is HIGH and the K input is LOW, as shown in row 3 of the table, the JK FF is in a set mode. When in the set mode, the JK FF becomes set on the next LOW-going clock pulse. If the FF is already in a set state when placed in a set mode, it will remain set regardless of the number of clock pulses applied. Therefore, when S_2 is open and S_3 is closed, in the circuit of Fig. 13-8, the FF will definitely be in a set state after S_1 is thrown up and down several times.

Row 4 shows that if both the J and K inputs are HIGH (or open), the FF is in the *toggle mode*. When in the toggle mode, the JK FF's outputs change states on each and every LOW-going pulse applied to the $\overline{C}_p$ input.

Sample input and resulting output voltage waveforms for the JK FF are shown in Fig. 13-9. Note that though the FF is placed in a set mode between clock pulses 2 and 3, this FF does not set until the third LOW-going clock pulse arrives. Simi-

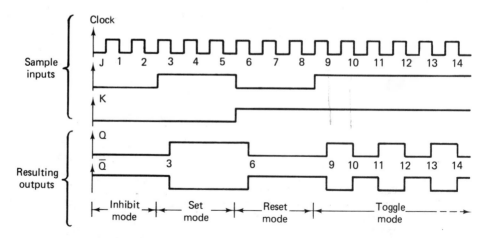

Fig. 13-9. Sample inputs and resulting outputs on the JK flip-flop.

larly, this FF is put in a reset mode between pulses 5 and 6, but it becomes reset only after the sixth pulse arrives. Also note that the output frequency, on the Q or $\bar{Q}$ output, is half the clock frequency when the FF is working in the toggle mode.

Summary

1. The JK FF has direct set and direct clear inputs that can be used for asynchronous operation.

2. The J, K, and $\overline{C_p}$ inputs are used for synchronous operation of the JK FF.

3. The direct set $(\overline{S_D})$ and the direct clear $(\overline{C_D})$ inputs work exactly like the $\overline{S_D}$ and $\overline{C_D}$ inputs of the D-type FF, which work exactly like the ACTIVE LOW $\bar{S}$ and $\bar{R}$ inputs of an RS flip-flop.

4. When both J and K inputs are LOW, the JK FF is in an inhibit mode, which instructs the FF to ignore all clock pulses.

5. When input J is LOW and K is HIGH, the JK FF is in the reset mode. When placed in this mode, the FF resets on the next LOW-going clock pulse.

6. When input J is HIGH and K is LOW, the JK FF is in the set mode. When the FF is instructed to work in the set mode, it becomes set on the next LOW-going pulse applied to its $\overline{C_p}$ input.

7. Because the 7476-type JK FF responds to LOW-going clock pulses, it is referred to as a trailing edge-triggered FF.

8. When both the J and K inputs are HIGH or open, the JK FF is in a toggle mode. In this mode the JK FF changes states on every LOW-going clock pulse.

Problems 13-3

1. Show how Q and $\bar{Q}$ will respond to the clock, J, and K inputs shown in Fig. 13-10. Note that the FF is initially reset; that is, output Q is LOW.

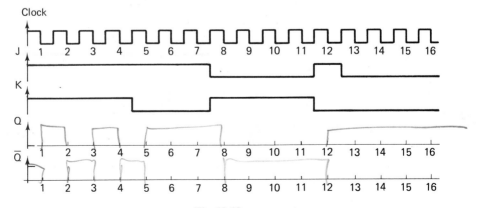

Fig. 13-10.

2. Resketch the circuit of Fig. 12-6, of the previous chapter, using JK FFs instead of RS FFs. Use space below.

3. Can the JK FF be used with a mechanical switch to construct a bounceless switch? __Yes__ Why? _____

Because it is triggered on the falling clock pulse. And the very action of Flip-Flop prevents bounces. ONCE SET THE SAME SIGNAL AGAIN & AGAIN DOES NOT change the output.

$\overline{S_D}$ & $\overline{C_D}$ SAME AS $\overline{S}$ & $\overline{R}$ INPUTS

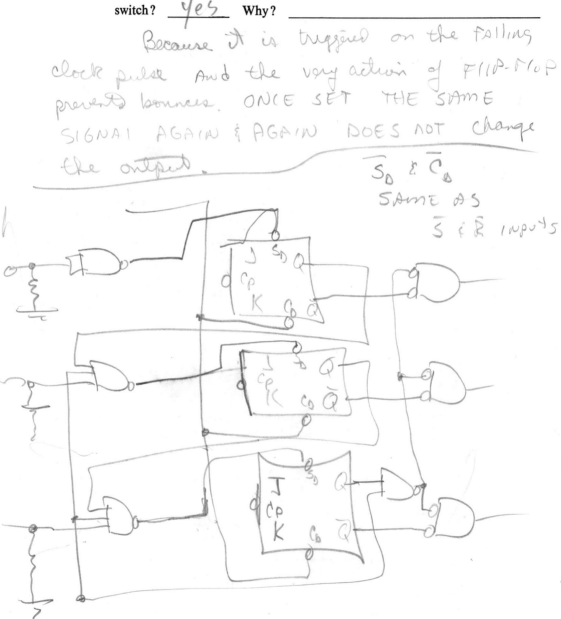

Experiment 13-1   D-Type Flip-flops

Purpose

To become familiar with the operation of the D-type flip-flop.

Equipment

Digital breadboard kit
7474 dual D flip-flop

Procedure

1. Wire the circuit of Fig. L 13-1. Leave S_3 LOW, and the C_p input should be normally LOW.

2. Apply power. Starting with switches $\hat{S}_1$ and S_2 in the L position, make the necessary changes, and fill in the table below. *Note:* When changing input switches, change only one at a time. That is, when going from the first to the second condition, leave C_D LOW and make S_D HIGH. Then leave S_D HIGH and make C_D LOW, etc.

S_D	C_D	Q	$\bar{Q}$
L	L	H	H
H	L	L	H
H	H	L	H
H	L	L	H
H	H	L	H
L	H	H	L
H	H	H	L
L	H	H	L
L	L	H	H

3. Now we shall check the synchronous operation. CLEAR the flip-flop with S_1; then make S_1 and S_2 both HIGH.

4. With S_3 LOW, CLOCK the flip-flop once by depressing the pushbutton switch. What is the state of the Q output? ____High to Low____

5. CLOCK the circuit several more times. What happens to the output Q? ____NOTHING   NO   CHANGE____

6. Next, make the D input HIGH. CLOCK the circuit once. What is the state of the Q output? ____Low to High____

253

7. Keeping the *D* input HIGH, CLOCK the circuit several more times. What happens to output *Q*?   <u>NO   C HAN 6E</u>

8. Experiment on your own, making the *D* input HIGH or LOW; then CLOCK the circuit several times until you are sure you understand the operation.

9. Make the C_D input LOW. Then make the *D* input HIGH, and CLOCK the circuit. What happens?   <u>Q RemAi n s LOW</u>

10. Now make S_1 HIGH and S_2 LOW. What is the state of output *Q*?
<u>High</u>

11. Make the *D* input LOW, and CLOCK the circuit. What happens to output *Q*?
<u>RemAin s High</u>

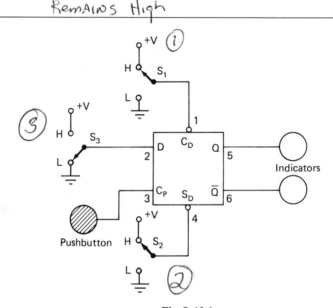

Fig. L 13-1.

Quiz for Experiment 13-1

1. To CLEAR the 7474, the C_D input should be made (HIGH, LOW).

2. To SET the flip-flop, the S_D input should be made (HIGH, LOW).

3. If both S_D and C_D inputs are LOW, the outputs will be (set, reset, both HIGH, both LOW).

4. If either the S_D or C_D inputs are LOW, the flip-flop (can, cannot) be CLOCKed.

5. Suppose both S_D and C_D are HIGH and Q is LOW. If D is made HIGH, the flip-flop will (set immediately, reset immediately, set when CLOCKed, reset when CLOCKed.)

6. Suppose S_D and C_D are both HIGH and Q is HIGH. If D is made HIGH, the flip-flop will (reset immediately, not change even when CLOCKed, reset when CLOCKed).

7. Synchronous operation refers to (the S_D and C_D operation, CLOCKed operation).

8. In synchronous operation, the Q output takes on the same state as the D input when CLOCKed (true, false).

9. Synchronous operation is possible only if S_D and C_D are both HIGH (true, false).

10. Asynchronous operation refers to the S_D and C_D inputs being independent of the CLOCK (true, false).

Experiment 13-2 JK Flip-flops

Purpose

To become familiar with the operation of JK flip-flops.

Equipment

Digital breadboard kit
7476 dual JK flip-flop

Procedure

Since the S_D and C_D inputs to the JK flip-flop perform exactly the same as those on the 7474 D-type flip-flop, we shall not repeat that part of the experiment. Whenever you are instructed to CLEAR the flip-flop, make the C_D input LOW and then return it to the HIGH position, and similarly for the S_D input. As before, both the S_D and C_D inputs should remain HIGH for synchronous operation.

1. Wire the circuit of Fig. L 13-2.

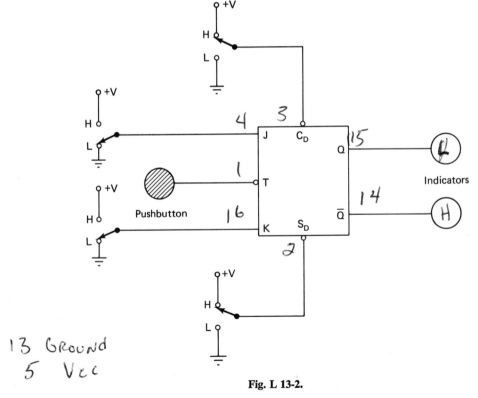

13 GROUND
5 Vcc

Fig. L 13-2.

256

2. CLEAR the flip-flop. Make both J and K inputs LOW. Then CLOCK the flip-flop by depressing the bounceless pushbutton switch once. What is the state of output Q? <u>STAYS LOW</u> CLOCK the flip-flop several more times. Is there any change? <u>   NO ChANGe   </u>

3. Now make the J input HIGH and the K input LOW. CLOCK the FF several times. What happens? <u>   Q   becomes High   </u>

4. Make the J input LOW again and the K input LOW. (The Q output should be HIGH from step 3.) CLOCK the FF several times. What happens? <u>NC   </u>

5. Now make the K input HIGH and the J input LOW. CLOCK the FF several times. What happens? <u>   Q goes LOW   </u>

---

6. Finally, make *both* J and K HIGH and CLOCK the FF several times. What happens? $\overline{Q}$ sLow Q $\rightarrow$ High   1ST pulse

        Q$\rightarrow$High Q $\rightarrow$ Low   2^{d} pulse

                    etc.

14

Counters

Introduction

JK flip-flops have many uses. Here we shall see how they are used and work in serial counters. Counters are used to reduce the frequency of a clock or to keep track of the number of incoming pulses and then initiate action when an appropriate number of pulses arrives. For example, in the rat-conditioning logic circuits discussed previously, we might want to count the number of times the rats request food. Thus if they exceed the number of tries we allow them, a counter will disable the feed system or execute an appropriate warning signal.

14-1 Serially Connected Flip-flops

The simplest serial counter is one of two JK FFs, as shown in Fig. 14-1(A). The set and reset inputs and the J and K inputs are tied HIGH or left open, causing each FF to work synchronously in a toggle mode. When toggling, each FF's Q outputs change state on each LOW-going signal on its $\overline{C_p}$ input. Note that the clock input drives the first (left) FF and that the output of this first FF drives the $\overline{C_p}$ input of the second FF. When the clock is running and if the FFs are initially in a reset state, this counter's action is as shown in Figs. 14-1(B) and (C). The numbers in the clock input column of the functional table represent the numbers of the LOW-going clock pulses applied to the $\overline{C_p}$ input of the first FF. The A and B columns show the Q outputs of the first and second FFs, respectively.

In both Figs. 14-1(B) and (C), note that in this case initially (clock input 0) both A and B outputs are LOW; that is, both FFs are in a reset state. Then after the LOW-

258

going clock pulse 1, output *A* goes HIGH (first FF sets). This HIGH-going output *A* does not set the second FF because only LOW-going inputs cause toggling. Then after clock pulse 2, output *A* goes back LOW. This LOW-going signal toggles the second FF, causing it to set; that is, its output *B* goes HIGH. After the next clock input 3, output *A* goes HIGH again, and output *B* remains HIGH. Then clock pulse 4 toggles the first FF, which in turn toggles the second, and thus both FFs return to a reset state. Therefore, two FFs, wired to work as a serial (2-bit) counter and driven by a clock, will *naturally* progress through 2^2 or 4 distinct states. It is important to note, in the table, that this counter counts in binary, output *A* being the LSB.

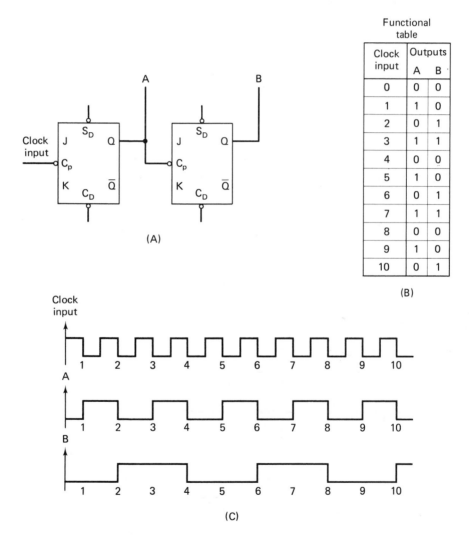

Functional table

Clock input	Outputs	
	A	B
0	0	0
1	1	0
2	0	1
3	1	1
4	0	0
5	1	0
6	0	1
7	1	1
8	0	0
9	1	0
10	0	1

(B)

(A)

(C)

Fig. 14-1. (A) JK flip-flops wired to work as a two-bit serial counter; (B) functional table of the two-bit serial counter; (C) timing diagram for the two-bit serial counter.

If we add another FF to the 2-bit counter, we get a 3-bit counter, such as in Fig. 14-2(A). With a clock input applied, it will naturally count through 2^3 or 8 states before starting over again. Note in Fig. 14-2(B) that the 3-bit serial counter also progresses in binary, with output A being the LSB. Also note in Fig. 14-2(C) that output A, as before, changes logic levels every time the clock input goes LOW. Output B, in turn, changes states every time the $\overline{C_p}$ input of the second FF goes LOW, which is when output A goes LOW. Likewise, output C changes every time signal B swings LOW.

As we would expect, four FFs in a 4-bit serial counter will naturally count through 2^4 or 16 states. Each additional FF simply doubles the number of possible states.

Fig. 14-2. (A) JK flip-flops wired to work as a three-bit serial counter; (B) functional table of the three-bit serial counter; (C) timing diagram for the three-bit serial counter.

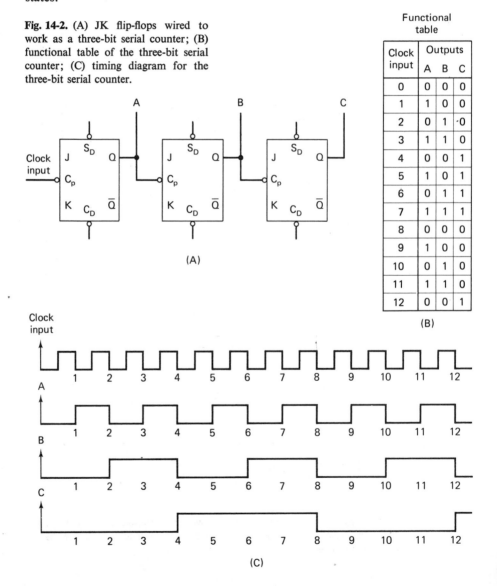

Functional table

Clock input	Outputs		
	A	B	C
0	0	0	0
1	1	0	0
2	0	1	0
3	1	1	0
4	0	0	1
5	1	0	1
6	0	1	1
7	1	1	1
8	0	0	0
9	1	0	0
10	0	1	0
11	1	1	0
12	0	0	1

(B)

Summary

1. JK flip-flops wired serially in a toggle mode will naturally count in binary.
2. The output frequency of the first FF is twice the frequency of the second FF, the output frequency of the second FF is twice the frequency of the third FF, etc.
3. The total number of natural states that a serial counter has is 2^n, where n is the number of FFs in the counter.

Problem 14-1

1. Referring to the 4-bit serial (binary) counter in Fig. 14-3(A), show how its A through D outputs change with each LOW-going clock pulse in the functional table in Fig. 14-3(B). Also finish the timing diagram in Fig. 14-3(C).

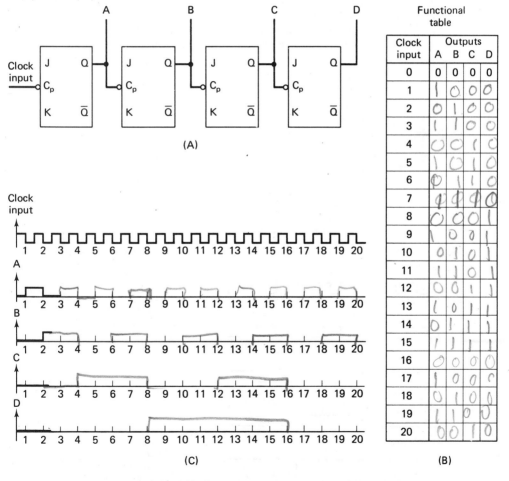

Clock input	A	B	C	D
0	0	0	0	0
1	1	0	0	0
2	0	1	0	0
3	1	1	0	0
4	0	0	1	0
5	1	0	1	0
6	0	1	1	0
7	1	1	1	0
8	0	0	0	1
9	1	0	0	1
10	0	1	0	1
11	1	1	0	1
12	0	0	1	1
13	1	0	1	1
14	0	1	1	1
15	1	1	1	1
16	0	0	0	0
17	1	0	0	0
18	0	1	0	0
19	1	1	0	0
20	0	0	1	0

(A)

(B)

(C)

Fig. 14-3. (A) JK flip-flops wired to work as a four-bit serial counter; (B) functional table of the four-bit serial counter; (C) timing diagram for the four-bit serial counter.

14-2 Altering the Natural Count Sequence

The natural counting sequence of a serial counter can be changed. For example, the 3-bit counter of Fig. 14-2 naturally counts through eight states. If some application demands a counter, say with seven states, one of the natural states can be skipped. The circuits of Fig. 14-4 show two ways this can be done. The circuit in Fig. 14-4(A) is wired to skip a state, the state with outputs A, B, and C all HIGH (equivalent to decimal 7). That is, the use of the NAND gate does not permit all outputs to *stay* HIGH *between* clock pulses. Thus as this modified 3-bit counter arrives to the state that is equivalent to decimal 7, outputs A, B, and C do go HIGH but only for an instant. At this instant, three HIGHs are applied to the input of the NAND gate, causing its output, the $\overline{\text{RESET}}$ signal, to go LOW. The ACTIVE LOW $\overline{\text{RESET}}$ signal output from the NAND resets all the FFs, causing their outputs A through C to go LOW and stay that way until the next clock pulse. Thus, as shown in the timing diagram for this circuit, outputs A, B, and C are all HIGH only momentarily, long enough to cause a LOW-going $\overline{\text{RESET}}$ pulse to each FF's $\overline{C_D}$ (direct clear) input. Therefore, immediately after the seventh pulse, but before the eighth, outputs A through C are all LOW.

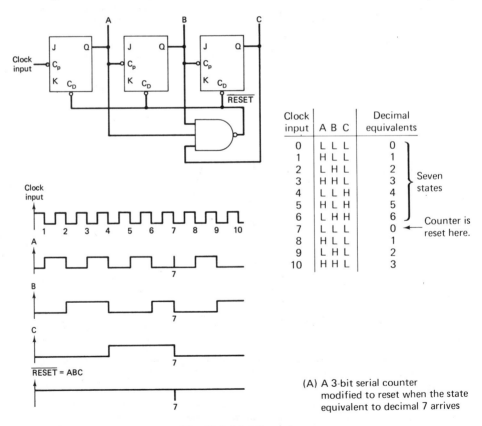

Clock input	A B C	Decimal equivalents	
0	L L L	0	
1	H L L	1	
2	L H L	2	
3	H H L	3	Seven
4	L L H	4	states
5	H L H	5	
6	L H H	6	
7	L L L	0	Counter is reset here.
8	H L L	1	
9	L H L	2	
10	H H L	3	

$\overline{\text{RESET}} = ABC$

(A) A 3-bit serial counter modified to reset when the state equivalent to decimal 7 arrives

Fig. 14-4. Mod 7 counters.

The circuit Fig. 14-4(B) is similar to the circuit in Fig. 14-4(A) except that it skips states zero and seven when driven by a series of clock pulses. That is, instead of being reset zero, the counter in Fig. 14-4(B) is preset to state one (a state equivalent to decimal 1). In this case, the natural state seven, with outputs *A* through *C* being HIGH, exists only momentarily, long enough to preset the counter. For the instant state seven exists, the *Q* outputs of the FFs are all HIGH, causing a momentary ACTIVE LOW $\overline{\text{PRESET}}$ signal out of the NAND gate. This pulse causes the first FF to stay set and the other two to become reset and thus presets the counter to a state equivalent to decimal 1.

The circuit (B) of Fig. 14-4 will repetitively progress through six states when a series of clock pulses is applied. Counters that count through six states are often called mod 6 counters. Similarly, counters that have 7 or 9 states are called mod 7 or mod 9 counters, respectively.

The output frequency of the square wave from the last FF in a serial counter is much lower than the frequency of the clock driving the first FF. If a 3-bit counter is repetitively counting through its eight natural states, the output frequency of the last FF is one-eighth of the clock input frequency. Similarly, then, output *C* of the mod 7 counter in (A) of Fig. 14-4 is one-seventh the clock input frequency. Counters, therefore, are frequently used as square-wave frequency dividers in digital systems.

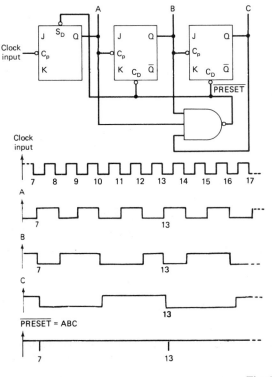

Clock inputs	A B C	Decimal equivalent	
0	L L L	0	
1	H L L	1	
2	L H L	2	
:	:	:	
6	L H H	6	Counter
7	H L L	1	is preset
8	L H L	2	here.
9	H H L	3	Six
10	L L H	4	states
11	H L H	5	
12	L H H	6	
13	H L L	1	Preset
14	L H L	2	here
15	H H L	3	
16	L L H	4	

(B) A 3-bit serial counter modified to preset to a state equivalent to decimal 1 **after state 6**

Fig. 14-4. (Cont.)

Summary

1. With additional gating circuitry, serial counters can be made to repetitively count through any number of states that is less than the counter's natural number of states.

2. The natural number of states is the number of states that a serial counter progresses through when no external gating is used to reset or preset the counter.

3. The natural number of states can be altered by resetting or presetting the counter.

4. A counter can be made to skip higher counts by using a gate to reset it.

5. A counter can be made to skip lower counts by using a gate to preset it.

Problems 14-2

1. With reference to the circuit of Fig. 14-5, in what states, set or reset, are the individual FFs in at the instant before the NAND gate's output goes LOW? FF *A* is ___HIGH___ , FF *B* is ___Low___ , FF *C* is ___HIGH___ .

2. The circuit of Fig. 14-5 is being (reset, preset) at decimal equivalent number ___5___ and therefore can be called a mod ___5___ counter.

3. The table in Fig. 14-5 shows the initial states of outputs *A* through *C*. Show how these outputs change, and their decimal equivalents, after each clock input pulse.

4. With reference to the circuit of Fig. 14-6, in what states are the individual FFs in at the instant before the NAND gate's output goes LOW? FF *A* is ___HIGH___, FF *B* is ___HIGH___ , FF *C* is ___HIGH___ .

5. The circuit of Fig. 14-6 is being (reset, preset) at the decimal equivalent number ___4___ . Immediately after being (reset, preset) this counter is in a state whose decimal equivalent is ___3___ .

6. The circuit of Fig. 14-6 can be called a mod ___2___ counter.

7. The table in Fig. 14-6 shows the initial states of outputs *A* through *C*. Show what logic states these outputs become, and their decimal equivalents, after each clock input pulse.

14-3 Counter Applications

We can return to the rat-conditioning logic system for an application of a counter. The rat-conditioning logic, we can recall, began with only combinational logic that required the rats to request food one at a time (Figs. 8-10, 8-11, 8-12, etc). We

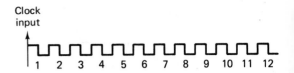

Clock input

Clock input	A B C	Decimal equivalents
0	L L L	0
1	H L L	1
2	L H L	2
3	H H L	3
4	L L H	4
5	L L L	0
6	H L L	1
7	L H L	2
8	H H L	3
9	L L H	4
10	L L L	0
11	H L L	1
12	L H L	2

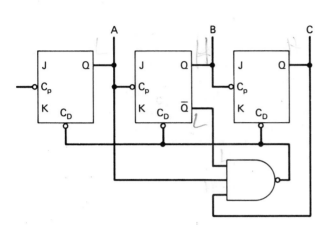

Fig. 14-5.

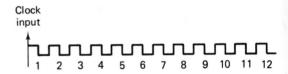

Clock input

Clock input	A B C	Decimal equivalents
0	L H H	6
1	H H H	7
2	H L L	1
3	L H L	2
4	H H L	3
5	L L H	4
6	H H L	3
7	L L H	4
8	H H L	3
9	L L H	3
10	H H L	4
11	L L H	3
12	H H L	4

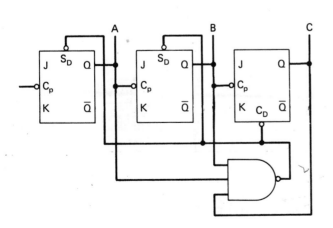

Fig. 14-6.

H H L

265

then modified the system to include sequential logic that required the rats to request food not only one at a time but also in a specific order (Figs. 12-6 and 12-7). That is, if the circuit, say, of Fig. 8-11 is combined with circuits of Figs. 12-6 and 12-7, Alfred must request food first, then Brenda, and finally Charlie. Otherwise they cannot get fed until the next feed-time period. In this combined circuitry, though Alfred is to request food first, there is nothing to inhibit his pushing his button repetitively thereafter provided that he does not do it when the busy light is on. Similarly, Brenda must request after Alfred, but after Alfred makes his request she can request many times as long as she does not do it at the same time another rat does. Of course, then, Charlie likewise must wait until Brenda requests at least once, but thereafter he can push his button repetitively. We shall now add another imposition on Alfred, Brenda, and Charlie by adding the circuit of Fig. 14-7 to the circuitry already mentioned. This circuit has a counter that counts the number of *single* requests made by any one of the rats.* It does this by monitoring

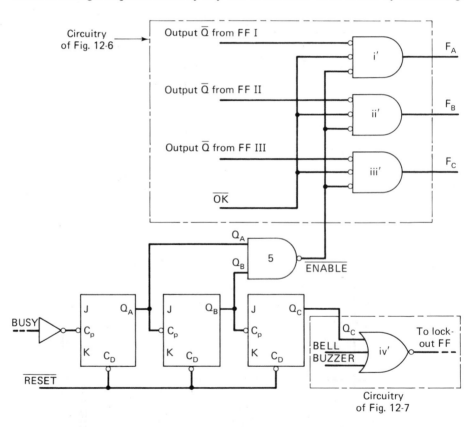

Fig. 14-7. Addition to rat-conditioning circuitry that allows the rats to get fed only if exactly three requests are made by them.

* The *A, B,* and *C* signals must be obtained through bounceless switches as shown in Fig. 12-9.

the BUSY signal via the inverter. Only if three and only three separate requests are made are the Q_A and Q_B signals HIGH, which generate an ACTIVE LOW $\overline{\text{ENABLE}}$ signal. The three-input NOR gates i′, ii′, and iii′ are able to respond to signals from FFs I, II, and III in Fig. 14-7 only when both the $\overline{\text{OK}}$ and the $\overline{\text{ENABLE}}$ signal are ACTIVE LOW. These three-input NORs replace the two-input NORs i, ii, and iii in Fig. 12-6. If the rats collectively request food more than three times in any feed-time period, the Q_C output of the third FF in Fig. 14-7 goes HIGH. This sets the lock-out FF via the three-input NOR gate iv′. NOR gate iv′ replaces the two-input NOR gate iv in Fig. 12-7. We can recall that the lock-out FF, once set, forces the rats to wait until the next feed time.

Counters used in a frequency divider are shown in the block diagram circuit of Fig. 14-8. Overall, this system receives and divides line frequency 60 Hz by 60, giving an output frequency of 1 Hz. The voltage divider, consisting of the resistor R and potentiometer POT, serves to reduce the 60-Hz source voltage to a value appropriate for the Schmitt trigger input. The Schmitt trigger squares up the input sine wave to make it more compatible for the first counter that works better with a logic-type input signal. This first counter is a mod 6 (divide by 6) counter. Its output frequency is one-sixth its input frequency or 10 Hz. This 10 Hz then drives the input of the mod 10 (decade or divide by 10) counter, whose resulting output is 1 Hz. A mod 10 counter is commonly called a decade counter because it counts by tens (decades).

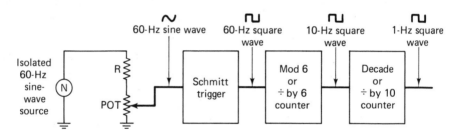

Fig. 14-8. Mod 6 and Mod 10 counters combined to work as a divide by 60 counter.

Problems 14-3

1. Show how to connect three JK FFs in a serial counter with appropriate gating that will reset the counter on each sixth clock input pulse.

2. Show how to connect four JK FFs in a serial counter with appropriate gating that will reset the counter on each tenth clock input pulse.

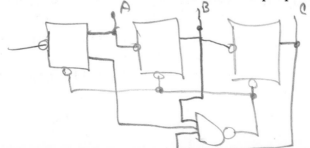

Experiment 14-1   Binary Counters

Purpose

This experiment will familiarize you with a 4-bit binary counter. You will learn how to make the 7493 chip count and how to reset it to zero.

Materials

Digital breadboard kit
7493 4-bit binary counter

Procedure

1. Wire the 7493 into the socket strip as shown in Fig. L 14-1 and apply power. With both toggle switches in the 1 position, the counter should be reset; that is, all outputs should be LOW. Pulsing input A with the bounceless switch should have no effect on the outputs.

2. Next, put both toggle switches to the 0 position. This will allow the chip to count when pulses are applied to input A_{in} (pin 14).

3. Depress the bounceless switch a few times. Notice that the counter outputs change states each time a *negative-going* signal is applied. The circles on the $\overline{C_p}$ inputs (Fig. L 14-1) show that the inputs are ACTIVE LOW; that is, a signal going from HIGH to LOW will toggle the inputs.

4. Experiment with pulsing the input and switching the reset toggle switches in various combinations, that is, either one or both toggle switches in 1 and 0 positions. Observe what happens to the outputs.

The set up conditions for counting and resetting are important for using the chip correctly. To make sure that you test every possible combination, experimentally check each of the following statements, and then circle *true* or *false* to show what you have learned.

a. The chip will count (outputs will change when input A_{in} is pulsed) if both R_0 inputs are grounded (true, false).

b. The chip will count if *either* input is grounded while the other is HIGH (true, false).

c. The chip will count if both R_0 inputs are HIGH (true, false).

d. Making both R_0 inputs HIGH causes immediate reset of outputs, regardless of the count number (true, false).

e. The chip will count if both inputs are left "hanging open," that is, disconnected (true, false). Explain why this is so.

When they are left open they are considered high

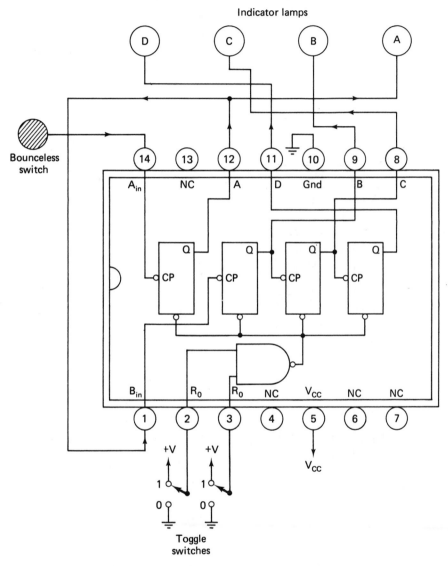

Fig. L 14-1. 7493 four-bit binary counter.

Both switches HIGH   Clear

NAND →0

5. Now that you know how to reset the counter, reset the outputs to zero and then ground at least one R_0 input. Then slowly depress the bounceless switch 16 times and fill in Table L 14-1. You should observe a binary progression of numbers.

6. Next, feed a 1-Hz clock into input A and observe the outputs. You should again observe the same progression of outputs as listed in the table. Try resetting with the toggle switches at any time during the count sequence. Does resetting occur as you expected? Explain.

D	C	B	A	Count
0	0	0	0	0
0	0	0	0	1
0	0	0	1	2
0	0	1	0	3
0	0	1	1	4
0	1	0	0	5
0	1	0	1	6
0	1	1	0	7
0	1	1	1	8
1	0	0	0	9
1	0	0	1	10
1	0	1	0	11
1	0	1	1	12
1	1	0	0	13
1	1	0	1	14
1	1	1	0	15
1	1	1	1	16

Tab. L 14-1.

Experiment 14-2   Modulo *N* Binary Counter

Purpose

You will learn to use the 7493 4-bit binary counter chip so that it will automatically reset at any predetermined count. This is called a *modulo N* counter. (*N* is the number of the count at which reset occurs.) This type of counter is very useful in frequency divider and computer circuits.

Materials

Digital breadboard kit
7493 and either a 7408 or 7400

Procedure

1. Hook up the 7493 as shown in Fig. L 14-2(A). Notice that the R_0 inputs are not connected to toggle switches but to outputs *B* and *C*. In Experiment 14-1, you learned that the counter will reset to zero when *both* R_0 inputs go HIGH. Thus in the circuit of Fig. L 14-2(A), when both *B* and *C* go HIGH, the counter will reset.

2. Apply power to the chip. (*Note:* When power is first applied, the counter may come on in any of 16 possible output states by sheer chance.) Disregard the starting condition, and pulse the bounceless switch until all outputs are LOW.

3. Starting with all outputs LOW, slowly depress the bounceless switch and fill in Table L 14-2(A).

If your circuit is wired correctly, your table should progress in binary up to the fifth count and then go back to all zeros on the sixth count and repeat all over again.

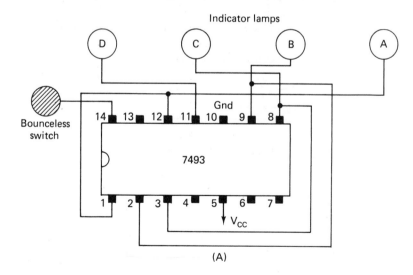

(A)

Fig. L 14-2.

4. Connect the 1-Hz clock to input *A* and observe that the six-count sequence repeats over and over. Since this counter resets every sixth count, it is called a *modulo 6* (mod 6 for short), or divide by six, counter. It can be used as a frequency divider. If the output is taken at output *C* and the input signal is applied to A_{in}, the output frequency will be one-sixth of the input frequency.

It is a simple matter to build any modulus counter. Notice that the R_0 inputs to the 7493 chip are actually ACTIVE HIGH inputs to a two-input gate. Thus all you have to do is look at the binary count table and determine which outputs go HIGH at the desired reset number. For example, in Table L 14-2(B), we see that if we start with all outputs in the zero state, the *first* time the *B* and *C* outputs both go HIGH is at the sixth count. Thus connecting them both to the R_0 inputs will cause the counter to reset at the instant both *B and C* go HIGH.

5. Shut off the power and disconnect the wire from the *B* output to the R_0 input. Tie both R_0 inputs together; that is, output *C* should feed both R_0 inputs. Now apply power and feed in a 1-Hz signal as before. At what count does the counter reset? __4__ . Explain why reset occurs when it does. __$C \rightarrow High$__

6. In Fig. L 14-2(B), show how you would wire the chip to build a mod 5 counter. Then wire the chip and see if it works. If it does not, examine the binary table and make corrections until it does work; then correct your drawing accordingly.

7. Next, examine the truth table and determine how you would wire the circuit to build a mod 10 counter. (This is also called a decade counter.) Draw your circuit on Fig. L 14-2(C). Wire it on the chip and make sure it works.

8. Suppose you need a mod 13 counter. Then you need a circuit, or gate, to detect the count of binary 13, which is 1101. But since the 7493 chip only has a two-input gate on the reset line, you must use some external gating to AND together the *D and C and A* outputs. On Fig. L 14-2(D), draw the diagram of your mod 13 counter, showing whatever external gating is needed. Build your circuit using either a 7408 or 7400 chip for your external gates. (You learned in a previous experiment how to use a NAND gate in place of an AND gate, and so either chip can be made to work.) Apply power and make sure the circuit works. Correct your diagram once the circuit works properly.

If you understand this experiment thoroughly, you should be able to build *any* modulus counter from mod 2 to mod 16 with the 7493 chip.

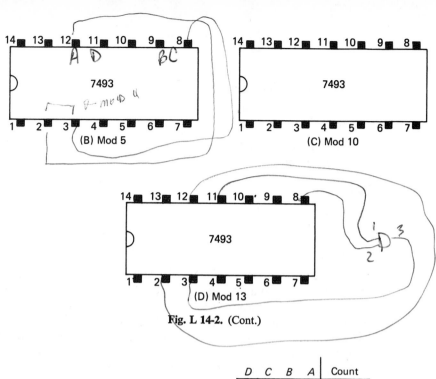

Fig. L 14-2. (Cont.)

D	C	B	A	Count
0	0	0	0	0
0	0	0	1	1
0	0	0	1	1
0	0	1	0	2
0	0	1	1	3
0	0	1	1	3
0	1	0	0	4
0	1	0	0	4
0	1	0	1	5
0	0	0	0	6
0	1	1	0	6
0	0	0	1	7
0	1	1	1	7
0	0	1	0	8
1	0	0	0	8
0	0	1	1	9
1	0	0	1	9
0	1	0	0	10
1	0	1	0	10
0	1	0	1	11
1	0	1	1	11
0	0	0	0	12
1	1	0	0	12
1	1	0	1	13
1	1	1	0	14
1	1	1	1	15

Tab. L 14-2A and B.

Experiment 14-3 Decade Counters

Purpose

You will become familiar with the 7490 decade counter, which is one of the most often used counters available.

Materials

Digital breadboard kit
7490

Procedure

1. Wire the 7490 decade counter as shown in Fig. L 14-3. Depress the bounceless switch until all outputs are zero; then slowly pulse input A in and fill in Table L 14-3. If your circuit is wired correctly, you should notice a binary count sequence up to the ninth pulse; then the counter resets automatically on the tenth pulse. The chip is internally connected to reset every tenth count without the need for reset signals to the R_0 inputs, as was needed for the 7493 chip. This chip is very useful in all sorts of decimal counting and measuring systems.

2. Next, connect both R_0 inputs to toggle switches, and drive input A_{in} with the 1-Hz clock. Experiment by switching HIGHs and LOWs to the R_0 inputs while the counter is counting. R_0 Both High Reset to 0

In your own words, explain the similarities and differences between the 7490 chip and the 7493 chip with regard to resetting.

3. Disconnect the bounceless switch from input A_{in}, and connect a toggle switch to input A_{in}. Reset the counter, and then ground at least one R_0 input. Now flip the toggle switch HIGH and LOW a few times while observing the outputs. Does the count progress in normal binary sequence? NO . Explain what you think is happening. (It will not be obvious what is happening by just observing the outputs because things are happening too fast to see. You will have to reason this one out.) THIS IS NOT A BOUNCEless switch AS IT BOUNCES iT COUNTS

Although the 7490 is internally connected to reset at the tenth count, it can also be used to build lower modulus counters, just as the 7493.

4. Disconnect the wire between the A output and the BD input (pin 12 to pin 1). Reset the chip normally and then drive the BD input (pin 1) with the 1-Hz clock.

A is
IGNORED

What happens to output A while the chip is clocked? NOTHING What is the modulus of the counter composed of outputs B, C, and D? MOD 5

274

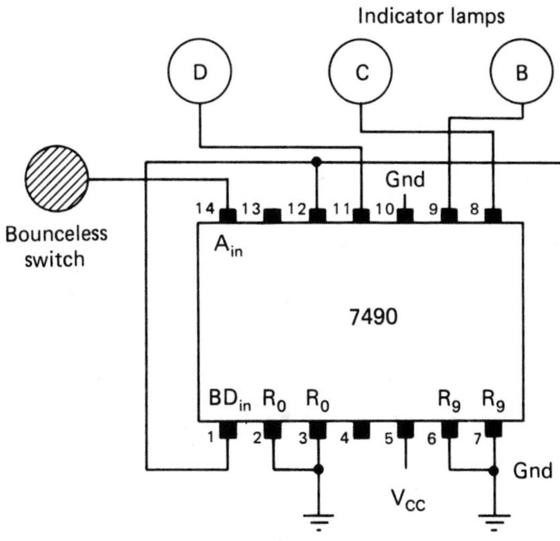
Indicator lamps
D
C
B
A
Bounceless switch
14
13
12
11
10
9
8
Gnd
A_in
7490
BD_in R_0 R_0
R_9 R_9
1
2
3
4
5
6
7
Gnd
V_CC

Fig. L 14-3.

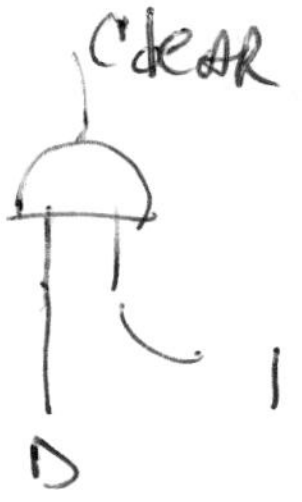
Clear
D

D → 1 Reset
mod 8

Tab. L 14-3.

D	*C*	*B*	*A*	Count
0	0	0	0	0
0	0	0	1	1
0	0	1	0	2
0	0	1	1	3
0	1	0	0	4
0	1	0	1	5
0	1	1	0	6
0	1	1	1	7
1	0	0	0	8
1	0	0	1	9
1	0	1	0	10

5. Now connect the bounceless switch to input A_{in}. Disconnect the clock from input *BD*, and reset the counter. (Leave input *BD* unconnected.) Depress the bounceless switch a few times. Does output *A* change states each time the switch is depressed? Yes (Switches between High & Low). Does output *B*, *C*, or *D* change states when the switch is depressed? NO STAY low

6. Next, connect the 1-Hz clock to input *BD* again. With the clock running, depress the bounceless switch input to A_{in} a few times at random. If your circuit is working properly, you should notice that output *A* acts as an independent mod 2 (divide by 2) counter and that the *B*, *C*, and *D* outputs act like a mod 5 counter.

7. Finally, with the 1-Hz clock still driving the *BD* input, try resetting the counter both with the *A* output HIGH and then with the *A* output LOW at various times during the *B*, *C*, and *D* count sequence. Do both counters reset together?

YES A → HIGH BCD counting All → Low (0)
A → Low BCD " All → Low (0)

15

Shift Registers, Latches, and Up/Down Counters

Introduction

Very commonly used digital devices are discussed in this chapter. How they can be interconnected to perform a useful function is also emphasized. As in preceding chapters, work with both the text and laboratory sections is very important. Each section supports the other to establish maximum understanding of the principles involved.

15-1 The Basic Shift Register

A shift register constructed with JK FFs is shown in Fig. 15-1. Its name somewhat describes what it does. It is able to accept serial digital data* and *shift* it to the right, from FF to FF. The term *serial data* refers to digital information that can be processed or transferred 1 bit with each clock input pulse. In the case of the 4-bit shift register of Fig. 15-1, a 4-bit word can be serially shifted into it and therefore be available at its *A* through *D* parallel outputs, after four clock pulses.

Serial data can be processed or transferred via a single pair of conductors. Telephone lines, for example, are commonly used to carry serial data between digital systems. Parallel data, on the other hand, require more conductors, but they can be processed or transferred much faster. The circuit of Fig. 15-1 is often used as a serial-to-parallel converter.

*The term data or data words, used in this chapter, refers to digital information in general. In computer language, data words, more specifically, are words that represent quantities or numbers as opposed to instruction words that are used to tell the computer what to do.

We learned previously that a FF is able to store (remember) a logic 1 or 0. The combination of FFs in Fig. 15-1 is able to store 4-bit words. Four-bit words enter this register by shifting in from the left by way of the SERIAL INPUT. The logic level on the SERIAL INPUT determines the level out of the first FF after the next LOW-going CLOCK PULSE. A HIGH on the SERIAL INPUT causes a 1 to shift into the first FF, that is, appear at output A when the CLOCK PULSE goes LOW. A LOW on the SERIAL INPUT causes a 0 at output A on the next LOW-going CLOCK PULSE. At the instant of the CLOCK PULSE, the logic level that was previously at output A moves over to B, and what was on output B moves over to C, and what was on C moves over to D, and what was on D simply disappears.

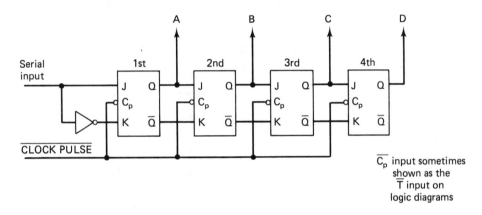

Fig. 15-1. Shift register.

The tables and timing diagrams in Fig. 15-2 show how 0101 (equivalent of decimal 5) and how 0111 (equivalent of decimal 7) are shifted into the register. In both examples, the FFs are initially in the reset state; that is, outputs A through D are initially LOW. Note in Fig. 15-2(A) that the SERIAL INPUT is initially HIGH. This instructs the first FF to set when the LOW-going CLOCK PULSE 1 arrives; that is, a HIGH SERIAL INPUT puts the first FF in a set mode. The second FF is instructed to reset by the first FF; that is, the first FF puts the second in a reset mode. The third FF in turn is told to reset by the second. And the fourth is instructed to reset by the third. Since initially the second, third, and fourth FFs are already reset, they remain reset when CLOCK PULSE 1 arrives.

Before CLOCK PULSE 2 arrives, the SERIAL INPUT signal goes LOW. This tells the first FF to reset. The first FF tells the second to set. The second tells the third to reset, and the third tells the fourth to reset. Thus, immediately after CLOCK PULSE 2, output A goes LOW, output B goes HIGH, and outputs C and D remain LOW.

This circuit's action on CLOCK PULSES 3 and 4 can similarly be analyzed. Note that after CLOCK PULSE 4, the A through D outputs are 0101.

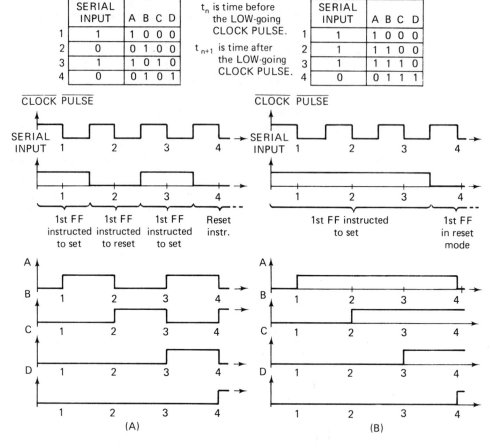

	t_n	t_{n+1}				
	SERIAL INPUT	A	B	C	D	
1	1	1	0	0	0	
2	0	0	1	0	0	
3	1	1	0	1	0	
4	0	0	1	0	1	

t_n is time before the LOW-going CLOCK PULSE.

t_{n+1} is time after the LOW-going CLOCK PULSE.

	t_n	t_{n+1}				
	SERIAL INPUT	A	B	C	D	
1	1	1	0	0	0	
2	1	1	1	0	0	
3	1	1	1	1	0	
4	0	0	1	1	1	

Fig. 15-2. Two examples of CLOCK PULSE and SERIAL INPUT signals and the resulting outputs on the shift register; (A) serial 0101 (decimal 5) shifted in; (B) serial 0111 (decimal 7) shifted in four pulses of the clock.

Problems 15-1

1. How many pulses will it take to shift a serial word into (a) a 5-bit shift register, (b) an 8-bit shift register, and (c) a 12-bit shift register?

2. Sketch a table like those of Fig. 15-2 but with eight rows instead of four. Show the outputs A through D if the serial input is HIGH for the first four clock pulses and LOW for the next four pulses.

15-2 MSI Five-Bit Shift Register

An MSI 5-bit shift register is shown in Fig. 15-3. The term MSI means medium-scale integration. Note that the five FFs, the gates, and inverters are all on a single IC. The IC gates and dual FFs covered in previous chapters are called SSI (small-scale integration) circuits. This shift register is very similar to the one discussed in the last section with the exception of the extra FF, data inputs, and controlling inputs. Note also that the CLOCK input is ACTIVE HIGH (without a circle) in this case. Because this register has five FFs, it is able to store (hold) words up to 5 bits long. Such words can be loaded into this register either serially or in parallel. These words can also read out serially or in parallel.

Up to 5 bits can be simultaneously loaded into this register by way of the P_A through P_E (parallel) inputs. Parallel loading must be preceded by a momentary ACTIVE LOW $\overline{\text{CLEAR}}$ input. This purges the register of all previous data, causing all the Q_A through Q_E outputs to go LOW asynchronously. Data on the P_A through P_E inputs will then enter this register when the LOAD input is pulled ACTIVE HIGH. Thus a HIGH on the LOAD input enables the NAND gates and allows any data on the P_A through P_E inputs to appear at the Q_A through Q_E outputs. This type of register can store the words loaded into it and therefore is frequently used as a temporary memory such as used in hand calculators.

Words up to 5 bits long can be serially shifted out of the register in a series of CLOCK pulses. Serial output data flow out of the Q_E output. Registers such as this, therefore, are used to convert parallel data to serial data, or to convert serial data to parallel data, or to temporarily store data that can enter either serially or in parallel. If words larger than 5 bit long are to be processed via a register, more than one 5-bit IC register can be used in cascade. These 5-bit registers are cascaded if the Q_E output of the first register is connected to the SERIAL INPUT of the next.

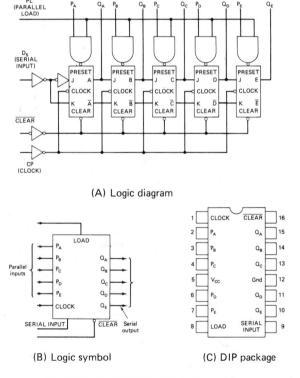

(A) Logic diagram

(B) Logic symbol   (C) DIP package

Fig. 15-3. The 7496 five-bit shift register.

Summary

1. Shift registers are able to accept serial input data, 1 bit with each clock pulse.

2. The number of FFs in a shift register dictates the number of bits that can be stored; four FFs can store up to 4-bit words, five FFs can store up to 5-bit words, etc.

3. Digital information stored in a shift register can be shifted out serially with a series of clock pulses or can be directly read out in parallel.

4. The 7496 5-bit register can accept digital information serially or in parallel.

5. Registers are frequently used as temporary memories.

15-3 The Up/Down Decade Counter

The up/down decade counter, as its name describes, is able to count up (increment) or count down (decrement) in BCD. The BCD words are read off the Q_A through Q_D outputs, output Q_A being the LSB; see Fig. 15-4. These words will either increase or decrease in value with each HIGH-going CLOCK input, depending on whether we make the DN/$\overline{\text{UP}}$ input LOW or HIGH, respectively. This counter will count only through legitimate 4-bit BCD words. Thus when the DN/$\overline{\text{UP}}$ input is LOW and the counter is incrementing, the highest count is 1001 (equivalent to decimal 9). After 1001, the next natural state is 0000, which starts the next up-count sequence. When the DN/$\overline{\text{UP}}$ input is HIGH and the counter is decrementing, the BCD values on the Q_A through Q_D outputs get smaller with each CLOCK pulse. After state 0000, the next natural state is 1001, which starts the next down-count sequence. This counter will not count, either up or down, unless its $\overline{\text{ENABLE}}$ input is ACTIVE LOW.

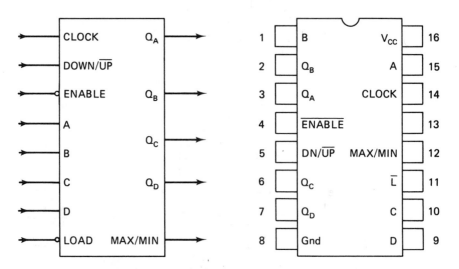

Fig. 15-4. (A) Logic diagram of the 74190 up/down counter and its (B) DIP package (top view).

This 74190 up/down counter can be reset or preset to any legitimate state (BCD number) via its A through D inputs. A BCD word applied to the A through D inputs will enter the counter and will either reset it or preset it, depending on the value of the input word, at the instant the $\overline{\text{LOAD}}$ input is pulled ACTIVE LOW. In other words, this counter ignores its A through D inputs while the $\overline{\text{LOAD}}$ input is HIGH. For example, the A and C inputs might be hardwired to the dc supply while the B and D inputs might be hardwired to ground. Thus the decimal equivalent of 5 is permanently wired to the A through D inputs and will preset the counter to state 5 when the $\overline{\text{LOAD}}$ input is pulled LOW.

The MAX/MIN output of the 74190 up/down counter goes HIGH for a period of about one clock pulse at the end of each 10-state count sequence. This MAX/MIN signal can be used to reset or preset its own or other counters.

15-4 The Four-Bit Latch

Latches are used for temporary storage of digital information. Commonly, they are used between a processing unit, such as a counter or register, and an output indicator, such as a decoder/driver and LED display; see Fig. L 15-4 in Experiment 15-4. The latch serves to read information from the counter or register and then applies this information to the display for a time long enough to enable the system operator to read it. Usually, the digital information in counters and registers is continually changing (updating) at a very rapid rate. Such rapid changes, if applied directly to a decoder/driver and LED display unit, would cause an unreadable display. That is, the display numbers, as viewed by the operator, would be changing so fast that he or she would not be able to read them. A latch between a counter and display device can be made to read the counter's updated information at regular intervals and apply it to the display for a few seconds at a time, long enough to be readable by a human observer.

Latches can be constructed with D-type FFs. They are also available in IC packages such as the 7475 unit shown in Fig. 15-5. This package contains the equivalent of four D-type FFs, their D inputs being D_1 through D_4. We can recall that a D-type FF reads the bit on its D input when a clock pulse is applied. That is, a HIGH on the D input causes the FF to set and the Q output to go HIGH on the next clock pulse, whereas a LOW on the D input causes the FF to reset and have a LOW on its Q output after the clock pulse. The 7475 4-bit latch has two enabling inputs; ENABLE 1-2 drives FFs (individual latches) 1 and 2 and ENABLE 3-4 drives latches 3 and 4 within this package. These enabling inputs work much like the clock inputs do on the D-type FFs. Often, these enabling inputs are externally wired together so that all four FFs are enabled simultaneously. When both enabling inputs are pulled HIGH, the data word on the D_1 through D_4 inputs is read into this 4-bit latch; that is, it is transferred to the Q_1 through Q_4 outputs, respectively. The $\overline{Q_1}$ and $\overline{Q_4}$ outputs, which are circled, are always complements of the Q_1 through

Q_4 outputs. After a 4-bit word is read into this latch, a LOW on the enabling inputs locks this word in and causes it to be displayed at the Q_1 through Q_4 outputs regardless of the data on the D_1 and D_4 inputs.

In a typical application, BCD outputs of a counter or register are applied to the D_1 through D_4 inputs of the 4-bit latch. The Q_1 through Q_4 outputs are applied to the inputs of a decoder/driver with a 7-segment display. Both enabling inputs are pulsed HIGH for just an instant every second or two. Thus, each time ENABLE 1-2 and ENABLE 3-4 pulse HIGH, this latch reads updated words and displays them.

Pin configuration

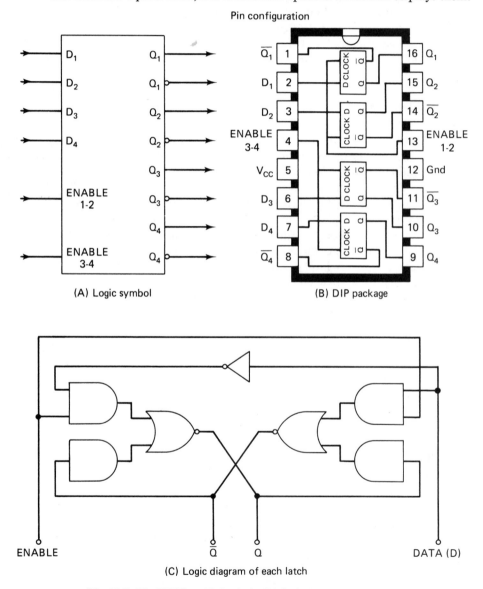

(A) Logic symbol

(B) DIP package

(C) Logic diagram of each latch

Fig. 15-5. The 7475 four-bit latch, its (A) logic symbol, its (B) DIP package, and the (C) logic diagram of each latch.

Summary

1. An up/down counter can be made to count up or down 1 binary bit with each clock pulse.

2. When both the $\overline{\text{ENABLE}}$ and DN/$\overline{\text{UP}}$ inputs are LOW, the 74190 up/down counter will count up with a series of HIGH-going CLOCK pulses applied.

3. When the $\overline{\text{ENABLE}}$ input is LOW and the DN/$\overline{\text{UP}}$ input is HIGH, the 74190 up/down counter will count down with a series of applied CLOCK pulses.

4. A HIGH on the ENABLE input stops the counter regardless of the number of input CLOCK pulses.

5. BCD words can be applied to the *A* through *D* inputs of the 74190 up/down counter for parallel loading, that is, for presetting the counter. BCD words on the *A* through *D* inputs of the up/down counter can preset it only when the $\overline{\text{LOAD}}$ input is pulled LOW.

6. Latches can serve as temporary memories and are commonly used to read rapidly changing digital information and to remember (hold) it for a few seconds.

7. The 7475 4-bit latch reads data via its inputs when its enabling inputs are HIGH. Words read immediately appear at the latch's outputs.

8. When a 7475 latch's enabling inputs are pulled LOW, the data previously read become locked in and remain available at its outputs. New data on the inputs are then ignored.

Experiment 15-1 Shift Registers Made with Flip-flops

Purpose

To become familiar with serial-in/parallel-out shift registers.

Equipment

Digital breadboard kit
(Two) 7476 dual JK flip-flops
(One) 7404 hex inverter

Procedure

1. Build the circuit of Fig. L 15-1. Notice that the toggle switch controls the serial input data and that the bounceless pushbutton switch acts as the clock. The outputs from all flip-flops are read simultaneously (in parallel) on the indicator lamps.

2. With the input switch in the LOW (0) position, apply power to the circuit. Depress the pushbutton switch four times to clear all flip-flops.

3. Now we shall shift a binary number into the register. Place the toggle switch in the 1 position.

4. Press the pushbutton switch once. List the states of the flip-flops:

$$\underset{1}{A} \quad \underset{0}{B} \quad \underset{0}{C} \quad \underset{0}{D}$$

5. Next, with the toggle switch still in the 1 position, press the pushbutton switch again. List the states of the flip-flops. __1__ __1__ __O__ __O__

6. Flip the toggle switch to the 0 position. Clock the register once. List the states of the flip-flops. __O__ __1__ __1__ __O__

7. Finally, flip the toggle switch to the 1 position, and clock the register once. List the states of the flip-flops. __1__ __O__ __1__ __1__
What number have you loaded into the register as seen by the parallel outputs? __~~ELEVEN~~ 00 11__

8. List the order in which you would apply HIGH and LOW signals to the serial input to shift the number 5 into the register. Before the first clock pulse __1__, before the second __0__, before the third __1__, before the fourth __0__.

9. Shift in the number 5 as you listed in step 8. Did it work? __yes__. Experiment by shifting other numbers into the register until you are sure you understand it.

284

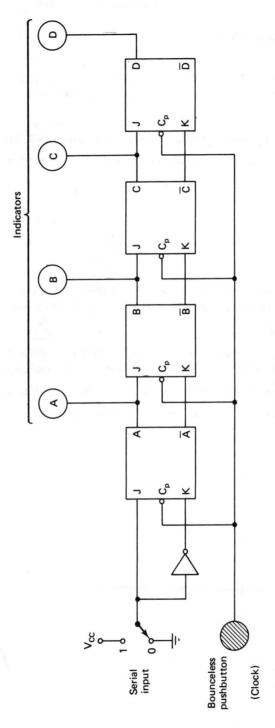

Fig. L 15-1.

285

Quiz for Experiment 15-1

1. Serial input shift registers come in a variety of lengths (number of flip-flops). If you were using an 8-bit shift register, how many clock pulses would you need to shift in a word?   *8* _____

2. In a shift right, serial input shift register, the (LSB, MSB) is shifted in first.

3. Ordinarily, a JK flip-flop has four modes of operation. They are

JK	Q
00	Remain the same
01	Reset
10	Set
11	Toggle

By connecting the inverter between the J and K inputs to the first flip-flop of the shift register, as shown in Fig. L 15-1, which two modes of operation are possible?   *on or off*   *set or reset*

4. If a 1 is placed on the serial input, the first flip-flop (sets immediately, resets immediately, sets when clocked, toggles when clocked).

5. Suppose you wanted to use the shift register of Fig. L 15-1 as a serial output register. Where would you take the output from?   *D* _____

Experiment 15-2 Integrated Circuit Shift Registers

Purpose

In Experiment 15-1, you built a 4-bit shift register using JK flip-flops. Now we shall study a chip with a 5-bit parallel-in parallel-out shift register. We shall use 7496 chips, as shown in Fig. 15-2(A). By using two or more of these registers, we can route data around inside a computer.

Equipment

> Digital breadboard kit
> (Two) 7496 5-bit shift registers

Procedure

1. Connect the two registers as shown in Fig. L 15-2(A). Note that the parallel inputs of Reg X are connected to toggle switches for loading in data. The parallel inputs of Reg Y are all grounded.

2. Apply power and reset both registers by connecting the $\overline{\text{CLEAR}}$ input (pin 16 on both chips) momentarily to ground. Then return the $\overline{\text{CLEAR}}$ inputs to a HIGH level.

3. Now flip the toggle switch connected to pins C and D of Reg X to a HIGH. LOAD these data (binary 6) into Reg X by momentarily removing the ground lead from the LOAD input (pin 8) and making it HIGH. Then return pin 8 to ground again.

4. Depress the pushbutton switch (CLOCK) five times. What do you observe at the Reg Y outputs after five CLOCK pulses?   _____O || O_____

5. Now, without changing any leads, CLOCK the inputs five more times. Now what do you see at the output of Reg Y?   _____ʇ ʇ ʇ ʇ ʇ   ɒ ɒ O O_____
   _____reset back to zer_____

6. Connect pin 9 of Reg X to a HIGH level and CLOCK both registers five times. What do you observe at the outputs of Reg Y?   _All lights light_____
   _____ 0000   00₀_____

7. Finally, CLOCK both inputs five more times. Now what do you observe at the outputs of Reg Y?   _____All on | | | |_____

287

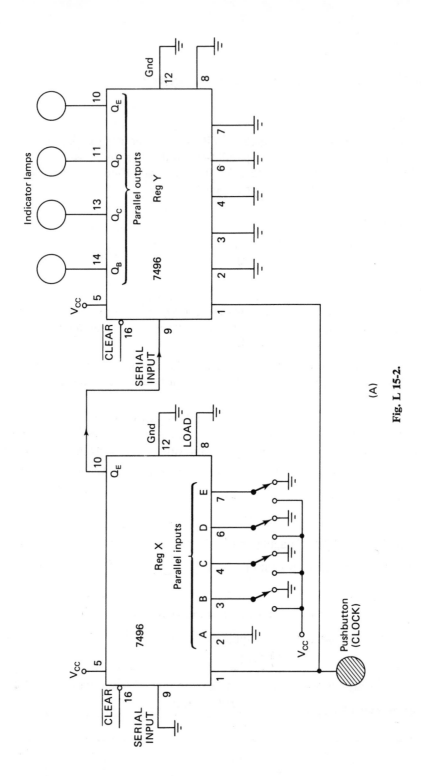

Fig. L 15-2.

8. To demonstrate a variation in the use of shift registers, we shall now build a *ring counter*. Wire the circuit of Fig. L 15-2(B). Note that output Q_E (pin 10) feeds back to the SERIAL INPUT (pin 9).

9. LOAD in the binary number 3. (Refer back to step 3 if you forget how to LOAD.) Be sure to return pin 8 to ground after loading. *Returns to 0011*

10. CLOCK the register five times by depressing the toggle switch. Explain what you observe at the *BCDE* outputs.   1.   0001

2   1000

3   1100

4   0110   5   0011

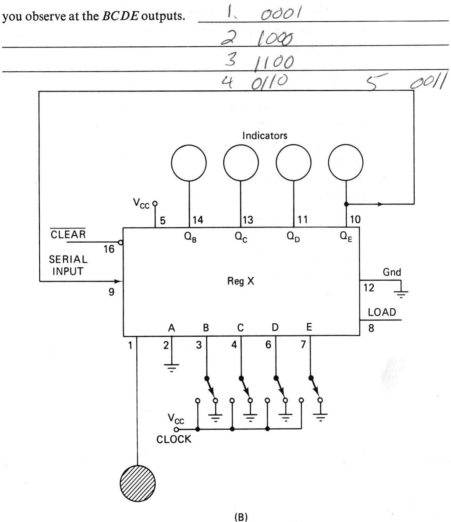

(B)

Fig. L 15-2. (Cont.)

Quiz for Experiment 15-2

1. To reset the 7496 shift register, pin 16 must be made (LOW, HIGH). While shifting data, pin 16 must be held (LOW, HIGH).

2. To LOAD data into the 7496 in parallel, the data to be loaded must be applied to inputs A, B, C, D, and E, and LOAD input (pin 8) must momentarily be driven (LOW, HIGH). During shifting, pin 8 must normally be held (LOW, HIGH).

3. Data are shifted to the (right, left) one position when the CLOCK goes from (LOW to HIGH, HIGH to LOW).

4. In step 4 of the experiment, depressing the pushbutton five times (made the circuit count to 5, transferred the contents of Reg X into Reg Y).

5. While the binary number 6 was being transferred to Reg Y, Reg X was being (loaded with another binary 6, fed all zeros via the grounded serial input).

6. In step 5, the contents of Reg Y after five clock pulses were (unpredictable, the same as the contents of Reg X before the transfer, obviously incorrect).

7. In step 7, the contents of Reg Y were (the same as Reg X before transfer, not determined by the contents of Reg X).

8. In a ring counter (random numbers are generated, the contents are shifted around from output back to input).

9. If the Q_E output of Reg Y in Fig. L 15-2(A) were fed to the serial input of Reg X, the LOAD inputs held LOW, and the circuit clocked, how many pulses would be needed until the original contents of both registers reappeared ?   10

Experiment 15-3   Up/Down Counters

Purpose

Up/down counters find application in digital voltmeters, in multiplier circuits, and in timing events, such as the blast-off of a rocket. We shall now see how to control the counter for different modes of operation.

Equipment

Digital breadboard kit
74190 decade up/down counter
7447 BCD-to-7 segment decoder driver
MAN 1   7-segment readout

Procedure

In this experiment, you will have to rely on your knowledge of ACTIVE HIGH and ACTIVE LOW terminology, and labeling of inputs and outputs, to determine how to operate the chip.

1. Let's start with the $\overline{\text{ENABLE}}$ input (pin 4). In order to activate the chip, the $\overline{\text{ENABLE}}$ input should be (LOW, HIGH). *Note*: The $\overline{\text{ENABLE}}$ input controls counting only. It has no effect on LOADing.

2. The clock input is ACTIVE (HIGH, LOW), indicating that the flip-flops in the counter are triggered when the CLOCK input goes from (LOW to HIGH, HIGH to LOW).

3. Pin 5 controls the mode of operation, that is, whether the device counts UP or DOWN. When a HIGH signal is applied to pin 5, the chip will count (UP, DOWN). Likewise, when a LOW signal is applied to pin 5, the chip will count (UP, DOWN).

4. The data input lines (pins 15, 1, 10, and 9) are ACTIVE (HIGH, LOW).

5. Outputs Q_A, Q_B, Q_C, and Q_D are ACTIVE (HIGH, LOW).

6. Finally, the MAX/MIN output will give a (HIGH, LOW) output when the counter overflows or underflows, that is, when counting UP, past 9, or DOWN, past 0.

7. After answering all the previous questions, you are ready to try using the chip. Wire the circuit of Fig. L 15-3. Look up the pin numbers for the 7447 and the MAN 1 in a previous experiment. Connect toggle switches to the DATA inputs (pins 15, 1, 10, and 9) of the 74190.

8. Put the proper HIGH or LOW on the $\overline{\text{ENABLE}}$ input so that the counter will not count. LOAD in a BCD number 3. (Input A is the LSB.) If you have done this correctly, you should observe the digit 3 displayed on the 7-segment readout. If so, go on to the next step. Otherwise, recheck your wiring, and recheck your understanding of the level required on pin 11.   OK

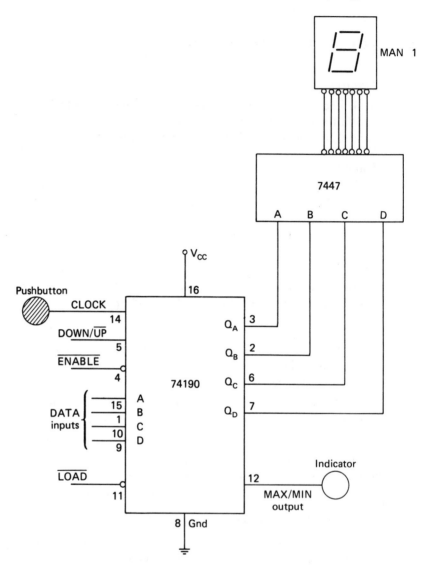

Fig. L 15-3.

9. Next, set the proper level on pin 5 to make the counter count up. Then enable the chip and manually depress the pushbutton clock several times. What happens? ____*counts up*_____ *on* *N iwh on to zero af*

What happens to the MAX indicator when the counter goes past the ninth count?

on n, wh to zero off

_____

10. LOAD in the number 7. Apply the proper control signal to make the counter count DOWN. Then pulse the pushbutton several times while watching the readout.

What happens? *counter down*

_____ .

What happens when the count goes past 0? *min lights*

man to 9 .

Experiment with LOADing and counting UP and DOWN until you feel you understand the operation.

Experiment 15-4   Quad Latch

Purpose

In Experiment 15-3, you used a 74190 as a decade counter. You saw the 7-segment readout display each digit as you counted up or down. In many applications, such as frequency counters and digital voltmeters, it is desirable to have only the final numbers displayed, rather than have the digits flicker while counting up or down. By inserting a latch between the counter and the decoder/driver, we can display the final number. The latch also serves as a temporary memory, since it retains (remembers) the previous count while freeing the counter to start counting again.

Equipment

> Digital breadboard kit
> 74190 decade up/down counter (or 7490)
> 7447 BCD-to-7-segment decoder/driver
> MAN 1 (or equivalent) 7-segment display
> 7475 quad latch
> 120-Ω, $\frac{1}{4}$-W $\pm 5\%$ resistor

Procedure

1. Construct the circuit of Fig. L 15-4. Note that the circuit uses a 74190, as in Experiment 15-3. However, since you will only be required to use it as an UP counter, a 7490 will work as well. There are many connections to make for this circuit, so take your time and recheck your wiring.

2. With switch S in the 1 position, depress the pushbutton switch several times. If your circuit is wired correctly, you should see the 7-segment readout count up to 9 and then reset to 0 on the tenth pulse. If this does not happen, recheck your wiring. If OK, go on to the next step. $0 \rightarrow 9 \rightarrow 0$

3. Depress the pushbutton several times until a 0 is displayed. Then place switch S in the 0 position. Next, depress the pushbutton five times. What number is displayed?   _____NO THING   DO_____

4. Now flip switch S to the 1 position. What number is displayed?

_____5_____

5. Flip switch S back to the 0 position. Then press the pushbutton three times. What number is displayed?   ____5   STAYS_____

6. Now flip switch S to the 1 position again. What number is displayed now?

_____4_____

7. Experiment with the latch by alternately placing switch *S* in the 1 position and pressing the pushbutton several times, and then placing the switch in the 0 position and pressing the switch several times. Try it both ways until you are certain you know how it works.

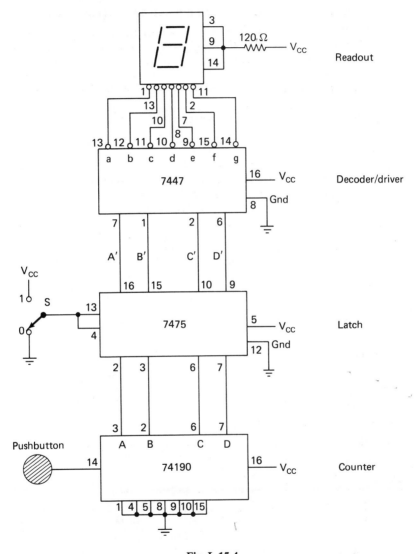

Fig. L 15-4.

Quiz for Experiment 15-4

1.   The quad latch contains four (RS, JK, D) flip-flops.

2.   When the CLOCK (ENABLE) inputs to the latch are HIGH, whatever logic level appears at the input to each flip-flop also appears at its output (true, false).

3.   When the CLOCK (ENABLE) inputs to the latch are LOW the outputs (toggle, follow the *D* inputs, retain the data that were on the *D* inputs just before the clock went LOW).

4.   A primary application of a quad latch, as used in this experiment, is to

      SeRve   AS   A   temporary   memory

5.   If you wanted to observe the current contents of the counter in Fig. L 15-4, you would place switch *S* in the (1, 0) position.

16

Arithmetic Circuits

Introduction

Many registers are used in typical computer circuits. Registers mainly serve to accept and store digital information. The registers are then able to apply this stored information, at proper times and in the proper way, to other various circuits. These other circuits are made to process information in many various ways. For example, in this chapter we shall see how registers are used, with other circuitry, to perform arithmetic operations such as addition and subtraction of binary numbers. Methods of adding binary numbers can be reviewed in Chapter 9. Subtracting techniques are discussed here. The laboratory projects of this chapter provide experience with basic, but typical, digital hardware that performs addition and subtraction.

16-1 Subtracting Binary Numbers

In elementary school, we learned how to subtract decimal numbers by first aligning them and their decimal points. The subtraction process then begins with the least significant digit. When the digit in the minuend is smaller than the digit of the subtrahend in the same column, we borrow from a more significant digit in the minuend. Binary numbers can be subtracted in the same way. Several examples are shown in Fig. 16-1, where examples (A) through (C) are quite simple in that no borrowing was required. That is, in example (A), 1 subtracted from 1 yields 0 in the 2^0 column. Then 0 from 0 in the 2^1 column yields 0, and 0 from 1 in the 2^2 column yields 1, etc. Examples (B) and (C) can similarly be analyzed.

Examples (D) through (F) in Fig. 16-1 involve a borrowing process. In the 2^0 column of example (D), a 1 must be borrowed from the 2^1 column in the minuend before subtraction can take place. This borrowing causes a 10 minuend in the 2^0 column. Subtracting a 1 subtrahend from a 10 minuend results in a difference of 1, as shown. That is, in any column that requires us to subtract 1 from 0, we must first borrow a 1 from the adjacent (more significant) column. Thus the 0 becomes 10 and the 1 subtracted from it yields a difference of 1; also note example (E). If the adjacent column also has a 0, it will have to borrow from the next left or more significant column. Therefore, if a 0 borrows a 1 from the left, it becomes 10. But if this 10 loans the right, it becomes a 1; note the resulting minuend after this kind of borrow/loan process in example (F).

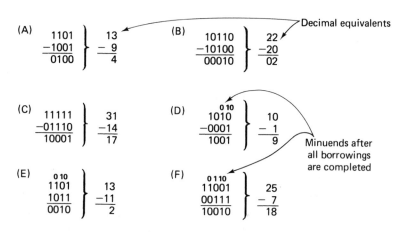

Fig. 16-1. Examples of binary numbers being subtracted.

Problem 16-1

1. Work each of the problems in Fig. 16-2. Check your answers by converting each of the minuends, subtrahends, and your differences to their decimal equivalents.

(A) 1111   (B) 1011   (C) 1101   (D) 11101
    −1001   −1010   −1011   −10011

(E) 11011   (G) 111111   (F) 100000
    −10111   −010101   −000001

Fig. 16-2.

16-2 Subtracting with One's Complements

Typically, digital computers perform subtraction by addition. That is, full adders, such as in the 7483 ICs, can be used to find the difference between two binary numbers. Subtraction by addition is performed by first *complementing* the subtrahend. A binary number is complemented when each of its bits is inverted. Examples of binary numbers and their complements are shown in Fig. 16-3. These

Fig. 16-3

Binary numbers	Their one's complements
0000	1111
0001	1110
0010	1101
0011	1100
0100	1011
0101	1010
0110	1001
0111	1000
1000	0111
1001	0110
1010	0101

complements are also known as *one's complements* or *true complements*. In a subtraction problem, if we add the one's complement of the subtrahend to the minuend, we get their difference less 1. A 1 is then added to this difference for a final answer. This process is best understood by examples and practice; see Fig. 16-4.

Note in each example that the subtrahend is first complemented, and then the complement is added to the minuend. This results in an extra 1 in the far-left column. This far-left 1 is then carried down to the least significant (2^0) column and is added to the previous answer. The final answer is the correct difference. This process is sometimes called the *end-around-carry* method of subtraction.

(A)
```
 1101        1101
-1001       +0110
           1 0011
            └──→ 1
             0100
```

(B)
```
 10110      10110 ←── Minuend
-10100     +01011 ←── One's complement of subtrahend
          1 00001
           └──→ 1 ←── End-around-carry of MSB
            00010
```

(C)
```
 11111       11111
-01110      +10000
           1 01110
            └──→ 1
            10001
```

(D)
```
 1010        1010
-0001       +1110
           1 1000
            └──→ 1
             1001
```

(E)
```
 1101        1101
-1011       +0100
           1 0001
            └──→ 1
             0010
```

(F)
```
 11001       11001
-00111      +11000
           1 10001
            └──→ 1
            10010
```

Fig. 16-4. Binary subtraction problems solved with one's complements and the end around-carry method.

Problem 16-2

1. Work each of the problems in Fig. 16-2 using one's complements and the
    end-around-carry method. Compare the results with your previous answers
    for these problems.

16-3 Parallel Add/Subtract Circuits

The circuit of Fig. 16-5 shows how the parallel adder circuit, discussed previously
in Sec. 9-11, can be modified to perform addition or subtraction. A 7487 IC, which
is an MSI true (one's) complementer, has been added. A functional table of this
IC is also shown in Fig. 16-5. Row 1 shows that if both the B and C controlling
inputs are LOW, the outputs are $\overline{A_0}$, $\overline{A_1}$, $\overline{A_2}$, and $\overline{A_3}$, that is, logically opposite to
the signals on the A_0 through A_3 inputs. Thus in this mode, the 7487 complements
each 4-bit input word. When the controlling input B is LOW while C is HIGH (row
2), the outputs are A_0, A_1, A_2, and A_3, which means that they are the same as
inputs A_0 through A_3. In this mode, therefore, the 7487 passes any 4-bit word on
the A_0 through A_3 inputs through to the Y_0 through Y_3 outputs. The controlling
input conditions shown in rows 3 and 4 cause all the outputs, Y_0 through Y_3, to be
HIGH or LOW, respectively.

   In the circuit of Fig. 16-5, the 7487 is wired to work in either of two modes, the
modes in rows 1 and 2 of its functional table. When this circuit's ADD/$\overline{\text{SUBT}}$ input
is pulled LOW, it will subtract the 4-bit word on the A_0 through A_3 inputs from the
4-bit word on the B_0 through B_3 inputs. Their difference appears at the S_4 through
S_0 outputs. When the ADD/$\overline{\text{SUBT}}$ input is HIGH, this circuit will add the 4-bit words
on the A_0 through A_3 inputs and B_0 through B_3 inputs.

16-4 Subtracting with Two's Complements

In the previous section we learned that we had to add 1 to the sum of the minuend
and the one's complement of the subtrahend in order to get the correct difference
between the minuend and the subtrahend. We can just as correctly add the 1 to
the one's complement before adding it to the minuend. When this is done, the
one's complement becomes a *two's complement*. The two's complement of the subtrahend added to the minuend gives the correct difference without the end-around-
carry step. Several examples of subtraction using two's complements are shown in
Fig. 16-6. Here we see each subtrahend first converted to its one's complement,
and then 1 is added to convert the one's complement to a two's complement. The
two's complement added to the minuend yields the correct difference. Note that
the 1 carry out of the MSB column, called an *overflow*, is dropped in each example.
In a digital sytem, this kind of overflow might typically be used to indicate the sign
of the answer.

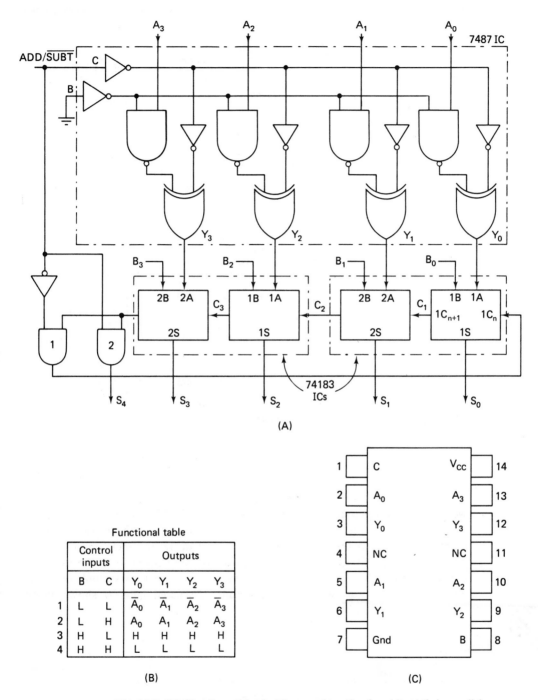

Functional table

Control inputs		Outputs			
B	C	Y_0	Y_1	Y_2	Y_3
1	L	L	$\overline{A_0}$	$\overline{A_1}$	$\overline{A_2}$	$\overline{A_3}$
2	L	H	A_0	A_1	A_2	A_3
3	H	L	H	H	H	H
4	H	H	L	L	L	L

(B)

1	C	V_{CC}	14
2	A_0	A_3	13
3	Y_0	Y_3	12
4	NC	NC	11
5	A_1	A_2	10
6	Y_1	Y_2	9
7	Gnd	B	8

(C)

Fig. 16-5. (A) Circuit capable of adding or subtracting four-bit words in parallel; (B) functional table for the 7487 complementer IC; (C) DIP of the 7487.

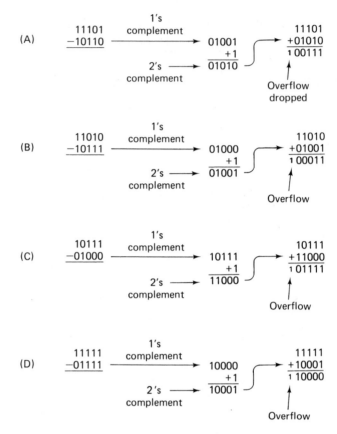

Fig. 16-6. Examples showing how to perform subtraction by adding with two's complements.

If we compare binary numbers with their two's complements (see Fig. 16-7), we can observe a pattern. Starting at the right with the LSB of each binary number and then working toward the left 1 bit at a time, we can see that the two's complement is the same as the binary number above it up to and including the first 1. Note, however, that after the first 1, each two's complement bit is the inverse of the binary bit in the same column. Circuitry that converts binary numbers to their equivalent two's complements, in a manner discussed here, is shown in the laboratory projects of this chapter.

Problems 16-3

1. Rework all the examples in Fig. 16-1 using two's complements.

2. Rework all the examples in Fig. 16-2 using two's complements.

3. Add a third two's complement column in Fig. 16-3. Use the technique of converting binary numbers to their equivalent two's complements, discussed the last paragraph of the previous section.

4. Rework all the examples in Fig. 16-4 using two's complements.

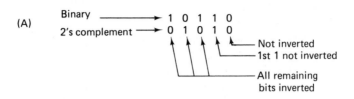

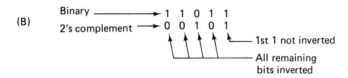

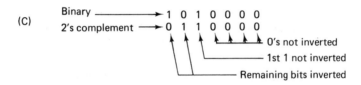

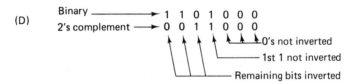

Fig. 16-7. Examples of how binary numbers are converted to their equivalent two's complements.

Experiment 16-1 Parallel Addition

Purpose

In previous experiments you worked with fairly simple-to-construct circuits. You checked out the operation of one or two chips working together. By now you have gained considerable experience with the individual chips, so from here on, we shall build more complex systems.

In Chapter 9 you worked with a parallel full adder. The binary numbers to be added were fed to the adder chip by means of toggle switches. In actual computers, the numbers to be added are fed to the adders via registers. In this experiment you will build a parallel full adder using registers and adders. You will see how registers are used to store a number and how the LOAD input can be used to isolate one register from another during the LOAD operation. You will also see how a *data bus* is used to selectively feed information from a single input unit, an encoder in this case, to two different registers.

NOTE: If this experiment, or any of the following experiments, requires more chips than you can assemble on your breadboard kit, we recommend that you work together with another student, each student building a part of the system on his own breadboard kit; then interface the two units to complete the system. This is the way design of large systems is done in industry. One engineer, or team, works on a small part of the overall system and then interfaces his part with the others to make the system complete.

NOTE: Whenever you interface two units, be sure that you tie the grounds of the two units together, that is, *use a common ground. Do not* tie the V_{CC} supplies together. Other than that, as long as your chips are compatible, for example, all TTL, you will not have any trouble in feeding the outputs of one unit to the inputs of the other.

Equipment

Digital breadboard kit (possibly two kits)
(Two) 74183 dual full adders
(Two) 7496 parallel-in/parallel-out shift registers
7404 hex inverter

Procedure

1. Study the diagram of Fig. L 16-1 carefully before starting construction. If the system is to be built on two breadboard kits, determine who will build what. Notice that the input to the system is a set of four toggle switches which LOAD the registers via their parallel inputs. In an actual computer, these switches would be replaced by either a keyboard encoder or a memory buffer register. In this experiment, switch the appropriate lines HIGH to LOAD each register.

Note also that the data bus connects the inputs of *both* registers to the encoder in parallel. However, only one register at a time is LOADed depending on the position of the LOAD A/LOAD B switch.

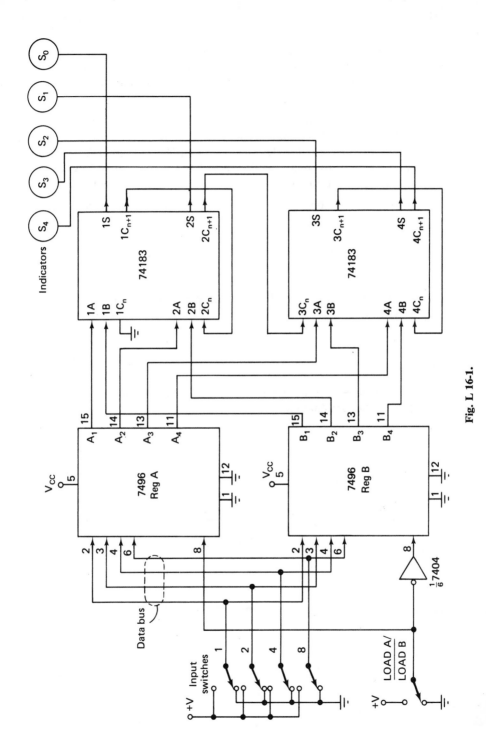

Fig. L 16-1.

2. Wire the entire system. LOAD all zeros into both registers by placing all four input switches in the 0 position and throwing the LOAD A/$\overline{\text{LOAD B}}$ switch up and then down. If your circuit is wired correctly, you should read all LOW outputs on the indicator lamps. If not, recheck your wiring.

3. LOAD the binary number 3 into Reg *A* by throwing the LOAD A/$\overline{\text{LOAD B}}$ switch HIGH; then throw inputs 1 and 2 HIGH. Next throw the LOAD A/$\overline{\text{LOAD B}}$ switch LOW. This last step disables the LOAD input of Reg *A* and allows the information on the data bus to change without affecting the contents of Reg *A*. Be sure to always make the LOAD input LOW *before* changing the data inputs.

4. Next LOAD the binary number 2 into Reg *B*. List the states of the output indicators.

$$S_4 \quad S_3 \quad S_2 \quad S_1 \quad S_0$$
$$0 \quad 0 \quad 1 \quad 0 \quad 1$$

5. LOAD the binary number 5 into Reg *A* and 6 into Reg *B*. List the states of the output indicators.

$$S_4 \quad S_3 \quad S_2 \quad S_1 \quad S_0$$
$$0 \quad 1 \quad 0 \quad 1 \quad 1$$

6. Experiment by LOADing various binary numbers into each register and see that all possible combinations work.

Experiment 16-2   Serial Addition

Purpose

In Experiment 16-1, you built a parallel adder, capable of simultaneously adding all bits of two binary numbers. Now you will build a serial adder. Although not so fast as the parallel adder, the serial adder requires only one full adder, regardless of the number of bits to be added. Therefore, the serial adder finds applications where speed is not so important as parts economy.

Equipment

>   Digital breadboard kit
>   (Two) 7496 5-bit shift registers
>   (One) 74183 dual full adder
>   (One) 7474 dual D flip-flop

Procedure

1. Study the diagram of Fig. L 16-2. Note that all the $\overline{\text{CLEAR}}$ inputs are tied together. Note also that the CLOCK inputs to both registers as well as the CLOCK input of the D flip-flop are all tied to the pushbutton. If you do not have sufficient indicators available, omit the S_4 indicator. However, you will get a better understanding if you interface two breadboard kits.

2. Build the circuit. Reset both registers by means of the $\overline{\text{CLEAR}}$ input. All indicators should read 0. Otherwise, check your wiring.

3. LOAD the binary number 3 into Reg *B* via the parallel inputs.

4. CLOCK the system five times by depressing the pushbutton five times. List the outputs of the indicators.

$$S_4 \quad S_3 \quad S_2 \quad S_1 \quad S_0$$
$$\underline{2} \quad \underline{0} \quad \underline{0} \quad \underline{1} \quad \underline{1}$$

5. Now LOAD the binary number 2 into Reg *B*.

6. CLOCK the system five times. List the outputs of the indicators. $\underline{0}$ $\underline{0}$
$\underline{1}$ $\underline{0}$ $\underline{0}$

7. LOAD the binary number 7 into Reg *B*.

8. CLOCK the system five times. List the outputs of the indicators. $\underline{0}$ $\underline{1}$
$\underline{0}$ $\underline{0}$

9(optional). You will get a better understanding of the operation of the serial adder by connecting indicator lamps to the SUM and CARRY outputs and the CARRY

307

inputs of the full adder. Then clear the registers, put a number into Reg *B*, and clock the system five times. Input another number into Reg *B* and clock the system five times. Observe all the indicators after *each* clock pulse. Try this several times until you are certain you understand the operation.

Quiz for Experiment 16-2

1. The 7496 5-bit shift register can be used in four different modes. They are (a) serial-in/serial-out, (SISO) (b) serial-in/parallel-out (SIPO), (c) parallel-in/serial-out (PISO), and (d) parallel-in/parallel-out (PIPO). In the circuit of Fig. L 16-2, Reg *B* is being used as a (SISO, SIPO, PISO, PIPO) shift register.

2. Reg *A* is being used as a (SISO, SIPO, PISO, PIPO) shift register. (The output appears on the indicators.)

3. In Experiment 16-1 both registers were being used as (SISO, SIPO, PISO, PIPO) shift registers.

4. An accumulator is a register used to hold the totals of several mathematical operations. Which register of Fig. L 16-2 is the accumulator? ____*A*____

5. If 8-bit shift registers were used instead of 5-bit registers, how many clock pulses would be needed for each addition after the registers have been LOADED?

6. Suppose that the *A* and *B* inputs to the full adder were both 1 and the CARRY IN were 0. What would be the SUM output? ____0____ What would be the CARRY OUT? ____1_____

7. With reference to Problem 6, after a clock pulse was applied, what would be the level of the CARRY IN (the output of the D flip-flop)? ____1____. What would be the state of S_4? ____0_____

8. When clocked, the D flip-flop always (toggles, takes on the state of the CARRY OUT, takes on the opposite state of the SUM output).

9. What is the primary purpose of the D flip-flop? _____
    ____Remembers   CARRY   Cary_____
    _____
    _____

10.   What happens to the SUM output of the adder when the system is CLOCKed?

<u>OUTPUT   APPEARS   AFTER All</u>

<u>clocks</u>

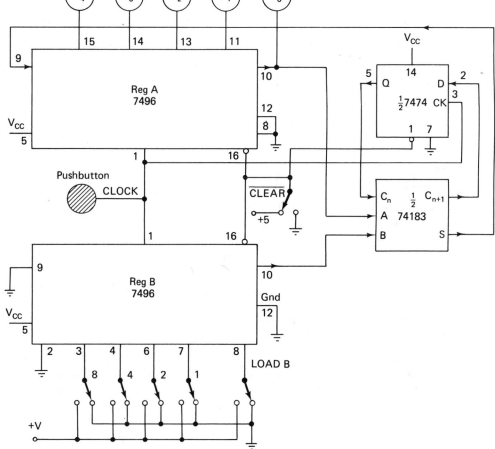

Fig. L 16-2.

Experiment 16-3   Serial Two's Complementer for Serial Subtraction

Purpose

In Experiment 16-2, you saw how a serial adder works. By using a two's complementer circuit along with the serial adder, you can subtract numbers. You will now build a serial two's complementer to see how it works. If possible, do not disassemble the circuit but save it for Experiment 16-4 to build a complete ADD/SUBTRACT circuit.

Equipment

> Digital breadboard kit
> 7474 dual D flip-flop
> 7400 quad two-input NAND
> 7404 hex inverter

Procedure

1. Study the circuit of Fig. L 16-3. Note that flip-flop II is *not* part of the complementer circuit. It is used to simulate the input flip-flop of a shift register. The actual output of the complementer is pin 8 of the 7400. The input to the complementer is toggle switch *S*. Normally, the input to the complementer is the output of a serial shift register. This will be made clearer in Experiment 16-4, when you interface it with the serial adder of Fig. L 16-2.

Indicator lamp *A* shows the logic level of the input bit. Lamp *B* indicates the output state of the complementer. Lamp *C* indicates the state of the first flip-flop in the shift register, so you will be able to see what is shifted into the register when it is clocked. Lamp *D* indicates when complementing is taking place.

2. Build the circuit of Fig. L 16-3. Be sure to connect V_{CC} and ground to each chip. Reset both flip-flops by placing a LOW level on the CLEAR inputs. Note that the $\overline{\text{CLEAR}}$ input of FF I is labeled $\overline{\text{ADD/SUBT}}$. When this line is held LOW, the level applied at the input (from switch *S*) passes through the complementer via gates 1 and 2. The output will always be the same as the input.

3. Make the $\overline{\text{CLEAR}}$ input to FF II HIGH, and the $\overline{\text{ADD/SUBT}}$ line LOW. With switch *S* in the LOW position, all indicators should be LOW. Otherwise, recheck your wiring.

4. Flip switch *S* HIGH and LOW a few times. Are *A* and *B* always the same? _yes_. Does *C* change? _No_. Why? (FF II is being cleared, FF II only can change when clocked.) Does *D* change? _No_. Why?

_____

311

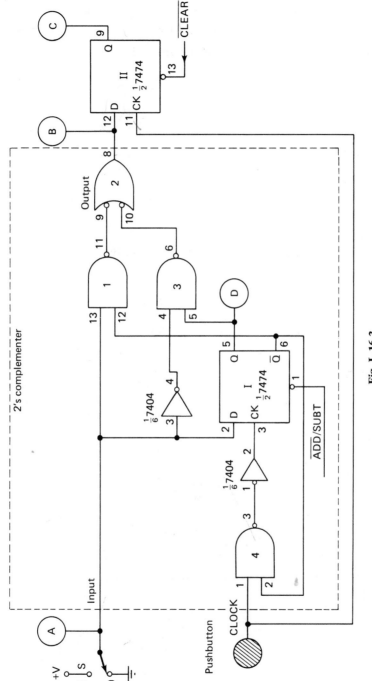

Fig. L 16-3.

5. With *S* in the LOW position, CLOCK the circuit twice by depressing the pushbutton switch. Does *C* change? __No__ . Why? (FF II is being cleared, 0's are being shifted into the *D* input, causing FF II to reset each CLOCK pulse.)

6. Throw switch *S* to the HIGH position. List the states of the indicators.

A B C D
1 1 0 0

Now clock the circuit once by pressing the pushbutton switch. List the states of the indicators.

A B C D
1 1 1 0

7. Flip switch *S* LOW again. List the states of the indicators.

A B C D
0 0 1 0

Now CLOCK the circuit once and list the states again.

A B C D
0 0 0 0

Repeat steps 6 and 7 a few times to make sure that you see what is happening.

8. Make the $\overline{\text{ADD}}$/SUBT line HIGH. With switch *S* in the LOW position, CLOCK the circuit once. List the states of the indicators.

A B C D
0 0 0 0

9. Now flip switch *S* HIGH. List the states.

A B C D
1 1 0 0

10. CLOCK the circuit once. List the states.

A B C D
1 0 1 1

11. Without changing switch *S*, CLOCK the circuit again. List the states.

$$A \quad B \quad C \quad D$$

1 0 0 1

12. Flip switch *S* LOW. List the states.

$$A \quad B \quad C \quad D$$

0 1 0 1

CLOCK the circuit once. List the states.

$$A \quad B \quad C \quad D$$

0 1 1 1

13. Experiment on your own by throwing switch *S* HIGH and LOW and CLOCKing the circuit after each throw. Also try CLOCKing two or three times between throws until you are sure how the circuit works.

Quiz for Experiment 16-3

1. Up to and including step 7, the circuit (did, did not) complement the input bits.

2. Explain both sets of indicator states in step 6._____

_____ Complement _____

_____

_____

_____

3. Both steps 6 and 7 show that *B* is the same as *A* when the $\overline{\text{ADD}}$/SUBT line is LOW (true, false).

4. Steps 6 and 7 show that the FF II output assumes the state of *B* when clocked (true, false).

5. Study your answers for steps 8, 9, and 10. Clocking the circuit in step 10 turned the complementer ON (true, false).

6. Was the first 1 bit complemented in step 10? ___Y_____

7. In step 11, a 1 bit was again being applied to the input, and then the circuit was clocked. Was this bit complemented? ___Y_____

8. Throwing switch S LOW in step 12 applied a (0, 1) bit to the input. Was this bit complemented? ___Y_____

9. The circuit of Fig. L 16-3 complements every bit *after but not including* the first 1. Suppose the binary numbers below were shifted through the two's complementer. Write the number that would appear in a shift register connected to the output for each. Assume that $\overline{\text{ADD}}/\text{SUBT}$ is HIGH.

    (a) 011010   1 0 0 1 1 0

    (b) 100010   0 1 1 1 1 0

    (c) 1001   0 1 1 1

    (d) 11111   0 0 0 0 1

    (e) 00000   0 0 0 0 0

Experiment 16-4   Serial Adder/Subtractor

Purpose

In this experiment, you will interface the two's complementer of Fig. L 16-3 with the serial adder of Fig. L 16-2. You will then have a system capable of adding or subtracting.

Equipment

See Experiments 16-2 and 16-3. It is recommended that two students or teams work independently, one building the adder and the other the complementer. Then, after checkout, the two circuits can be interfaced. Be sure to use a common ground.

Procedure

1. After checking each circuit, the adder of Fig. L 16-2 and the complementer of Fig. L 16-3, insert the complementer between the Reg *B* output and the full adder input, as shown in Fig. L 16-4. Note that FF II of Fig. L 16-3 has been

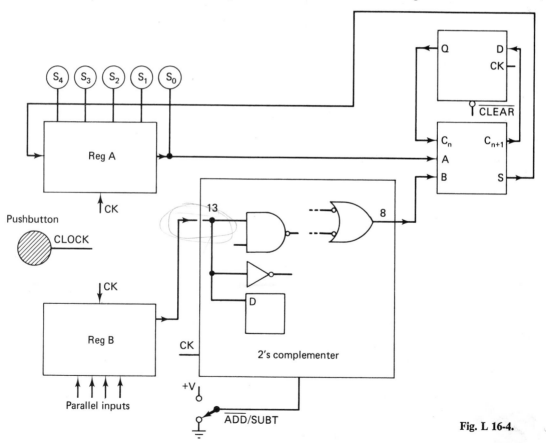

Fig. L 16-4.

315

omitted. The output of NAND gate 2 is used as the complementer output. The two's complementer output is fed directly into the *B* input of the full adder.

Notice that all clock inputs (for the shift registers and D flip-flops) are tied together. That is, all circuits are clocked synchronously.

2. Clear all registers. Throw the $\overline{\text{ADD}}$/SUBT switch LOW. LOAD the binary number 6 into Reg *B*, and clock the system five times. List the states of the Reg *A* output.

0   0   1   1   0

3. Next, LOAD the number 5 into Reg *B*, and add by clocking five times. List the states of Reg *A*.   *0   1   0   1   1*

4. Now we shall subtract a number from that in the accumulator. Throw the $\overline{\text{ADD}}$/SUBT switch to the SUBT position. Parallel LOAD the number 4 into Reg *B*. Then clock the system five times. List the states of Reg *A*.   *0   0   1*

1   1

5. Experiment on your own by adding or subtracting any number from the total in the accumulator to see how it works.

NOTE: Each time you want to subtract, you must first clear the complementer flip-flop by flipping the $\overline{\text{ADD}}$/SUBT switch LOW and then HIGH again. Otherwise, the output from the complementer will not be the correct two's complement.

Appendix I

BASIC RULES FOR THE USE OF TTL DEVICES*

1. Spare inputs should be connected to used inputs if the fan-out permits and otherwise connected to the V_{CC} power line via a resistor of value 1 kΩ or greater. This is particularly important for the preset and clear asynchronous inputs.

2. Gates from the same package may be paralleled where necessary for better driving capability.

3. Interconnection lengths of 12 in. or less (capacitance of about 50 pF) are unlikely to give ringing problems; lengths up to 24 in. are possible with good ground arrangements. Greater length will probably require line-driving precautions.

4. Wired-OR can be performed at the output terminals of open collector networks; however, a speed penalty is incurred by the introduction of a resistive pull-up.

5. In calculating system speeds, due allowance should be made for the maximum set up and minimum clock pulse width times on flip-flops, as well as the propagation delays of the elements used.

6. If relays are driven from TTL circuitry, care must be taken to ensure that the load connection wires to the relay contacts do not introduce noise into the logic system. This can be done by allowing these wires only to enter the logic system enclosure at a point close to the relay contacts, or in extreme cases by also shielding the relay.

7. Similarly, external inputs should be brought on to the printed circuit connections at right angles to the other wiring, the printed circuit itself being laid out to ensure least coupling between inputs and other connections.

8. If system speed is high, allowance should be made when calculating power supply requirements for the increased network supply currents due to current

*Courtesy of ITT Semiconductors.

spiking and line driving. An allowance at 10 MHz of 15% for spiking and up to 0.5 mA per each gate node for the line driving will be adequate for this.

9. Decouple every 10 gates or their equivalent in MSI functions with 0.01- to 0.1-μF capacitors of R.F. rating.

In conclusion, a careful perusal of the data sheet together with the points mentioned above will help in achieving a trouble-free logic design at the first attempt.

Appendix II

PARTS LIST FOR LABORATORY EXPERIMENTS*

Integrated circuits (TTL)

2	7400 quad two-input NANDs
	7402 quad two-input NOR
	7404 hex inverter
	7408 quad two-input AND
	7413 dual Schmitt NAND
	7432 quad two-input OR
	7447 BCD-to-7-segment decoder/driver
	7450 AND/OR/invert
	7474 dual D flip-flop
	7475 quad latch
2	7476 dual JK flip-flops
2	7490 decade counters
	7493 4-bit binary counter
2	7496 5-bit shift registers
2	74183 dual full adders
	74190 decade up/down counter

CMOS devices

	4001A quad two-input NOR
	4007A complementary pair plus inverter
	4049A hex inverter

Miscellaneous

1	MAN 1 (or equivalent 7-segment readout)
1	555 timer

*Quantities are one each unless otherwise noted.

319

Resistors (all $\frac{1}{4}$-W, $\pm 5\%$)

	3 MΩ
	1.5 M
	1 M
	100 K
2	56 K
2	51 K
2	20 K
	10 K
2	4.7 K
	3.9 K
	3.3 K
	2.2 K
2	2 K
	1.5 K
2	1 K
	330 Ω
2	270 Ω
2	240 Ω
	220 Ω
3	120 Ω
	100 Ω
	27 Ω

Potentiometers ($\frac{1}{2}$ W)

1 MΩ
500 K
100 K
50 K
10 K
1 K

Capacitors (all 15 WV dc or higher)

	100 μF
2	25 μF
	1 μF
	0.5 μF
2	0.1 μF
3	0.025 μF
	0.02 μF
	0.01 μF
	0.001 μF

Transistors

> 3 or 4 each *NPN* and *PNP* silicon (any type)

LEDS

> 2 red and 2 green, small 15-mA type

Diodes

> 12 silicon (any type) and 3 germanium

Switches

> 3 SPDT toggle
> 2 SPST momentary pushbutton

Filament transformer

> 12.6 V or 6.3 V ac, low current

Speaker

> 8 Ω (optional)

Test equipment

> dc scope, electronic voltmeter, sine-wave signal generator (audio)

Appendix III

ANSWERS TO SELECTED PROBLEMS

Chapter 1

Problems 1-1

1. HIGH because the diode is reverse biased.   **3.** About 20 V.   **5.** Approximately zero.   **7.** About zero.   **9.** The supply voltage E across the diode, 0 V across R.

Problems 1-2

1. Full sine wave, none.   **3.** Clockwise.   **5.** −dc.   **7.** +dc.

Problems 1-3

1. LOW.   **3.** HIGH.   **5.** LOW.   **9.** AND.   **11.** OR.   **13.** (a) 0 V, (b) 12 V, (c) 0 V, (d) 0 V.   **15.** (a) 12 V, (b) 0 V, (c) 0 V, (d) 0 V.   **17.** (a) 5 V, (b) 5 V, (c) 5 V, (d) 0 V.

Chapter 2

Problems 2-1

1. HIGH.   **3.** LOW.   **5.** LOW.   **7.** HIGH.   **9.** LOW.

	Q_1	Q_2	Q_3	Q_4	A	B	C	D
11.	ON	ON	ON	ON	ON	ON	ON	OFF
13.	ON	OFF	OFF	OFF	ON	OFF	OFF	ON
15.	ON	ON	ON	OFF	ON	ON	ON	ON
17.	OFF	OFF	ON	ON	OFF	OFF	ON	OFF

Problems 2-2

1. Saturated.   **3.** (a) 0 V, (b) 0 V, (c) 5 V.   **5.** 5 V, does, zero.   **6.** HIGH, LOW.   **7.** 0 V, does not, 5 V.

Chapter 3

Problems 3-1

1. OFF, HIGH.   **3.** ON, HIGH, OFF, LOW.   **5.** OFF, ON, 0 V.   **9.** Q_1 is ON; Q_2, Q_4, and Q_6 are OFF.

Chapter 4

Problems 4-1

1. HIGH.   **3.** LOW.   **5.** Inverter.   **7.** Inverter.

9. $\overline{W}$

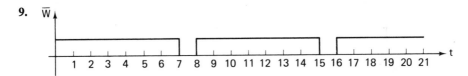

11. $\overline{Y}$

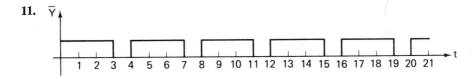

Chapter 6

Problems 6-1

2. Waveforms on pins 8 and 12 are inverted versions of the waveform at pin 13; pins 10 and 13 have the same waveforms.

Problems 6-2

3. LOW.   **5.** LOW.   **7.** HIGH, LOW, HIGH, LOW.   **9.** HIGH.   **11.** LOW.

Chapter 7

Problems 7-1

1. *C.*   **3.** *A.*   **5.** *G.*   **7.** *E.*   **9.** Gates 1, 3, 5, 7, *B, D, F,* and *H.* **11.** 1.
13. *C.*   **15.** 4.   **17.** *F.*   **19.** *H.*

Chapter 8

Problems 8-1

1. $A + \bar{B}$.   **3.** $L = (A + \bar{B})(\bar{A} + B)$.   **5.** Output of i $= B\bar{C}D$, of ii $= CB\bar{D}$, of iii $= \bar{B}DC$, of iv $= B\bar{C}D + CB\bar{D} + \bar{B}DC$.

Table II

7.

1		2		3	4	5
Inputs		Ouputs of Inverters		Output of AND Gate *a*	Output of AND Gate *b*	Output of OR Gate *c*
A	*B*	$\bar{A}$	$\bar{B}$	*AB*	$\overline{AB}$	*M*
0	0	1	1	0	1	1
0	1	1	0	0	0	0
1	0	0	1	0	0	0
1	1	0	0	1	0	1

Problems 8-2

1. NAND gates 1 through 4 are replaced with AND gates; NAND 5 is replaced with an OR.
3. NOR gates 1 through 4 are replaced with OR gates; NOR gate 5 is replaced with an AND.
5. Logically opposite.

Problems 8-3

1. Simply replace each of the four gates with three-input NANDS.
2.

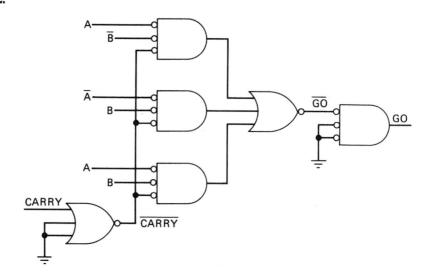

3. Simply replace each of the four gates with NOR gates.

4.

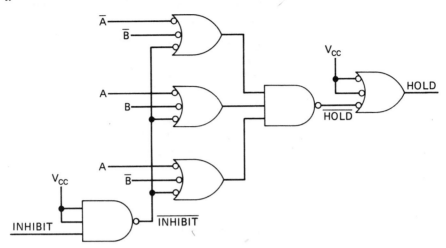

Chapter 9

Problems 9-1

1. (a) 30, (c) 55, (e) 204, (g) 238, (i) 256, (k) 429.   **2.** (a) 100100, (c) 1011100, (e) 10000000, (g) 11111111, (i) 100000100, (k) 111111111.

Problems 9-2

1. R_a, R_b, R_c.

Problems 9-3

1. (a) 0101 0001, (c) 0111 0101, (e) 1001 0000, (g) 0101 0000 0001, (i) 0011 0101 0011, (k) 1001 1000 0111.
2. (a) 97, (c) 57, (e) 594, (f) 731, (h) 897, (j) 9081.

Problems 9-4

1.

3	D_3 and D_4	$\bar{a}, \bar{b}, \bar{c}, \bar{d}, \bar{g}$
5	D_6 and D_7	$\bar{a}, \bar{c}, \bar{d}, \bar{f}, \bar{g}$
9	D_{14} and D_{15}	$\bar{a}, \bar{b}, \bar{c}, \bar{f}, \bar{g}$

Problems 9-5

1. (a) 100010, (c) 1000000, (e) 1111100, (g) 1101010, (i) 10011110.

Problems 9-6

	C_4	S_3	C_3	S_2	C_2	S_1	C_1	S_0
1	0	1	0	1	0	1	0	1
3	0	0	0	1	1	1	1	0
5	0	1	1	1	1	0	0	1
7	1	0	0	0	0	0	0	0

Problems 9-7

1.

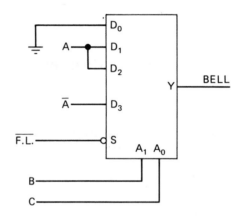

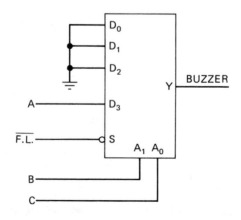

Problems 9-8

1.

$\bar{A}$	$\bar{B}$	K
L	L	L
L	H	H
H	L	H
H	H	L

$$K = (\bar{A} + \bar{B})(A + B).$$

3. Exclusive OR.

5.

Y_L	Z_L
L	L
L	L
L	L
H	L
L	L
H	L
H	L
H	L

7. (a) 9, (b) none, display remains blank, (c) 7.

9.

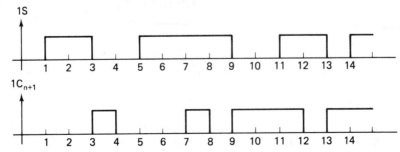

Chapter 12

Problems 12-1

1.

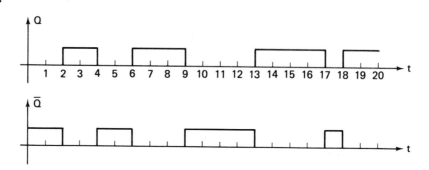

2. The FF will stay reset regardless of the throws of the switch because both inputs are always HIGH.

3.

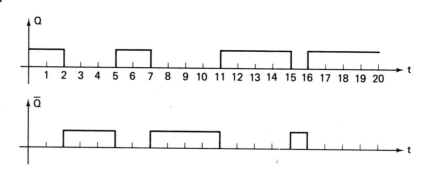

4. The FF will stay set regardless of the throws of the switch because both inputs are always LOW.

Chapter 13

Problems 13-1

1. HIGH, HIGH, unstable.   **3.** HIGH, LOW, set.   **5.** HIGH, LOW, set.
7. LOW, HIGH, reset.   **9.** LOW, HIGH, reset.   **11.** LOW, HIGH, reset.

Problems 13-2

1. Not lit.   **3.** Lit, HIGH.   **5.** Lit, HIGH.   **7.** Go HIGH, light.
9. Stay lit, stay lit.   **11.** Stays out, stay lit.   **13.** Stay out, light, stay out.

Problems 13-3

1.

$\bar{Q}$ is always logically opposite of Q.

Chapter 14

Problems 14-2

1. HIGH, LOW, HIGH.   **2.** reset, five, five.

3.

Clock Input	A	B	C	Decimal Equivalents	
0	L	L	L	0	
1	H	L	L	1	Repetitively counts
2	L	H	L	2	through five
3	H	H	L	3	states
4	L	L	H	4	
5	L	L	L	0	← Reset here
6	H	L	L	1	
7	L	H	L	2	
8	H	H	L	3	
9	L	L	H	4	
10	L	L	L	0	← Reset here
11	H	L	L	1	
12	L	H	L	2	

Problems 14-3

1.

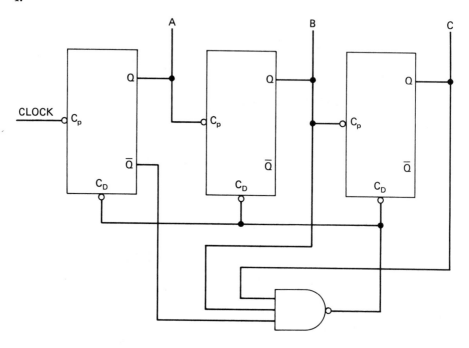

Index